THE

INTERNET

ATLAS

THE

INTERNET

ATLAS

Richard Dinnick

PARKGATE
BOOKS

First published in 2000 by
PRC Publishing Ltd,
Kiln House, 210 New Kings Road, London SW6 4NZ

This edition published in 2000 by
Parkgate Books Ltd
London House
Great Eastern Wharf
Parkgate Road
London SW11 4NQ
Great Britain

British Library Cataloguing in Publication Data:
A catalogue record for this book is available from the British Library.

ISBN 1 902616 69 3

Printed and bound in China

Illustrated Library.com

Visit *Illustrated Library* where you can view thousands of books and images,
compiled from some of the world's finest publishing houses, all on one site.
Our site offers a vast spectrum of content, from Alistair Cooke to Zen Interiors;
from history, art, and gardening to sports and children's books.

http://www.illustratedlibrary.com

Contents

Introduction

The Internet is here to stay. Many people have said to me over the years that the Internet is just a flash in the pan or a passing fad. It isn't. It's a communications revolution that's sweeping through the world and nothing will ever be the same again. Inventions, such as the telephone and the television, do not come close to the Internet in terms of the changes the Internet has, and will, bring about.

This phenomenal era of change has been driven primarily by the combined forces of email and the 'world wide web' (or just 'web'). Email is the way most people experience the Internet for the first time and because of its similarity to something we are all familiar with - regular mail - it is a good introduction to new technology.

Email lets you communicate with any other individual in the world, providing he or she has an email address. And you no longer need to be tied to one Internet Service Provider, or even be in one country to send and receive them. With web-based email services, such as those discussed later in the book, you can just access a web site and sign up for free email.

Indeed, here we have an example of how email has been affected by the other driving force of the Internet - the web. You can read more

about the development of the Internet, and where the invention of the world wide web fits into it, in the section entitled **History**, but the web has been instrumental in making the Internet the success it is today.

The web allows you to move between different sites with ease. Instead of having to type in each address, you merely click on a link and you are instantly transferred to another web page. The nature of the world wide web means that it is also a multi-media experience of pictures, animation, film, music, and sounds whereas, before the web's invention, the Internet had been silent and made up of text alone.

This multi-media experience means that, as a surfer of the web (i.e. one who visits web sites), you can get so much out of it.

If you are a movie buff, you can download and watch trailers of the latest blockbusters. Sports fans can watch edited highlights of the most recent (or archive) baseball games or rugby matches. Music aficionados can listen to chart topping songs or classical concertos. Farmers can watch satellite weather forecasts to see if an anticyclone threatens their crops or livestock. Business people can check live stock market reports. Those who cannot see can listen to the latest news. All this is possible from anywhere in the world.

And that is just the multi-media part of the web. The Internet is the biggest single source of information anywhere on the planet and most of it is freely available to you, and your children, and your grandparents. Think of the possibilities.

Most of the world's universities, libraries, art galleries, museums and places of higher education are online. This means that if you are interested in a special subject - be it archaeology or the works of Vincent Van Gogh - you will find thousands of relevant web sites.

Many users of the Internet have found solace on the web when they, or a loved one, is diagnosed with a rare or life-threatening condition. They have been surprised to find how many universities, institutes and companies carry out research into the very ailment about which they have been unable to find a book. The web also has many thousands of support groups as well as professional doctors and specialists – all at your fingertips.

You can, of course, find information on other more pleasant topics - perhaps you are trying to trace the roots of your family history, research the background of your home town, or discover who are the great men and women of your country (or anyone else's). The web will help you. If you are feeling nostalgic you can certainly find out when that old make of car you used to drive stopped rolling off the production line; or if Vivien Leigh or Grace Kelly ever really looked that

Introduction

good. If you have favorite authors, you can establish whether or not you have read all their books. And if you haven't, you can then buy them.

E-commerce is the buzzword for the end of the old century and the beginning of the new. What it means for you is that almost anything you could ever need (and quite a lot that you don't yet realise you need) is out there - just a few clicks of a mouse away.

The ability to purchase online means you can go shopping for items at cheaper prices than the local or even national stores. You will find goods that you may not be able to find easily - such as out of print books, or long-deleted vinyl LPs. You can buy your groceries online; go clothes shopping; complete or start a CD, video or DVD collection; shop for gifts at any time of the year, upgrade your computer or buy some wine. Most retailers are represented on the web - indeed there are many that only exist in cyberspace.

The wonders of the web will also let you do many things that might surprise you. It is quite possible for you to buy a car, a boat, or even a house on the web. You can trade stocks and shares, buy insurance, or even open and manage a bank account. You can do almost anything and there are over one billion web pages out there to help you.

That, some say, is the main drawback of the world wide web. There are simply too many web sites. Certainly it can make searching for what you are looking for more complicated and over long. That is the purpose of this book. To help you cut through the cyber chaff to get at the web wheat.

I have chosen the best web sites for almost every conceivable situation you may find yourself in online. Some are included because they are popular - visited and commended by millions of people. Others I have included because they are more off the beaten track and offer an extraordinary function or service, an unparalleled expertise, or a different angle on the subject.

Where I haven't listed specific sites, I have given tips and tricks that will help you to use the web's many excellent search engines to their full capacity. For the web changes constantly. Sites are redesigned, their popularity wax and wane. Mergers take place, companies are taken over, and firms go bust. But never fear, you will find the very best, and the most unlikely to be replaced or usurped, contained in this volume.

History of the Internet

The Internet is a vast communications network, transmitting data in the form of words, pictures, animation, audio and video, to and from an ever-growing number of computers worldwide. Like so many technological advances - such as the jet engine or nuclear power - the Internet owes its existence to the Military. However, before the Internet came into being, there were several historical developments that were key to its creation and implementation.

Way back in 1836, the way humans communicated changed forever when William Cooke and Charles Wheatstone patented the Telegraph. This ushered in the first period of communication over long distances, or telecommunications, as it became known. This form of communication also introduced the idea of a binary language in the form of Morse Code - a series of dots and dashes - that is, in effect, very similar to modern computer language which is made up of ones and zeros.

Between 1858 and 1866 the first transatlantic cables were laid, allowing communication between the US and Europe. The technology may have changed little (some cables laid in 1866 were still operational almost a century later) in the last 140 years, and cables are still the main conduits of intercontinental telecommunication, including the Internet.

Cable and Morse technology was followed in 1876, by Alexander Graham Bell's invention of the telephone. Today, it is still telephone

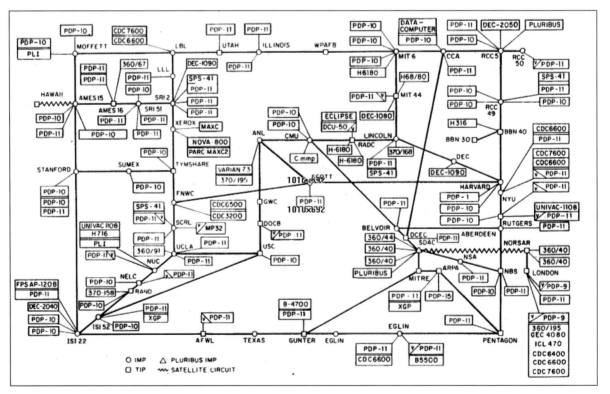

exchanges that provide the backbone for Internet connections. This stepping stone in the Net's history was followed, in 1957, by the launch in the former Soviet Union of the world's first artificial satellite, *Sputnik I*. This heralded true global telecommunications, as today satellites augment the cable network in transmitting data around the world in a matter of seconds.

The launch of *Sputnik I* was also key in the development of the Internet, as the US was forced to re-evaluate its use of technology in its military forces. As a result, the Advanced Research Projects Agency, or ARPA (www.arpa.mil), was set up in 1958 within the Department of Defence (DoD). Since that time, ARPA has ensured a US lead in applying state-of-the-art technology for military capabilities, and to prevent technological surprise from her adversaries. Between 1962 and 1968, the US military made many advances that would eventually be used in the creation of the Internet.

Now called the Defence Advanced Research Projects Agency (DARPA), the Agency's mission is to 'develop imaginative, innovative and often high risk research ideas offering a significant technological impact that will go well beyond the normal evolutionary developmental approaches; and, to pursue these ideas from the demonstration of technical feasibility through the development of prototypes systems'.

Until the proliferation of Soviet nuclear intercontinental ballistic missiles (ICBMs), the US military's computer network was organised in such a way that one well-placed bomb would have effectively shut down the whole thing. This was because one central mainframe computer controlled the US military system, including the launch of the American nuclear arsenal. Only the central computer could issue orders to the rest of the network and co-ordinate the country's defence.

It had also discovered that, when detonated, nuclear weapons send out a wave of radiation called an electromagnetic pulse. This pulse disables anything using a microchip processor that is switched on at the time of attack.

To counter this double threat posed by strategic nuclear weapons, ARPA came to the conclusion that the US military had to de-centralise its command structure. So, instead of one master computer controlling all functions of the system, a network of smaller computers was set up. This ensured the security of the US chain of command as networks can withstand large-scale destruction.

Networks also mean that there is more than one route a message can take when being sent from one point to another. If one section of

History of the Internet

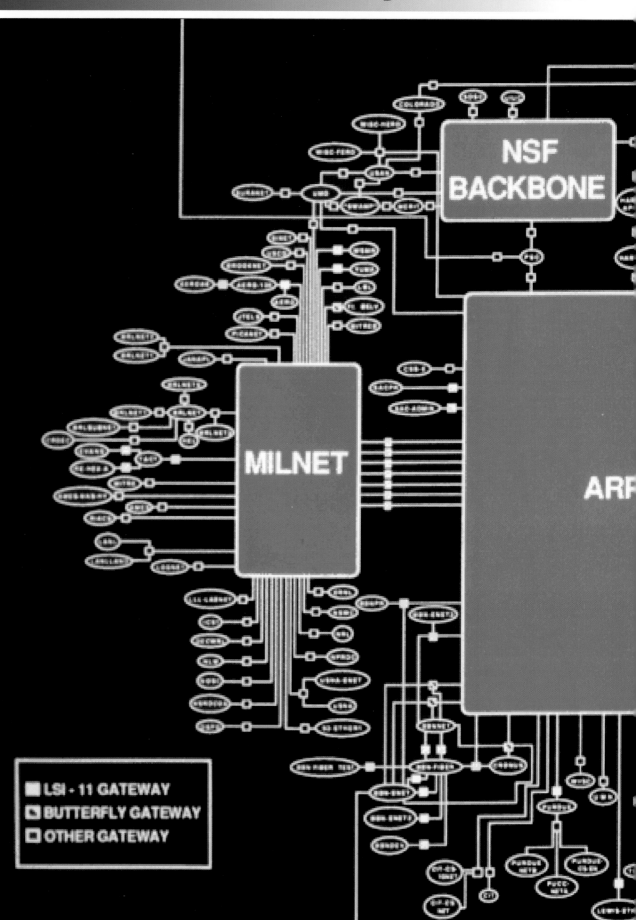

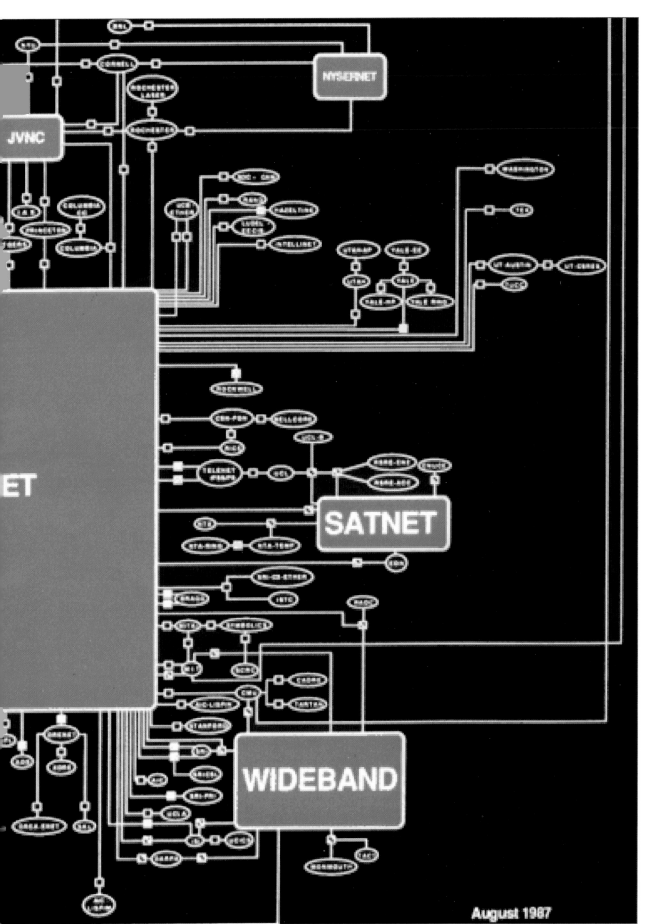

NYSERNET

JVNC

ET

SATNET

WIDEBAND

August 1987

the network is destroyed, messages can still get through by alternative routes.

In July 1961, Leonard Kleinrock of the Massachusetts Institute of Technology (MIT) published the first paper on a system of communication known as packet-switching (PS). This paper was called 'Information Flow in Large Communication Net'. In the PS system, data is split into tiny 'packets' capable of taking different routes through a network to reach its destination.

The PS system would make the military communications system difficult to penetrate, as anyone attempting to eavesdrop on a message would only be able to decipher the packets being routed through the section of the network being tapped. So ARPA adopted and developed the technology for its own use.

There were three teams working on the development of PS technology, including ARPA. In the US, RAND (a contraction of the term research and development), America's foremost Cold War think-tank initially set up to aid the US Air Force in its research, had been looking at packet-switching since 1964. While in the UK, the National Physical Laboratory (NPL) had been working on the technology under Donald Watts Davies, who actually coined the term 'packet'.

After working independently for several years, the three teams finally met in October 1967 when the Association for Computing Machinery, or ACM (the world's first educational and scientific computing society, founded in 1947), held a symposium on 'Operating Principles' in Gatlinburg, Tennessee.

Two years later, in 1969, the DoD commissioned ARPA to set up a military network that used PS technology. This network became known as ARPANET, and involved the setting up of several 'nodes' or information distribution points, at some of the universities involved in research into networking and PS systems. The first few nodes were set up at UCLA, the Stanford Research Institute (SRI), the University of California Santa Barbara (UCSB), and the University of Utah.

These four universities could transfer data between their computers on dedicated high-speed telephone lines. The computers could even be programed remotely from the other nodes, which meant scientists and researchers could share one another's computer facilities long-distance.

Charles Kline was the first person to use the system to transfer data packets from UCLA to SRI. Although this initial communication resulted in the system crashing when the letter 'G' of the word LOGIN was entered, this simple act has now been identified as the

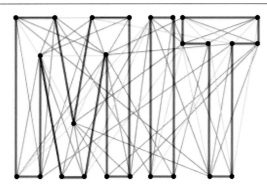

massachusetts institute of technology

spotlights - Civil and Environmental Engineering
Millennium Colloquium

Tether Survey

news - events and research summaries

academics - admissions, schools, courses

research - labs, centers, and programs

administration - offices and programs, capital campaign

resources - services, students, alumni

campus life - activities, personal home pages

map - how to get around MIT, virtual tour

search - [   ] Go

○ MIT   ○ Directory   ○ Personal Pages

77 Massachusetts Avenue · Cambridge, MA 02139-4307 USA · 617.253.1000

Windows Technologies   **Microsoft**

ows Home Pages |

Site Index

This index lists the family of Windows Technologies Web sites. Each site provides in-depth information about each technology, and is specifically designed to meet the needs of general users, analysts, business decision makers, or the press. Each site also includes pointers to related information that can be found on our other Windows Web sites.

Internet Explorer
Want to know what it's all about? Internet Explorer brings you the Web the way you want it so it's easy to find what you need, whether it's on your computer's hard drive, a local area network, or on the Internet. You can rely on the Internet Explorer site to keep you up to date on Internet Explorer news, Internet Explorer's latest features, and industry reviews from the Internet press. We also offer Internet Explorer for Windows 3.x, Macintosh, and UNIX.

Outlook Express
With Microsoft's Outlook Express, sending and receiving e-mail is a snap. Make your own stationery, find long-lost friends, broadcast e-mail across your company or yak it up in a newsgroup. And while you're busy doing this, Outlook Express can screen your incoming mail if you ask it to, so you don't have to worry about junk mail piling up in your Inbox. We also offer Outlook Express for Windows 3.x, Macintosh and UNIX.

NetMeeting
With Microsoft NetMeeting, you can hold face-to-face conversations with family, co-workers, and friends around the world. You can collaborate with one person or a group of people—drawing to illustrate an idea on a shared whiteboard, exchanging calendars with other parents to plan who can pick up after soccer practice, or during a discussion, edit a document on someone else's computer. The NetMeeting site keeps you up to date with compatible products and easy-to-follow instructions about how to find who else is meeting on the Net.

Windows Media Technologies
Browse the best development resource for streaming media solutions. Windows Media Technologies have assembled a thorough list of tools and information for developers to peruse, evaluate, and learn about what the Windows Media Technologies can do. You'll find deployment tools, author and developer resources, technical information, and content samples. You'll also find comparison information, logo and branding information, and download links.

Windows Media Player

birth of the Internet. The date was October 29th, 1969. By 1971, ARPANET consisted of 15 nodes, and communication over the network was augmented by the invention of a program that let scientists send notes to each other. This system became known as email. One year later ARPANET connected 40 machines, and the masses got their first glimpse of the new technology when the nascent network was demonstrated to the public for the first time.

It was about this time that the Internet Working Group (INWG) was created to standardise the way that computers communicated with each other, called 'protocols'. It was the first time the word Internet had been used.

ARPANET continued to grow and, in 1973, became an international network with the inclusion of connections at University College London, and the Royal Radar Establishment in Norway. Indeed, this year saw many advances that formed the basis for the Internet we know today.

Over the next few years, ideas key to the functioning of the Internet were developed. These included Ethernet (how local networks of computers are connected), Gateway architecture (how large networks perhaps of different configurations and specifications can be

Corporate Information

Home | Events/Training | Subscribe | About Microsoft | US/Worldwide | Downloads | MSN.com |

Top links:

Inside Our Site

Jobs

Piracy

Press News

Investor Relations

Other resources:

Corporate Profile

Living Our Values

Microsoft's History

Bill Gates' Home Page

Diversity

Accessibility

Community Giving

Fast Facts

Microsoft Worldwide

What We Do

Since its inception in 1975, Microsoft's mission has been to create software for the personal computer that empowers and enriches people in the workplace, at school and at home. Microsoft's early vision of a computer on every desk and in every home is coupled today with a strong commitment to Internet-related technologies that expand the power and reach of the PC and its users.

As the world's leading software provider, Microsoft strives to produce innovative products that meet our customers' evolving needs. At the same time, we understand that long-term success is about more than just making great products. Find out what we mean when we talk about Living Our Values.

Corporate headquarters:
One Microsoft Way
Redmond, WA 98052-6399
Telephone: (425) 882-8080

connected together), and FTP, or File Transfer Protocol (how computers send and receive data).

ARPA's original standard for communication was known as NCP (Network Control Protocol) but, as these technologies were developed, a new, more sophisticated standard came into being. Known as TCP/IP. The TCP bit stands for Transmission Control Protocol, and converts messages into streams of packets at the source, before putting them back together as coherent messages at the destination. IP, or Internet Protocol, became the standard method of identifying that destination by giving it a numerical address.

Throughout this time of amazingly quick advances, it was noted by the military that its network was not being used to share computer facilities half as much as it was being used as an electronic postal system. Scientists were busy sending emails that let them collaborate on other research projects, send personal messages, swap news, and even share jokes. They all had user accounts on ARPANET with their own personal addresses for electronic mail.

This set-up led to the inception of the 'mailing list', a technique for automatically sending identical messages to any number of network users. Inevitably, one of the first big mailing lists was called SF-LOVERS, for fans of science fiction. All these activities were frowned upon by the US government, but that didn't stop them from happening.

Although the military side of ARPANET remained strictly monitored, other networks now started to link to the original. In 1974, the first commercial version of ARPANET, called Telenet, was launched and, by 1977, other networks were even using TCP/IP to link to ARPANET.

From the military's point of view, the trouble with inventing a decentralised computer network (designed to link up as many military computers as possible), was that not just military computers could join the network. As the computer revolution took off, universities all over the world found themselves with computer networks, as did large corporations, and TCP/IP software was readily available to the public.

So it was difficult to stop those universities, corporations, and even individuals, from linking to ARPANET. This is when the Internet really began to take off. As a result, ARPANET as a secure means of control for the US military machine became defunct in 1983, when the military segment of the Internet broke away to become today's MILNET. ARPANET was still there, but it was now just another network on the ever-expanding universe of linked computers. A year after MILNET was set up, the US National Science Foundation joined the

History of the Internet

Internet, through its Office of Advanced Scientific Computing. The NSFNET, as it was called, took the technologies and ideas developed in the 60's and 70's and built on them, using faster and faster computers in conjunction with faster and faster links. Indeed, NSFNET made three major upgrades of the system in 1986, 1988 and 1990.

This massive growth in terms of coverage and technology was helped by other major organisations joining the Internet. The National Air and Space Administration (NASA), the National Institute of Health, and the Department of Energy, all signed on for the digital revolution.

As the Internet grew, it became important for networks to be identified for messaging purposes. So, in 1984, the idea of top level domains and Domain Name Servers (DNS) was born. As the majority of networked computers on the Internet at this time were American, they became grouped by the six basic Internet domains of: Government (.gov), Military (.mil), Educational (.edu), Commercial bodies (.com), Non-profit-making Organisations (.org), and computers used as gateways between the networks (.net). The .net domain later also became used for bodies that were Internet based.

Countries outside the US, simply adopted top level domains relating to their geographic locations; .fr for France, .de for Germany, .ie for Ireland, .co for Columbia, etc. There are now many exceptions to these rules, such as the UK and Australia, both of which adopted a series of upper level domains made up for the most part of the existing American domains, followed by their own top level domain (such as .gov.uk and .com.au).

Further developments in the establishment of the Internet were now happening thick and fast. In 1987, the number of hosts on the Internet reached 28,000, and the Net witnessed its first major commercial uses when what was to become one of the world's biggest Internet Service Providers (ISP), UUNET, was set up.

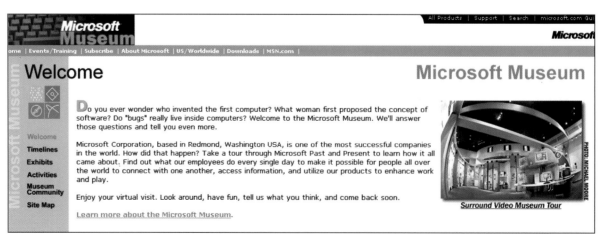

The National Center for Supercomputing Applications (NCSA) at the University of Illinois at Urbana-Champaign is the leading-edge site for the National Computational Science Alliance (Alliance). In this capacity, NCSA anchors all Alliance teams and oversees the administration of all Alliance programs. NCSA leads the Alliance in its mission to maintain American preeminence in science and technology.

The center's user services division has been expanded to assist the large volume of researchers migrating to the Alliance from other supercomputing centers. The computing resources embraced by the Alliance include all the major high-performance computing platforms. NCSA is increasing its own computing capabilities, particularly its distributed shared memory systems. NCSA has the largest unclassified 512-processor distributed shared-memory architecture in the world, which will be continually upgraded to meet the needs of the research community.

NCSA is one of the five original centers in the National Science Foundation's Supercomputer Centers Program. During the decade covered by that program, the center earned a reputation for innovation and aggressive applications in high-performance computing, visualization, and desktop software. Its virtual environment laboratories are among the most advanced in academia, with three different projection-based display systems -- the CAVE, the ImmersaDesk, and the Infinity Wall. In the early 1990s, Caterpillar Inc. demonstrated virtual reality's potential for industrial research when the company slashed months from its production schedule by prototyping its wheel loader almost entirely in NCSA's virtual environments. NCSA Mosaic, the Web browser that launched a billion-dollar industry, is a product of the center.

The following year, Internet Relay Chat (IRC) - the standard for chat rooms across the Net - was developed and by the end of the 1980's the very founder of the Internet itself, ARPANET had become defunct - a victim of its own success. Ironically, its subscribers scarcely noticed, because the Internet as a whole had now adopted all of the former military network's functions.

At the beginning of the 1990's, the expansion of the Internet had been so rapid, that there were now some 300,000 Hosts, over 1,000 Newsgroups, and File Transfer Protocol (FTP) became widespread as a method of transmitting documents online. Internet Service Providers, such as CIX and The World, began to widen Net access.

The Internet now had all the building blocks it needed to reach the phenomenal proportions it has achieved today. Academic, scientific, medical, military and commercial bodies of information, have become available to anyone with a Net connection. Email messages have become the norm for many of the aforementioned organisations. The Net has text, images, graphics, sound files, and database functionality.

What it lacked was the user-friendly interface we are familiar with today. This final piece of the jigsaw arrived in 1991 when Tim Berners-Lee, an Englishman working at CERN, the European Particle Physics Laboratory, developed the World Wide Web. Technically an Internet-based hypermedia initiative for global information sharing, the 'web' or 'www' as it is less often referred to, quickly sped up access to those forms of information mentioned above, anywhere in the world. Although initially non-graphic, the web and the method of traversing it - the browser (also developed by Berners-Lee) -

Bill Gates' Web Site - Microsoft Internet Explorer

File Edit View Favorites Tools Help

Back Forward Stop Refresh Home Search Favorites History Mail

Address http://www.microsoft.com/billgates/

Bill Gates
Microsoft Chairman

HOME | WRITING | BIOGRAPHY | SPEECHES | NEWS | GIVING |

Welcome to my Web site.

Here you can find information about my and interests; look at transcripts of spe given over the years; read essays and written about the many ways technolog and improving our lives; and learn how Melinda, and I are supporting causes th important to us — in our own communit the world.

You can also read about *Business @ the Thought*, a book I wrote to help organiz technology to manage information and k fundamentally new ways.

Bill Gates
Chairman
Microsoft Corporation

Search Bill Gates' Web Site

[   ] GO

PressPass Web Site

Edit   Discuss

ground
s I've
ns I've
hanging
fe,

around

d of
s use
dge in

revolutionised modern communications forever, by allowing the creation of web sites.

From then on it was as if a snowball had been pushed from the top of a very high mountain. The web developed at an amazing pace, gathering and creating new technologies to make it the most exciting medium in the world. In 1992, at which time there were more than one million hosts, multimedia pushed the Internet in the new direction of entertainment, and the term "Surfing the Internet" was coined by Jean Armour Polly (today one of the world's foremost Internet consultants). Also at this time, a part-time computer programmer called Marc Andreessen was working at the University of Illinois' National Center for Supercomputing Applications (NCSA). He had a plan for putting together a user-friendly graphical front-end piece of software, featuring point-and-click navigation, that would really make the world wide web an exciting place to be. Its name was Mosaic.

By 1993, Andreessen's free Mosaic browser had taken the Net by storm, growing to 20 million copies within a year and a half. Within a year of developing his browser, James Clark, the founder of Silicon Graphics, contacted Andreessen via email to talk about setting up a new company. By the beginning of 1994, Andreessen had set up what he called Mosaic Communications, which became Netscape Communications in November of that year. Ironically, it was that year too, that the Net celebrated its 25th anniversary.

Between then, and when it celebrated its 30th anniversary in 1999, the Internet had witnessed the arrival of practically every kind of business and individual onto its systems. Traditional online dial-up systems such as the US's CompuServe and America Online (AOL), as well as the UK's Demon and Freeserve, have all helped to spread the usage of the Internet. The registration of domain names ceased to be free, and became commercial. Microsoft, which at first scoffed at the idea of the Internet and the web, dived into the market in 1996. With its Internet Explorer browser, and many web-related software programs, Microsoft has since become arguably one of the most important players in the Internet market today.

Now the Internet is estimated to have more than one billion web pages, being looked at by some 200 million Net users. Every major company in the world has a web site or is planning an online presence. Most of the world's governments, armed forces, charities, universities, and some 18 million individuals all have web sites you can visit. With these figures only set to rise, the story of the Internet thus far will only be the first chapter when the medium's complete history is written - at some indeterminate point in the distant future.

ISP's & Internet Use

How many people are online? This is the most difficult Internet question to answer as no one knows for sure. There are many surveys, all of which use different measuring processes and all of which come to slightly different conclusions. Most surveys are only as good as the representative cross section they poll, and all are out of date by the time they are released. So, the right answer is: "it's impossible to gauge".

That said, if you examine the majority of surveys published, you can make an educated guess as to how many people are online, both by region and by country. That gives you the total number worldwide. One of the best survey sites on the web belongs to the Irish firm of Nua (www.nua.ie), from which a lot of these figures come.

So how many people are online? Well, collating all the data, it appears that the Internet is used by almost 250 million people worldwide. This is a tiny proportion (just over 4 per cent) of the world's population of 6 billion, but remember that according to figures from the World Bank (www.worldbank.org) only about 15 per cent of the world's population (900 million people) has access to a telephone. You will find the figures for the different regions and countries detailed under their individual headings.

What the breakdown of these figures reveals is that there are many more users in the developed nations than in so-called third world countries. For example, the huge gap in the number of users the US/Canada have and those in the Middle East means that the Internet Service Provider (ISP) market will be bigger and more diverse in North America than it will be in Arab nations.

Some countries operate a system in which ISPs do not compete in a free market economy, and where Internet users must instead connect through a government-controlled central access point. Where Internet access is not completely controlled by the state, ISPs come in many shapes and sizes. The smallest are the local ISPs, peculiar to a specific region or city. Next come the national ISPs, and then the international ISPs such as **AOL** or **PSINet**. Many countries' national telephone companies are also ISPs, giving them a head start in the brand awareness stakes. This idea of brand has also allowed many companies, that previously had nothing to do with either telecommunications or the Net, to enter the market in a strong position.

A major factor in the spread and popularity of different ISPs in different countries is the cost of local calls. In the US, local calls are unmetered. This means that you are charged a flat rate for local calls, no matter how long you stay on the phone. In many countries, however, the telephone companies do not offer unmetered local or

Internet calls, and the price of ISP connection and subscription remains prohibitively high.

What follows in this section is a subjective attempt to identify the foremost ISPs for home use in given countries or regions of the world. In judging the service providers I have, where possible, taken into account the number of subscribers, the importance in the market and the impact they have had. I have also included facts and figures detailing the number of ISPs in each region, and taken a brief look at the state of the service provider business in that region.

Bear in mind that, due to the ever-shifting nature of the Internet and its markets, the following can only be taken as an approximate guide.

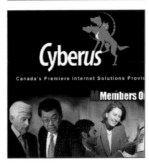

US

According to the latest report from Reuters, the US has approximately 120 million Internet users, comprising equal numbers of men and women. This is an increase for American women online of 32 per cent on 1999 figures. The overall figure is creeping ever closer to 50 per cent of the population.

The biggest story in the US ISP market of recent times was the AOL merger with Time Warner. The deal - creating a company worth almost $350 billion (around £220 billion) - brings together 142 million clients across the world and media properties such as Netscape, CompuServe, *Friends*, Warner Brothers Studio, and CNN.

Taken together, the top seven ISPs account for more than 50 percent of all US residential ISPs subscriptions, with the remaining subscriptions distributed across a highly fragmented market. Within this market, an increasing number of users are signing up with local and regional telephone company-owned ISPs. These ISPs are highly ranked by consumers in terms of customer service and speed of connection, and it is this local market which is expected to record significant growth over the next few years.

ANS/TLIC
One of the nine biggest ISPs in the USA

www.tlic.com/isp/ans_entry1.htm

AOL US/CompuServe

Interactive Services
The biggest ISP in the world, with over 20 million subscribers, is also one of the USA's top providers.

www.aol.com

AT&T WorldNet

One of the US's top national ISPs and portals and voted *PC World*'s Best Buy 1999.

www.att.net

EarthLink

One of America's national ISPs, now exclusively linked to Apple.

www.earthlink.net

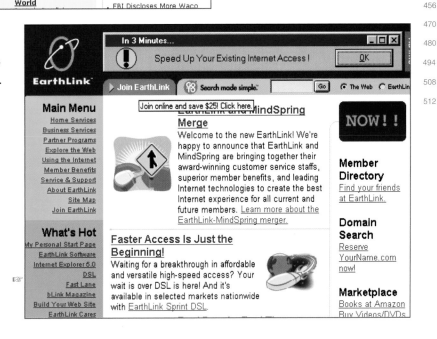

GTE Internetworking/BBN

One of the major ISPs in the US, about to merge with Bell Atlantic.

www.bnn.com

IBM Global Network

Key ISP player in the US, just acquired by AT&T.

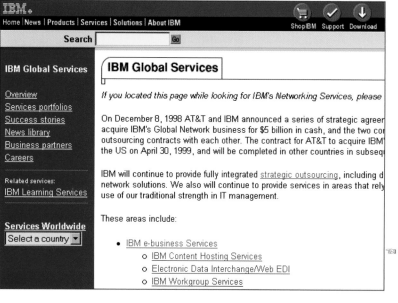

www.ibm.com/globalnetwork

www.att.com/globalnetwork

MCI WorldCom Internet (Cable & Wireless)/UUNET (Pipex Dial)

Two massive Internet service and telecom companies, both part of the same company.

www.mci.com

www.uu.net

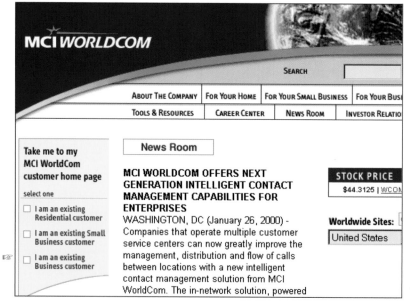

Microsoft Network

The national ISP owned by the biggest company on the planet.

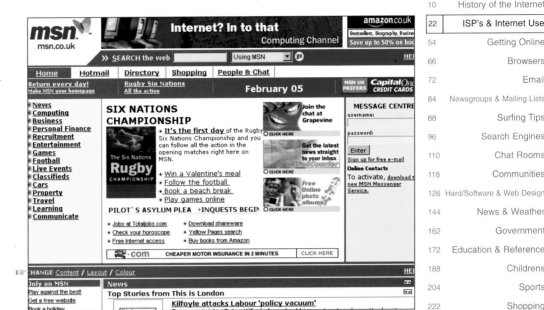

www.msn.com

MindSpring

One of the largest American ISPs, which took over Netcom. Plans to merge with EarthLink (page 25).

www.mindspring.com

www.netcom.com

Prodigy

This national service provider claims to have one of the fastest rates of growth among US ISPs.

www.prodigy.com

PSINet

One of the world's largest ISP companies and a major player in the US.

www.psinet.com

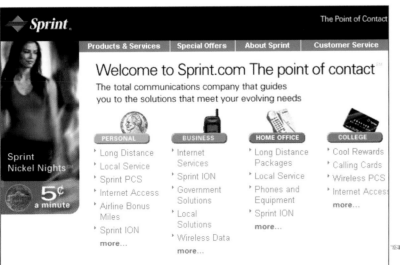

Sprint

One of the US's biggest ISPs, in merger talks with MCI WorldCom (page 26).
One of the world's largest ISP companies and a major player in the US.

www.sprint.com

UK

The UK ISP market was shaken up at the end of 1998 by the introduction of the 'free' ISP model. This model did not charge subscribers a connection or monthly fee, instead it skimmed some of the call charges, made money on premium rate technical help lines and depended, to a great degree, on advertising revenue.

The first of these free ISPs was **X-Stream**, but the electronics retail company Dixons soon joined it and, because of its nationwide distribution network and bigger budget, soon overtook the innovator. Indeed, **Freeserve** (as the service is called) soon overtook **AOL**, which had been the UK's top ISP for some time. Many companies jumped on the free ISP bandwagon, and there are now over 600 ISPs in the UK covering some 13 million users. Roughly half of the UK's ISPs offer paid-for subscription services.

In late 1999 **AOL** struck back by offering a flat dial-up rate of 1p a minute, and in early 2000 BT introduced unmetered Internet calls at differing rates starting at £6.99 (around $11) for evening or weekend access, and a staggering £39.99 (around $64) for unmetered Internet access at all times. It is expected that this price will fall as the British Government sees cheap unmetered calls as vital to the success of e-commerce and becoming a wired nation.

AOL UK/CompuServe/Netscape Online

AOL is number two in the UK with over 600,000 subscribers. CompuServe is top ten, and Netscape Online is well rated too.

www.aol.co.uk
www.compuserve.co.uk
www.netscapeonline.co.uk

BT Internet/ BT Click/LineOne

The telco has three top UK ISPs; the first paid-for, the other two free.

www.btinternet.com
www.btclick.com
www.lineone.net

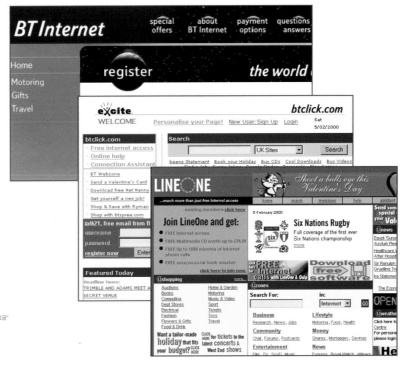

Cable & Wireless Lite/Cable & Wireless Internet

C&W is the main competition to BT offering the free 'Lite' service and the paid-for 'Internet' service.

www.cwcom.net

Demon

The original £9.99 a month ISP, started by Cliff Stanford. Now owned by Thus (ex-Scottish telecom).

www.demon.net

Freeserve

The country's biggest ISP. It's free with over 2.8 million subscribers.

www.freeserve.net

Global Internet

This paid-for ISP has won *Internet Magazine*'s Best ISP of the Year Award twice.

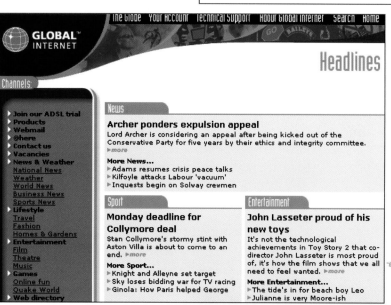

www.global.net.uk

IC24

One of the fastest-growing free ISPs from *The Mirror* newspaper.

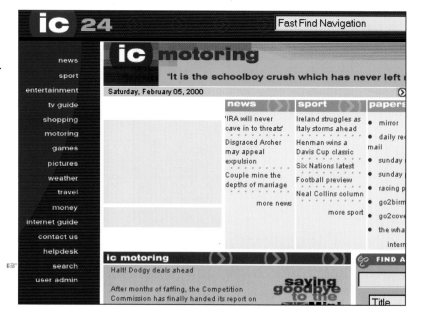

www.ic24.co.uk

UUNet (Pipex Dial)

Not the power it once was in the UK, but still one of the nation's major players.

www.uk.uu.net

MSN

Still in the top 10 ISPs, but now concentrating on its portal.

www.msn.co.uk

Stray Duck

One of the few free call ISPs with staying power.

www.strayduck.co.uk

Virgin Net

Converted to free ISP in 1999. Now one of the UK's top 10 with several hundred thousand subscribers.

www.virgin.net

X-Stream

The UK's first free ISP, and now also the third biggest with almost 700,000 subscribers.

www.x-stream.co.uk

CANADA

The Canadian ISP market is pretty much dominated by American service providers, but there are some homegrown providers. These Canadian ISPs tend to concentrate on areas up to province size, rather than attempt to go nationwide.

The market is quite fragmented with the domestic market supporting an estimated 800 ISPs. These 800 ISPs are currently catering for approximately 40 per cent of Canada's population (13 million users) that is online.

Most recently, Canada has been in the sidelines of an ISP/telco mergers and acquisi-tions battle that has been raging in the US market.

AOL Canada/CompuServe   www.compuserve.ca

Two of the biggest Canadian ISPs with 130,000 and 50,000 subscribers respectively.

www.aol.ca

Cyberus

A new entrant to the national
ISP market, but one to watch.

www.cyberus.ca

Galaxynet-Canada

The big US ISP that's bigger in
Canada.

www.canadadrive.com/canada

Online-Pro

One of Canada's leading ISPs.

www.online-pro.com

PSINet/iStar

Another two companies coming
together to form a market
leader.

www.psi.ca
www.istar.ca

Sympatico.ca

The self-proclaimed home for
Canada on the Internet.

www.sympatico.ca

AUSTRALIA & NEW ZEALAND

Around six million Australians and just under one million New Zealanders use the Internet, according to figures dating from 1999. While New Zealanders have been polled on their thoughts about Internet censorship and responded that the Net should police itself, the Australian Government has had other ideas.

Australia has introduced passing of censorship legislation to govern the distribution of illegal and offensive content on the Internet. Under amendments to the Broadcasting Services Bill 1999, the Australian Broadcasting Authority (ABA) is authorized to seek out such content, and to require offending ISPs to remove the content from their servers. This move has shocked the Internet community around the world as Australia is considered one of the major Internet countries.

Australia boasts over 650 ISPs in a very fragmented market. The two leading ISPs, **OzEmail** and **Telestar**, share 47 per cent of the market, while the next biggest has only five per cent. Asia/Pacific research specialists, IDC, have predicted that 20 per cent of the country's existing ISPs will be out of business by 2002. However, the same prediction of consolidation was made for the UK ISP market and, so far, that has not happened - the reverse, in fact.

Actrix

One of New Zealand's oldest ISPs - established in 1989.

www.actrix.co.nz

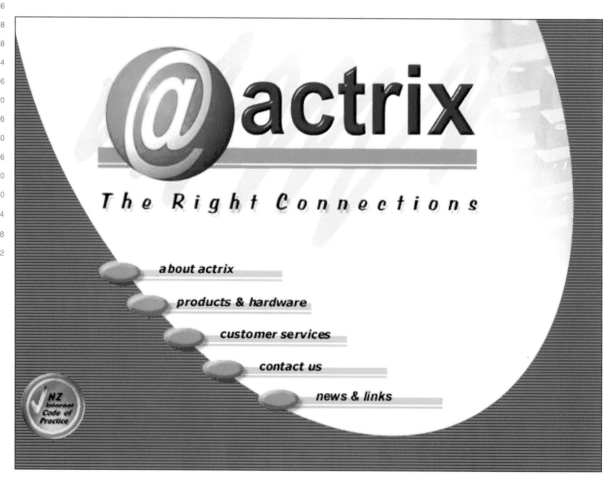

AOL Australia

New entrant to the Australian ISP market from the world's number one ISP.

www.aol.com.au

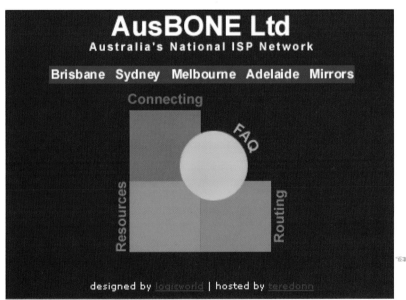

AusBONE Ltd

An upstart co-operative taking on the big ISP players.

www.ausbone.net

ICONZ

One of New Zealand's nation-wide ISPs.

www.iconz.co.nz

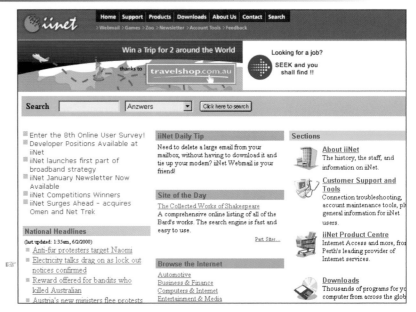

iiNet

One of Australia's largest ISPs, with a focus on Western Australia.

www.iinet.net.au

Internet4Free

Australia's first free ISP launched in early 1999.

www.in4free.com.au

MacroTec

One of Australia's main ISPs with high-speed access and low prices.

www.australia.net.au

Optus (Cable & Wireless)

The second largest telco in Australia and an ISP player.

www.optus.net.au

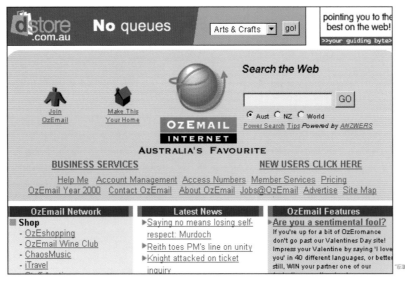

OzEmail

Australia's leading ISP with some 27 per cent of users.

www.ozemail.com.au

Telstra/Bigpond

Australia's largest telco with a 20 per cent share of the market. Also active in NZ.

www.telstra.com.au

www.telstra.co.nz

Telecom

One of New Zealand's leading ISPs.

www.telecom.co.nz

World-Net

Lower prices and faster access have made World-Net one of New Zealand's top ISPs.

www.world-net.co.nz

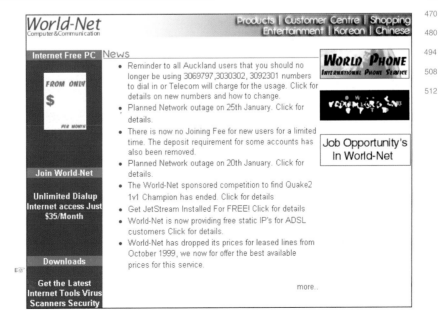

EUROPE (including Russia)

Although it is impossible to detail here the ISP market in every European country, those with the largest number of Net users are: Germany (10 million), Italy (7 million), France (6.5 million), Russia (5.5 million), Sweden (4 million), Spain and the Netherlands (3 million each), Norway, Denmark and Finland (all with 2 million each), Turkey, Poland and Belgium (1.5 million each), and Switzerland (1 million). All other countries have fewer than one million Internet users, and the total for Europe and Russia is 55 million.

While Germany has a very high level of internet use and its market is dominated by the big players, Italy has a reputation for having the lowest Internet penetration levels in Europe (around 5 per cent). This is changing due to the introduction of free ISPs. Indeed, the whole of Europe has witnessed an explosion in the number of free ISPs, with France and Spain also greatly affected.

Ireland must be considered a potential growth area due to its use of English, but the biggest potential in Europe must be in Russia. However, the future for its ISPs is not looking so rosy. Although there is vast,

untapped potential in terms of users, the Russian Prime Minister, Vladimir Putin, is known to be examining ways of regulating the Internet and access to it.

AOL Germany

The first of AOL's ISPs outside the US to hit one million subscribers. AOL also has a dedicated service in France.

www.germany.aol.com

www.france.aol.com

Eunet/kpn Qwest

With services in almost all European countries (Belgium, Spain, Finland, France, etc), Eunet is one of the largest ISPs in the region.

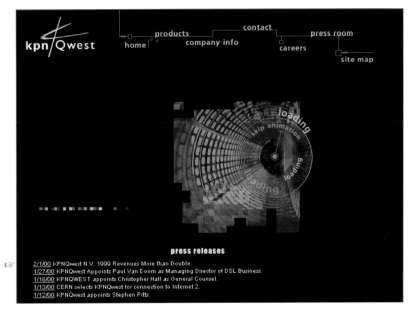

www.eunet.com

T-Online

Owned by Deutsche Telekom, T-Online is the biggest ISP in Europe.

www.t-online.de

Telefonica SA

Spain's leading telco and a recent entrant to the ISP market.

www.telefonica.es

Liberty Surf (French)

The most popular free ISP in France with 150,000 subscribers.

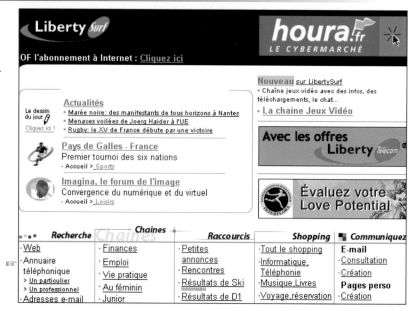

www.libertysurf.fr

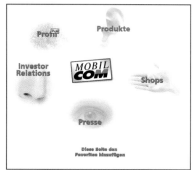

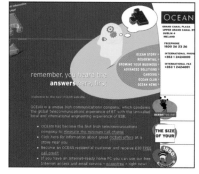

Mobil Com (German)

One of the most popular ISPs in Germany.

www.mobilcom.de

Ocean Free (Irish)

BT-backed leading free ISP, accounting for 10 per cent of the Irish market.

www.ocean.ie

Eircom Net

Ireland's second biggest free ISP with a big share of the market.

www.eircom.net

Relcom

The biggest ISP in Russia founded in 1990.

http://statserv.relcom.ru

Telia

Sweden's national telco and
biggest ISP merged with
Norway's biggest telco, TeleNor,
in late 1999.

www.telia.se

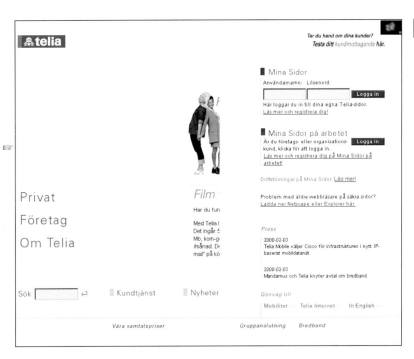

Tiscali

Italy's first free ISP with around
650,000 subscribers.

www.tiscali.it

SOUTH AMERICA

Increased competition among local providers in the Latin American ISP market is forcing down the cost of Internet access, but local call charges remain high and can inhibit growth in the number of Net users. It is hoped that the emergence of free ISPs will change this. If the current situation persists, it is believed that Internet access by mobile phone and cable TV will surpass that of PCs in five years. At the moment the figure for Net users is 7.5 million.

Defining the number of people accessing the Net in South America is an inexact science, but latest estimates show that there is a concentration of Internet use in Brazil (5 million), Mexico (one million) and Argentina (half a million). All the other countries in the region have figures way below this, with the smallest number of net users to be found in Haiti (only 4,000).

AndineT

Colombia's biggest ISP operating out of the country's capital, Bogota.

www.andinet.com

AOL Brazil

The global brand is one of South America's leading ISPs.

www.br.aol.com

Ciudad Internet/Prima

Argentina's leading ISP, part of Grupo Clarin media company.

www.ciudad.com.ar

CompaqNet

New ISP from the computer manufacturer hopes to corner the South American market.

www.compaq.com.mx

Telefonos de Mexico/Telmex

Mexico's biggest ISP with
around 350,000 subscribers.

www.telmex.com.mx

PSINet

Has bought many Brazilian ISPs
to make it one of the country's
major players.

http://corp.psinet.com.br

AFRICA

Although there are 2.5 million Internet users in Africa, around 1.5 million of these can be found in South Africa. South Africa has twenty serious players in the market, each of which has a subscriber base in excess of 10,000. The total number of dial-up accounts is almost 600,000, compared to Egypt which has 207,200, Morocco that has 32,500 and Tunisia with 15,000.

Against all the odds, the first ISP has opened for business in Somalia, bringing one of the few remaining unwired African countries online. However it only has 100 users. Only two countries are now technically without access, Eritrea and Congo-Brazzaville. Africa's land-line telecommunications system is so poorly developed that it is quite possible for the continent to bypass the PC, and go straight to wireless use of the Net.

Vodacom/Yebo!net/World Online

The multi-branded company, arguably the biggest ISP in South Africa, also offers services to other African nations.

www.vodacom.co.za
www.worldonline.co.za

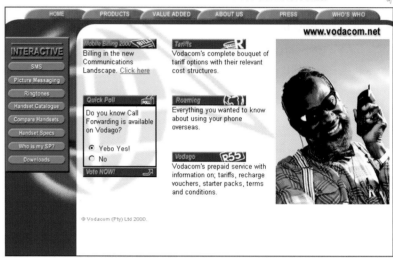

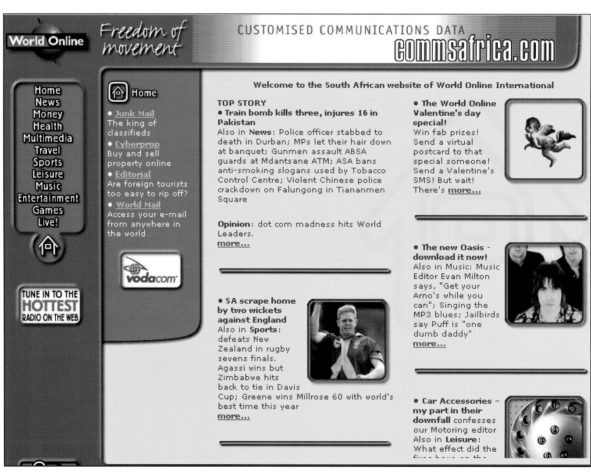

MIDDLE EAST

The Middle East is perhaps the most difficult region to assess, as it is so diverse. The region is plagued by problems such as poor infrastructure, prohibitive telecommunications costs, lack of awareness, and the absence of cooperative policy between government and private sectors.

The biggest story in the Middle Eastern ISP market has been the opening up of the Saudi-Arabian market. This is followed by the awarding of a top level domain (.ps) to Palestine. Israel is the biggest player in the Internet market in this region - Palestine, for example, has no direct connection to the Internet backbone, so its ISPs must all go through an Israeli owned ISP. Israel has between 12 and 13 per cent of its households online. The area has about 1.5 million Internet users, with only four countries rating over 100,000 users: Israel (600,000), United Arab Emirates (204,300), Lebanon/Syria (132,200), and Saudi Arabia (112,500).

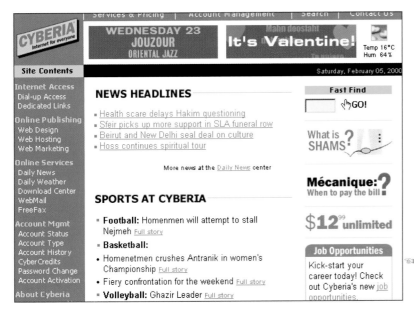

Cyberia

Established in 1996, Cyberia is Lebanon's leading ISP.

www.cyberia.net.lb

Emirates Internet/Etisalat

The Middle East's foremost ISP since 1995.

www.emirates.net.ae

Gulfnet International

Kuwaiti Government sanctioned ISP, also responsible for rebuilding the country's telecommunications system after the Gulf War.

www.moc.kw

NetVision

The favorite ISP in Israel.

www.netvision.net.il

Sahara Network

The first, and now the leading, ISP in Saudi Arabia.

www.sahara.com.sa

SurFree

Israel's first free ISP.

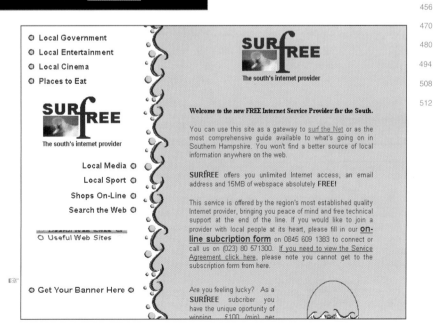

www.surfree.co.il

ASIA

As is the case with Europe and the Middle East, Asia has a very varied ISP market - some countries being state controlled, others only having ISPs under license, and some enjoying the same free market as the West. The major difference between Europe and Asia is that the vast majority of its Internet potential is untapped. The four major countries in the region in terms of use and potential are China, India, Japan and Taiwan. They account for more than 50 per cent of Internet users in the whole of Asia.

China currently has over 9 million Internet users, which sounds relatively high until you remember that China's population is over one billion. It is estimated that as the number of

Chinese online rises sufficiently, and the country becomes more open to free trade, the current domination of English as the language of the web will be over. As it is, China has over 14,000 ISPs (all government controlled), over a quarter of which are based in Beijing, where the majority of users are.

Until the end of 1998, the Indian government held a monopoly on Internet access. Since then, it has granted over 70 licenses to companies to start Internet service provision. Probably the biggest barrier to growth of the Internet in India is the lack of PC penetration across the country. Estimates currently suggest India has 3 computers per 1,000 inhabitants. The country currently has approximately 100,000 Internet

users. Almost 13 million people subscribe to online services in Japan. Small ISPs in particular are experiencing high growth levels. **Nifty** with over 2 million subscribers, however, has seen little growth. In Taiwan, where there are now over two million Internet users and over 100 ISPs, the story is quite different. There the market is dominated by the largest seven ISPs, which account for over 90 per cent of users.

Other countries in the region all have fewer than one million users. South Korea tops the list with 200,000, followed by the Philippines with some 150,000. Next come Singapore and Thailand (both with 100,000), with Malaysia (60,000) and Indonesia (30,000) bringing up the rear.

AOL Japan/AOL Hong Kong
Although not as big in this part of the world, AOL is - as ever - one to watch.

www.jp.aol.com

http://aol.com.hk

Biglobe

The second most popular ISP in Japan is also big in Taiwan.

www.biglobe.ne.jp

Broline.com

One of the Philippines new entrants to the ISP market, but one to watch.

www.broline.com

China.com

Active in Taiwan, as well as specifically Hong Kong, this company has some major partners such as AOL and the online advertising specialist, **24/7**.

www.china.com
www.hongkong.com
www.taiwan.com
www.cww.com

ISP's & Internet Use

China Online

Reputedly China's biggest ISP.

www.chinaonline.com

Eureka@Online/EOL

Now the second biggest ISP in Sri Lanka, pundits believe it could take first place soon. Already has a 25 per cent market share.

www.eureka.lk

HiNet

Taiwan's leading ISP with the greatest bandwidth.

www.hinet.net

Internet Thailand

The country's premier service provider was also its first, launched in 1995.

www.inet.co.th

IUOL

The first Chinese government-approved ISP, which acts in accordance with China's telecommunications department.

www.iuol.cn.net

Mantra Online

Also set up Bharti BT Internet, the British telco's Indian arm, it is one of the major players in the Indian ISP market.

www.mantraonline.com

MosCom Internet

The Philippines' first ISP.

www.mozcom.com

@nifty

Japan's number one ISP.

www.nifty.com

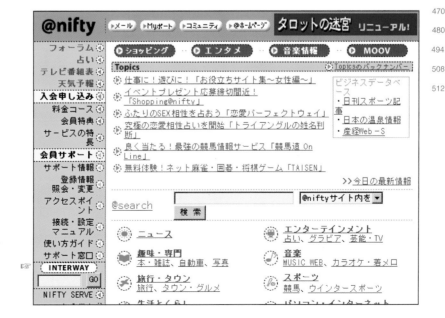

Pacific Link/PI

One of Indonesia's and Singapore's premier ISPs with great terms and conditions.

www.pacific.net.id

Satyam Infoway

India's largest privately owned ISP, part of India's major technology company Satyam.

www.satyam.net.in

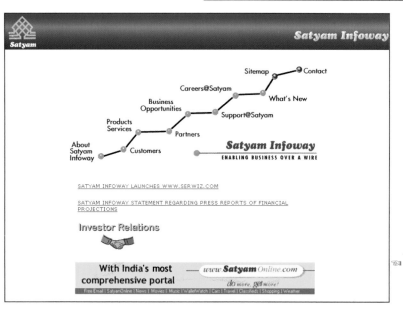

SEEDNet

One of Taiwan's leading service providers.

www.seed.net.tw

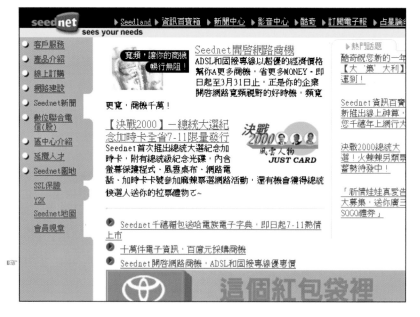

TMnet

Telekom Malaysia's ISP, which is claimed to be Asia's biggest provider with 350,000 subscribers.

www.tm.net.my

VSNL/MTNL/DoT

Indian government telecom provider and first (also biggest) Internet service provider in India.

www.vsnl.com

VNN

One of Vietnam's leading ISPs.

www.vnn.vn

Getting Online

It's a bit of a misconception that connecting to the Internet is complicated - it's getting easier every day with the technology becoming what experts term 'invisible' and 'pervasive'. Although most of the world connect to the Internet through their computers – be they Apple Macs or PCs – there is an increasing number of other devices that can access the Net, from computer games consoles to mobile phones and even kitchen appliances.

Before we look at the more unusual way of getting on the Net, let's ensure that you can get online with your computer. All you need are five things: a computer, a modem, a telephone line, an account with an Internet Service Provider (ISP) and some software. If you are uncertain as to how to go about choosing an ISP, see the chapter in this book on ISPs to find one in your geographic location.

In the most basic connection, the key to the process is a Modem. This name is a contraction of the technical phrase 'Modulator/Demodulator' that means it acts as a translator between your computer and the telephone system. Your computer communicates using digital signals, while the telephone uses tones and pulses. Modems translate the telephone signals into digital signals that your computer can understand and vice versa.

These modems come in many forms and speeds, and the most basic difference is the two distinct physical types. One is internal and the other external. As the names suggest, an internal modem is actually part of your computer, while an external one is a separate piece of hardware.

The faster your modem is, the better your experience of the Internet will be. A modem's speed is measured in bits (a quantity of information) per second. Although there are many 28.8kps modems still in use, most modern computers have a 56kps (capable of transferring 56,000 bits of information per second), which is also known as a V90.

As an aside here, it should be pointed out that the fuss made about the Internet connectivity of the recently released Sega *Dreamcast* games console was all due to its having a 56kps modem built in. Although this is a novelty for a games system and allows owners of the console to play with others over the Net, it is nothing special.

Until recently, the 56kps was the pinnacle of speed you could expect without upgrading to an expensive dedicated telephone line known as a leased line (of which more later). For a few years Net users have had the option of an ISDN (integrated services digital network) connection, which can transmit data up to 128kps.

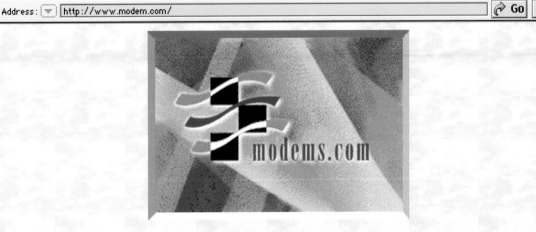

You've made it!

Welcome to modems.com, the most helpful and easy-to-use source for modems information on the Internet.

Modems.com is a public service brought to you by Zoom Telephonics, Inc. We believe in the importance of having up-to-date, accurate information about modems and related technologies. Although our opinions will inevitably come through on occasion, it is our intention to be objective in the information that we present in this forum. We welcome all comments, suggestions and submissions. Over the next few months and years, we intend to continually expand our menu of modem related topics. We hope you will find this site helpful and informative, now and in the future.

Copyright 1995-2000, Zoom Telephonics, Inc. All rights reserved.

Reference | Upgrades | Zoom | Hayes | AdSubtract

Introducing AirPort

AirPort 1.1 Update
If you purchased an AirPort product, you will want to upgrade your base station and card to AirPort version 1.1, which features improved user experience, new functionality such as active roaming, and a preview version of the software base station .

The AirPort Base Station contains a 56K modem and a 10 BASE-T Ethernet port for connecting to a phone line, cable modem, DSL modem or local area network for terrestrial Internet access.

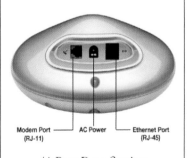

Modem Port (RJ-11)   AC Power   Ethernet Port (RJ-45)

AirPort Base Station

ISDN is prevalent in the small to medium sized enterprise sector, particularly among printers, media companies and the like. This is because it lets companies not only get a fast connection to the Net, but also send and receive large documents. However, ISDN is not supported by every ISP, so if you're going to make the move, ensure you have an ISDN compatible ISP. Be warned that it can be uneconomical, especially if inadvertently left on.

Whatever, the problem, ISDN is ultimately used as an interim or temporary measure. If you do not have unmetered access (a set charge paid on a monthly or regular basis for unlimited Internet calls) you are charged by the minute to use the Net, which is expensive. If you, or your company, have several people using the Internet at different times, it might be an idea to move up a level to a leased line permanent connection.

A leased line will cost you the same set fee for Net access, at any time, for any period you wish. The real price difference is in connection, as a leased line must come straight to your door from the ISP.

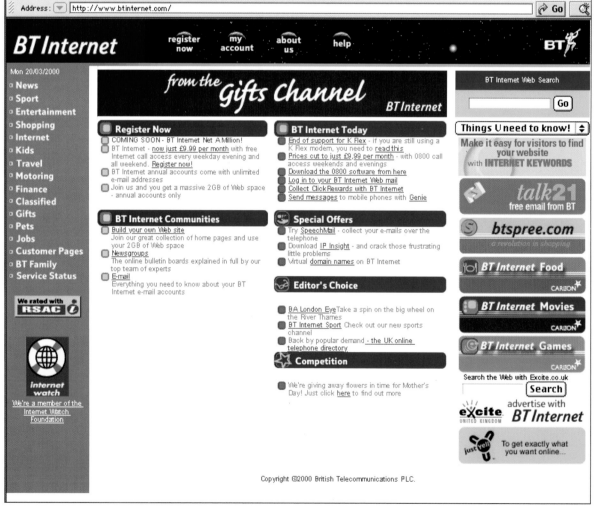

Then there are cables and boxes that have to be installed, but the set fee gives you peace of mind when the time comes for the phone bill to be paid. You certainly don't need a leased line if you only spend a few hours a week online, but the advantages for heavy users are great. In terms of speed, we're talking between 1.44 Mbps (megabits per second) and 45 Mbps.

Another alternative to using a leased line is the cable modem. This type of modem is capable of transmitting data at up to 10 Mbps. Unless you have a leased line, this is about the fastest connection you can get in your home now. The system is so fast because it uses the same 'pipes' as cable TV. This is not to be confused with Web TV, and once again, not every area has the facility.

The problems with ISDN, leased lines and cable modems may be eliminated by a technology that renders old copper telephone wires capable of transmitting data at roughly the same speed as a cable modem. This technology is known as DSL (digital subscriber line), of which the best known in the UK is ADSL (asynchronous digital subscriber line) while in the US there are several standards including SDSL, xDSL, IDSL and many others. Whatever the system, DSL basically takes the old phone line and uses it as three different high-speed lines. The first handles voice traffic, the second is used for uploading data (only about 650kps), and the third for downloading data at a much faster 9 Mbps.

In the UK, only BT can offer DSL connections. The UK's telecommunications regulatory body, OFTEL, has announced plans to change this, but nothing will come into effect until 2001. When it is rolled out nationwide in the summer of 2000, DSL connections will cost ISPs £90 (around $144) a month for a 512kps connection. This will not be the price the ISP charges the customer, so we can expect it to rise to over £100 a month. That said, DSL connections should be far cheaper than current options when they become available early next year. In the US, you can buy a permanent, unlimited access connection for $49 (around £32) a month.

There are also other ways to connect to the Internet that have cropped up in the past year or so. The most important technology is called Wireless Application Protocol which lets specially equipped mobile phones have access to specially designed web sites. WAP basically gives hand-held mobile devices the extra ability to offer a web-like experience. Although this next generation of phones and Personal Digital Assistants (PDAs) will be WAP-enabled, they will not have access to the web, but a section of the Internet that only WAP devices will be able to read.

UNDER CONSTRUCTION...

"By 2004, one-third of all Europeans — more than 219 million consumers — will regularly use their mobile phones to access Internet services."
Forrester Research, dec. 99

WAP.COM is your guide to the wireless internet.

QUIZ - Win a handsfree set for your cellular phone

Click here

Join our mailinglist now – Be the lucky winner of a new Motorola T2288 WAP-phone. A new winner every day !!!

Your email: [ ] [Submit]
The winner for March 19 was Jason Ho, Malaysia.
Previous winners

WAP has been described as a solution looking for a problem and, so far, it has two drawbacks. The first is that although it seems to be the buzzword in Europe at the moment, the North Americans are not enthusiastic as the two continents have very different mobile telephone systems that are generally not compatible. The other drawback is that sites will have to be redesigned in Wireless Mark-up Language (WML), the WAP equivalent of Hyper Text Mark-up language (HTML) the basic design programing language of the web.

The other, much talked about method of connecting to the Internet has been over the TV. With the advent of digital and interactive TV, much has been said about the possibilities of systems such as Web TV, Microsoft's Internet via the TV service. With Web TV the idea is for you to be able to send email to friends and family, surf the Internet, and interact with new forms of entertainment.

Open is another system set up by BT, BSkyB, HSBC, and Matsushita to provide interactive TV services via digital satellite and/or the household phone line. Open itself claims not to be the Internet on TV. Instead, Open offers its "own range of interactive services - all specially designed to be secure".

Whatever the name of these new systems, the forms of entertainment on offer look quite similar. The idea of programs – not just movies – on demand is appealing, as is the renting of software/games, and the ability to intermingle advertising and programing so seamlessly, means that the ad of today will become defunct. Naturally, you will be able to take part in polls (and vote in elections}, chat with other viewers during Interactive TV programing, and automatically program your VCR. The possibilities seem endless, and yet, Internet through the TV hasn't got very far. Making predictions about technology is a bit like trying to negotiate a minefield with a basket of apples and some flour – one foot wrong and it's all so much pie in the sky. That said, there are a few things that can be said with relative confidence about the future of Internet connectivity.

The main thing about the future is that the Internet will be everywhere – not just on your PC, TV, mobile phone and PDA in the shape of the web. When I say the Internet will be everywhere, I mean that goods that communicate using the Internet will be everywhere. Already there are houses that have built-in networks that allow you to program the lighting, heating and security systems from one central control panel. Soon, you will be able to monitor and change those controls remotely from the office or from the car.

All very handy, but some experts would go further. IBM and BT envisage futures where the following scenario might be played out.

You will be driving home from work and the car will detect a fault in one of its systems. It will automatically know what is wrong and how to fix it. So it will go onto the Internet and shop for the best price at the local garages. It will know how far to go in its search, because you will have programmed it with perameters for just such an occasion.

Once it has found the best price, your car will check with your office computer system, PDA and/or mobile phone, to see what time and day is convenient in your schedule for it to book an appointment. Having established this it will make the necessary arrangements. You get to know via voice and/or email message from the car. As you are marveling at modern technology, the car is also busy working out the best route home to avoid traffic jams or any other delay, as well as mapping the route with a global positioning satellite.

Anyone at home will know what time you're due, because your car will have alerted him or her with a very good ETA. Once you reach home, the house will alter lighting, temperature and even your entertainment schedule to your mood. In the kitchen you will take out some food from the fridge and place it in the oven.

You do not have to read any instructions, as the fridge will now be in communication with the cooker/microwave to tell it how long, and at what power setting, to cook the food. It will also have communicated the consumption of the food to your local store or supermarket, which will in turn add the items to your next delivery, to ensure you don't run out. This may all sound a little far fetched, but the technology is almost all in existence today. The point is it will not be long (in some cases they are already here!) before everyday items like kettles, toasters, fridges and cars will be Internet-ready, and using the Net as a means of making your life easier.

QuickTime

hot picks

SXSW 2000 P

SXSW. QuickTime coverage of concerts, film premieres, interviews and more...

Windows 2000

Deploying Windows 2000: I
We've got the tools to ease
2000. For starters visit our
and check out the upcoming
Conference and other trainir
represent a large corporatio
you covered with links to a c

■ **Office 2000 Learning Center: Get the Resources You Need**

■ RealNe
Media

■ **Microsoft and Andersen Consulting Expand Alliance**

■ X-Box
Games

■ **Microsoft Launches Virtual Golf Tour with $100,000 Grand Prize**

■ Micros(
Techn(

More N

DOJ vs. the Freedom to Innovate

Jobs at Microsoft

Subscribe to our Newsletter

sh

Tł
B
In

IBM®

Home | News | Products | Services | Solutions | About IBM   ShopIBM Support Down

Search [   ] Go

News
Current stories
Previous stories
Webcasts
Events
Publications

More news
-> Announcement letters
-> IBM Press room
-> Lotus press releases
-> Tivoli press releases
-> NetObjects press releases

Full story

Major initiatives, partnerships encourage wireless web

IBM working with Cisco, Ericsson, Intel, Motorola, Nokia, Palm and Symbian

IBM will undertake major initiatives to make the wireless Web ready for e-business. The initiatives include key business partnerships and integrated products and services from IBM that will help both wireless providers and enterprises develop and deploy new mobile solutions for e-business. In addition, IBM announced new customers working with the company to pioneer breakthrough mobile e-business applications and services.

IBM is working with Nokia, Motorola and Cisco, three of the leading providers of infrastructure for wireless networks, to provide the foundation for new wireless data services for businesses

IBM and Nokia intend to cooperate in enabling network operators, ISPs and ASPs to deliver wireless e-business services to their enterprise customers. The initiative will involve the mutual exchange and collaboration on key application-enabling technologies, such as Wireless Application Protocol via the Nokia Artus Messaging Platform, Nokia-developed location-based technologies, IBM servers, and voice recognition and transcoding technologies.

IBM and Motorola intend to create an offering that would serve as a 'voice and data engine' so businesses can easily develop and access wireless applications and services.

For example, carriers could use the offering to allow businesses to provide mobile workers real-time access to email, stock quotes, news and corporate resources via wireless devices. The companies plan to establish a joint solutions center to create a flexible framework based on a combination of technologies from both companies. The initial framework will be available in the second half of this year.

Cisco is working with IBM to develop the next generation of wireless networks for both enterprises and service providers. By combining Cisco's expertise in networking for the Internet with IBM?s open platforms for wireless applications, Cisco and IBM will jointly address the increasing demand for e-business solutions on the mobile Internet, through the provision

GETTING THE MOST FROM YOUR PC CONNECTION

Acrobat

Many web sites store files in Acrobat format, and if you want to view them, you'll need software called Adobe Acrobat Reader. Acrobat lets you convert any document into a Portable Document Format (PDF) file, with its original appearance preserved (such as a page from a magazine).

www.adobe.com/acrobat

Address: ▼ http://www.adobe.com/products/acrobat/

Adobe

PRODUCTS   ABOUT ADOBE   REGISTRATION   SUPPORT   SEARCH/SITEMAP   PERSONAL ADOBE   FEEDBACK

ADOBE STORE   SHOPPING CART   WEB   PRINT   MOTION   ePAPER

◀ Products

Adobe Acrobat

support   related products   user forums   tutorials   buy now

The essential tool for universal document exchange

Tired of colleagues not being able to open your documents? Frustrated by software and platform incompatibilities that destroy your documents' look and feel? You need Adobe® Acrobat® 4.0 software. It's the most reliable, efficient, and effective way to share information electronically. Acrobat lets you convert any document - including entire Web sites - into an Adobe Portable Document Format (PDF) file, with its original appearance preserved, and then distribute it for viewing and printing on any system. Powerful markup tools make electronic review a snap, so you can collaborate more easily and productively than ever before.

Do you already own Acrobat 4.0 for Macintosh? You'll want to get the Mac plug-ins, which provide Web capture, digital signatures, and other features previously available only in Acrobat 4.0 for Windows.

Current version: 4.05
Platforms: Macintosh, Windows
System requirements
Language versions

▶ Buy this product

Got a Second?
Help us know how you
use Adobe products

Key Features

- Convert any document to Adobe PDF
- Mark up and annotate PDF documents
- Apply security options and digital signatures
- Create PDF Web forms
- Integrate PDF files with Web servers and e-mail
- Do late-stage text and image editing on PDF files
- Reuse text, graphics, and table data from PDF files
- Retain and print sophisticated PostScript® 3™ graphics

Solutions

- Review and mark up documents electronically
- Protect document security for worry-free distribution

Adobe Acrobat at Work

Try Acrobat Reader with Web Buy
View sections from popular books for free! Web Buy lets you download encrypted content from the Web and unlock it. This Adobe technology is a fully integrated component of Adobe Acrobat and Acrobat Reader (version 4.05, English only).

Adobe ePaper® Solutions
Paper - it's everywhere and it's not going away. Yet, as companies around the globe strive to incorporate e-business practices at "Internet speed," paper alone just doesn't cut it. Here's how you can intelligently bridge the gap between paper and digital documents - and improve your workflow.

Acrobat 4 and Accessibility
Access.adobe.com includes tools that help visually impaired users access Adobe PDF documents by converting PDF into simple HTML or ASCII text. Conventional screen-reading programs then synthesize the text as audible speech. Read the white paper (PDF: 447 KB / 8 pages) outlining future plans to enhance the accessiblity of Adobe PDF files and try out accessible PDF forms.

Flash and Shockwave

Flash lets you view animated images, movie clips and the like without having to wait for them to download. This is called streaming. Shockwave lets you view interactive web content like games, business presentations, entertainment, and ads through your browser.

www.macromedia.com

`http://www.macromedia.com/`

macromedia
add life to the web

日本 américa latina asia pacific brasil canada deutschland españa france italia sverige uk ...

products
Learn about our lineup of breakthrough products.

ebusiness
A complete solution for building your eBusiness Infrastructure.

support
Get the support you need to make the most of our products.

about us
Company information for customers, investors, job seekers, press, and fans.

jobs
We've got a job for you!

gallery
See the best of the Web in our sites with life gallery.

membership
Become a member and subscribe to the Macromedia Edge, a monthly newsletter tailored to your preferences.

shockwave.com
Visit shockwave.com to enjoy games, toons, music, and more.

downloads
Get free downloads from

This site uses Flash extensively. We recommend you install the free Flash Player.

If you know you have Flash Player installed, click here.

news headlines
The latest headlines from Macromedia for March 2000.

▶ Flashforward2000
Burgess and Lynch to deliver keynote at world's first Macromedia Flash conference and exhibition.
▶ Macromedia membership center
Join today and subscribe to your personalized newsletter, the Macromedia Edge.
▶ NBCi.com delivers with Flash
NBC Internet uses Macromedia Flash on their new broadband portal.
▶ Intuwave and Macromedia ally
Partnership brings high-impact Macromedia Flash content to wireless devices.
▶ Director 8 Shockwave Studio
The new studio is ideal for creating magnetic Web sites and producing Shockwave content.
▶ Macromedia Web World in June
Join your colleagues in Seattle for five days of in-depth sessions on Macromedia Web solutions.
▶ Watch Stan Lee's superheros!
Enter The 7th Portal, Stan Lee's newest Webisode, featured exclusively on shockwave.com.
▶ We've got a job for you!
Job spotlight: Direct Sales Representative. Find work you love. We've got lots of openings.

sites that add life to the web
What happens when you add life to your Web site? Check out how these leading companies did it with Macromedia products.

altoids   winstar   levi strauss & co.   mandalay   boston herald

QuickTime

Software that lets you play and edit digital video, as well as other types of media on your computer. Fox and Disney favor it for their sites.   www.apple.com/quicktime

RealPlayer

This plug-in lets you play movies and sound files of the kind that you
have to download before you can enjoy them.

www.real.com

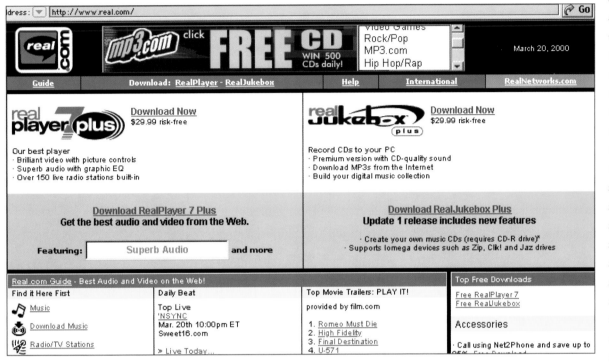

Windows Media Player

A similar piece of software to the real Player, but only compatible with
certain files, s if you want to be able to play all those multi-media clips,
you'll need this software to complete the set.

www.microsoft.com

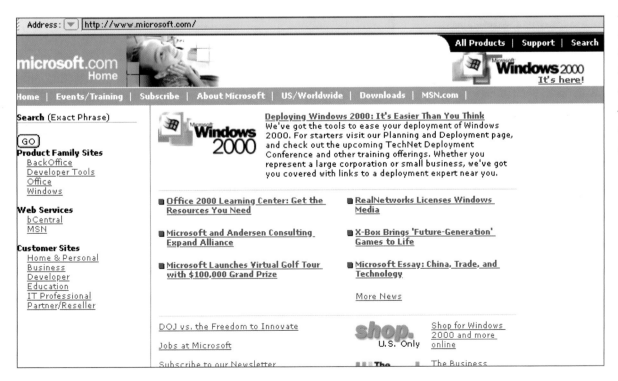

Browsers

To connect to the Internet and view the world wide web, you will need a piece of software called a **browser**. This special tool will allow your computer to download and display pages from the web. Don't worry too much about getting hold of a browser as the chances are you already have one. Many come bundled with the software, or as part of Internet Service Provider (ISP) software, which is often already installed on a computer when you buy it.

Although it is estimated that there are over 300 different browsers in existence, Netscape's Navigator and Microsoft's Internet Explorer (IE) are the two main browsers in use, with Internet Explorer now becoming the browser of choice. These two software programs come in many versions but, at the time of writing, the latest versions are IE5 and Netscape 4.6. If you haven't got either of them, don't worry as they are free and you can download them direct from their makers' sites. In the UK, you will find the latest versions of both pieces of software on the cover mounted CD on Internet-related publications, such as *Internet Magazine.*

You can set many controls in your browser to speed up navigation, or to stop the chil-dren from seeing unsuitable sites. To help you, let's take a brief look at how your browser is made up. Apart from the large display window for showing web pages, a browser has several bars above it that let you adjust your browser's controls. Netscape Navigator and IE have three of these that fulfil similar functions.

Under the title bar that displays the software name comes the menu bar. This lets you open the control menus of your browser - to open a new document, print a page, copy some text or shut down the program, for example. Below this is the navigation bar with a row of buttons that let you

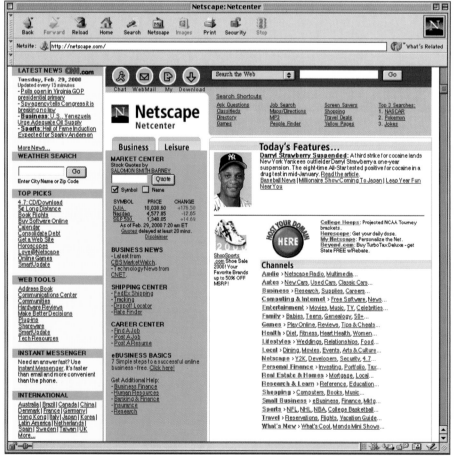

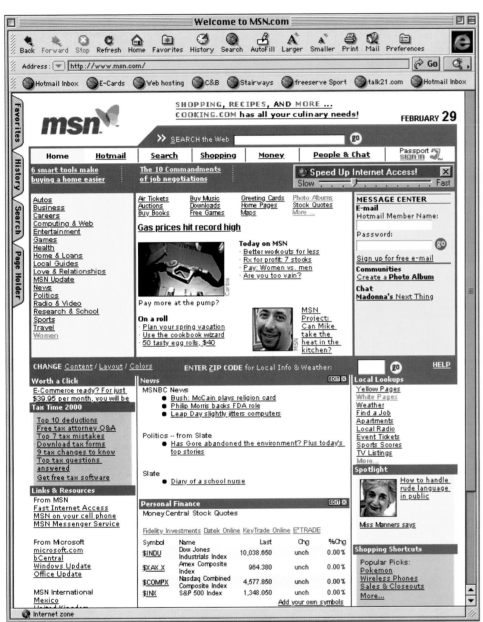

control your browser without accessing the menu bar. IE and Netscape Navigator (as well as the less common browsers) share similar buttons.

Both of these popular browsers have a 'Back' and 'Forward' button. These let you move between pages you have viewed. The 'Home' button takes you to the page set up in your browser as the first page you see when you connect to the

Net. 'Print' lets you print the page you are looking at, while 'Stop' is useful for preventing a page from loading when it has stalled. The 'Refresh' and 'Reload' buttons perform the same function of reloading a page after you have stopped it or if you have changed your settings.

The 'Search' button will help you find things online by taking you to appropriate search

engines. You can make IE and Netscape Navigator remember sites you have found by adding them to your 'Favorites' or 'Bookmarks'. These buttons actually display those sites you have chosen. As with the less popular browsers, IE and Netscape Navigator have separate functions that we cannot go into in great detail here, but you will find full user guides on their respective web sites.

Internet Explorer

Microsoft's late entrant to the market, Internet Explorer, has become the most popular browser in the world. It has overtaken Netscape Navigator in the number of new versions that have been released, and is now the browser of choice with most Internet Service Providers - even AOL, which now owns Netscape.

www.microsoft.com/windows/ie

It works *faster* to save you time

New to the Net?
Web enthusiast?
Building a business?
Today's Highlights

Download Now
International Downloads
Order the CD

Tell us what you think about Internet Explorer 5.01!

Download Internet Explorer 5.01--the newest version of Internet Explorer with 56-bit encryption! Internet Explorer 5.01 not only displays Web pages faster, it's designed to save you time on the things you do most often. It's never been easier to get online, find the information you need, and just do stuff faster. You can also order Internet Explorer 5 on CD.

For customers in the U.S. and Canada, you can download the high encryption (128-bit) upgrade package for Internet Explorer 5.01!

Netscape Navigator

Used to be the unrivalled king of the browsers, Netscape Navigator now has to play second fiddle to Microsoft's Internet Explorer. The browser was designed off the back of the original Mosaic browser and is generally favored by Apple Mac users. The latest version is 4.7 and a newer one is expected shortly.

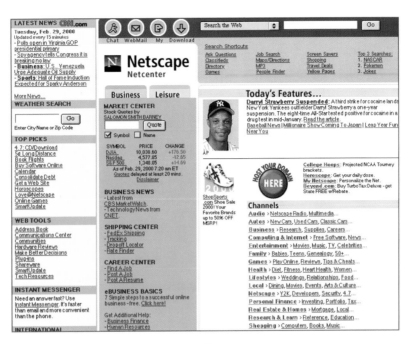

http://home.netscape.com/browsers/index.html

N Netscape

You are here: Home > Netscape > Browsers

Netscape Communicator and Netscape Navigator

Click for Long Distance savings   Get 128-Bit Encryption Here!   Get FREE email!

Choose a Product ▼ Go

Netscape Communicator combines Netscape Navigator, the world's most popular browser, with a suite of Internet tools for high-performance Internet mail, web page creation, and instant messaging.

Get Information About Communicator and Navigator

By Product
Communicator

Navigator

By Type of User
Home and Small Business

Corporations

ISPs

Browser Update Notice

If you are using an older version of Netscape Navigator or Netscape Communicator (version 4.05 or earlier), you may wish to update your Netscape browser to ensure a continued smooth experience while conducting secure on-

Highlight

MY stock quotes, MY news, MY weather, MY horoscope, MY sport scores, MY NETSCAPE

About Communicator and Navigator

Data Sheets
FAQs
In the News
Future Versions
How to Get Browsers
Browser Plug-ins
Performance

Amaya

The world wide web Consortium's own browser and a relatively simple one it is too.

www.w3.org/Amaya

Amaya - W3C's Editor/Browser

Activity Statement | Documentation | Mailing list | FAQ

Try MathML. With Amaya you can edit complex mathematical expressions within HTML pages through a WYSIWYG interface. See some examples.

Download Amaya

New! This release includes support for HTML 4.0 and XHTML and new features like the horizontal scrolling, the ability to print with style, and the possibility to work either on the HTML view or on the source view. The new release also improves the accessibilty of Amaya for people with disabilities and for people who prefer to use the keyboard. With Amaya, one can download, test, edit and publish CSS style sheets as well as HTML pages. Profiles allow you to customize the application according to your HTML expertise and a mechanism of templates can help users who frequently create the same kind of HTML pages.

- Amaya 2.4 public release (17 December 1999)
- Source code of Amaya 2.4 public release (17 December 1999).
- RPM distributions are also available at http://rpmfind.net/linux/RPM/amaya.html.

Amaya is covered by the W3C Copyright Statement. Please read it carefully before downloading the software. That icon can be inserted in your Web pages when they are created and edited by Amaya.

The Cello Internet Browser

This file was last updated on April 9, 1994.

The latest edition of Cello is version 1.01a.

What Cello is and does

Cello is a multipurpose Internet browser which allows access to the myriad information resources of the Internet. It supports WorldWideWeb, Gopher, FTP, CSO/ph/qi, and Usenet News retrievals natively, and other protocols (WAIS, Hytelnet, Telnet, and TN3270) through external clients and public gateways. It can be used to view hypermedia documents, including inlined images, text, and digital sounds and movies. Cello was developed by Thomas R. Bruce of the Legal Information Instit at Cornell Law School.

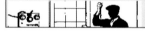

Cello

Multi-purpose Internet browser that supports the more straight-forward web-related media by itself, but will need help for anything complicated.

www.law.cornell.edu/cello/
cellotop.html

Lynx

The best-known text only browser that cuts out extraneous pictures, animation and video.

http://lynx.browser.org

Lynx

Lynx is a text browser for the World Wide Web. Lynx 2.8.2 runs on Un*x, VMS, Windows 95/98/NT but **not** 3.1 or 3.11, on DOS (386 or higher) and OS/2 EMX. The current developmental version is also available for testing. Ports to M are in beta test.

- How to get Lynx, and much more information, is available at Lynx links.
- Many user questions are answered in the online help provided with Lynx. Press the '?' key to find this help.
- If you are encountering difficulty with Lynx you may write to **lynx-dev@sig.net**. Be as detailed as you can about the URL where you were on the Web when you had trouble, what you did, what Lynx version you have (try '=' key), and what OS you have. If you are using an older version, you may well need to upgrade.

Maintained by lynxdev@browser.org

Mosaic

The first ever browser is still going and used by many devotees.

Welcome to NCSA Mosaic, an Internet information browser and World Wide Web client. NCSA Mosaic was developed at the National Center for Supercomputing Applications at the University of Illinois in Urbana-Champaign. NCSA Mosaic software is copyrighted by The Board of Trustees of the University of Illinois (UI), and ownership remains with the UI.

Jan '97

The Software Development Group at NCSA has worked on NCSA Mosaic for nearly four years and we've learned a lot in the process. We are honored that we were able to help bring this technology to the masses and appreciated all the support and feedback we have received in return. However, the time has come for us to concentrate our limited resources in other areas of interest and development on Mosaic is complete.

All information about the Mosaic project is available from the homepages.

www.ncsa.uiuc.edu/SDG/Software/ Mosaic

| The Mozilla Organization | Mozilla News | 4 February 2000 | Status Update | 1 February 2000 |

The Mozilla Organization
At A Glance
Feedback
Get Involved
Newsgroups
License Terms
Newsbot

Developer Docs
Roadmap
Projects
Ports
Module Owners
Hacking
Get the Source
Build It

Testing
Download
Bugzilla
Bug Writing

Tools

Mozilla Localization Project
Join the Mozilla Localization Project. Their goal is to ship as many language packs for M14 as possible. Projects are underway in 16 different languages. Localized versions of M13 are already available in Japanese and German.

Macintosh Compiler Update
Due to popular demand, the Macintosh build system is moving from CodeWarrior Pro 4 to Pro 5. Mac developers will need to update their build environment. See bug 25949 and the mozilla mac newsgroup for more details.

Open Source Crypto Announced
Thanks to relaxed US export regulations, we can now host security and cryptographic code. For more details, see our press release and Mozilla Crypto FAQ. The Sun-Netscape Alliance has announced that it will contribute Open Source PKI Projects to

This week's update contains news on ZopeMozilla, Mail/News, Composer and XPToolkit...
more...

Download Mozilla

Mozilla is an open-source web browser, designed for standards compliance, performance and portability. For more info about us, read Mozilla at a Glance. We provide these binaries for testing and feedback. Use bugzilla to report bugs.

Milestone 13
M13 is our Alpha release. Use it as your main browser and find as many bugs as possible as we work to release a beta. Use Fullcircle packages to report crash data and

Mozilla.org

The open source browser that you could modify if you wanted to. M13 (the first alpha version) now available.

www.mozilla.org

Opera

One of the few browsers that charges anything and this one costs $35 (around £22).

Home

Program Info
Features
Keyboard Navigation
Plug-ins
Try It - Buy It
Download
Prices
Purchase
Expired Opera
Services
My Opera
OperaMail
Technical Support
Special Needs
Discussions
Mailing lists
Explore Opera
Affiliate Programs
Opera Products
Press
Tools
Opera Ports
Company
Awards
Guestbook

OPERA *The Browser Made For You!*

Search our site:

[   ] go

Download Opera!

- Opera for Windows 95/98/NT4/2000
- Opera for Windows 3.x/NT3.51
- Opera for BeOS
- Opera for Linux

About Opera for Windows

The most recent English Language version of Opera for Windows is 3.62 Beta 6.

This upgrade is free for registered users of Opera version 2.12 and up. Select your version for download below.

Opera for windows is fully functional for 30 days of usage after installation--the software is not crippled in any way. After the 30 days of usage it will expire and it

www.opera.com/download.html

Email, or electronic mail to give it its full title, is the part of the Net most used in everyday life. While some businesses do not allow 'surfing' of the Net, they would be foolish to disallow email, for this newest form of communication is the main reason for businesses to connect to the web.

The reasons for its popularity are not hard to see. It is both more efficient and better suited to business communication than a telephone call - an email tends to be brief and to the point while having the added bonus of carrying documents, pictures or sound. Email improves on the postal system, as it is not bound by the constraints of time or distance and, compared to either a phone call or a postal charge, the cost is a fraction.

In order to send and receive emails, you will either need email software, or a web-based email system. Most Internet Service Providers (ISPs) provide you with at least one email address for one of these systems. In the case of a paid-for connection service, you are likely to be given an email program as part of the ISP's software package, probably bundled with the browser. As part of the ISP's paid-for service, it will provide you with at least one email address - and more normally at least three.

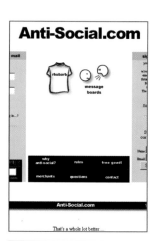

 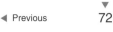

The form of an email address identifies people in much the same way as an addressed envelope, and is broken down into two constituent parts. The first (the bit before the '@' symbol) will identify the person to whom the email address belongs. This first section is usually the name, title or initials of the individual. It could also be a set of numbers, or a mixture of the two. Some people prefer to use an Internet nickname or handle, which can be anything you like.

The section of the address after the '@' symbol refers to the domain to which the user belongs. This will either be the name of the ISP or web-based email service the individual uses, the company he or she works for, or a combination of the two.

Using the multiple email addresses given to you by your ISP you can set up additional addresses, either for you, your partner, your children or maybe your employees. You may even choose to use different addresses not for people, but for aspects of your life or business. It's worth thinking about how you'd use extra email addresses, and finding an ISP who'll accommodate those needs.

To send an email all you need do is open your email software, start a new message, fill in the email address of the recipient, type in a short phrase to act as the subject, complete your message and click on 'send'. It's as simple as that. No country's postal system is involved. Email is sent and delivered all day every day. The only restriction is how often the person receiving the email checks his or her mailbox, and whether the email server is operating properly. Not only can you add the aforementioned extra documents or files - termed 'attachments' - but you can choose to 'cc' or copy people in on your message. This saves having to write the same message to each person you need to inform of, for example, a meeting.

In the case of the free ISP model, it is unlikely you will receive email software. Instead the ISP will offer you a free, web-based service. On the surface, web-based email works in much the same way as normal email, but they are completely different systems. If you have email software, messages sent to you are routed through your ISP to your mail server, and then downloaded onto your computer when you connect to the web and check your email. Those messages then reside on your computer's hard drive until you delete them. Most reputable ISPs will let you send and receive as many messages of (almost) whatever size you like. Moreover, storage space is only limited by the memory of your computer.

When you sign up to a web-based email service, you are given a small amount of space on the company's servers, and told what you can and cannot do in terms of sending and receiving messages.

Limitations on the size of attachments are common, and the amount of memory you have for the storage of emails is kept small. Whether you use your own, or a web-based email service's software, there are many ways you can improve the process to get the most from it. In general you can just think of email as normal post. When you start using it, you'll see that your software comes ready with 'in' and 'out' trays. This is so that you can keep track of what was sent or received, when and by whom. Also, like normal mail, the more correspondence you enter into, the more you'll need an address book. You can operate without one by simply selecting an old email from the person you're writing to from the 'in' tray, and clicking on the reply button. But you don't need to go this rather long-winded way round. All email software is different, but you should find the address book controls under one of the main pull-down menus on the opening screen of your email program, or one of the options presented to you on the web site of your free email account.

Some will let you create a new entry by just right clicking your mouse when the sender's email is open. Others - such as **Eudora** (at www.eudora.com) - let you create nicknames within an address book, where you can store email addresses and a raft of other information. Most email systems let you administer your messages using a labeling

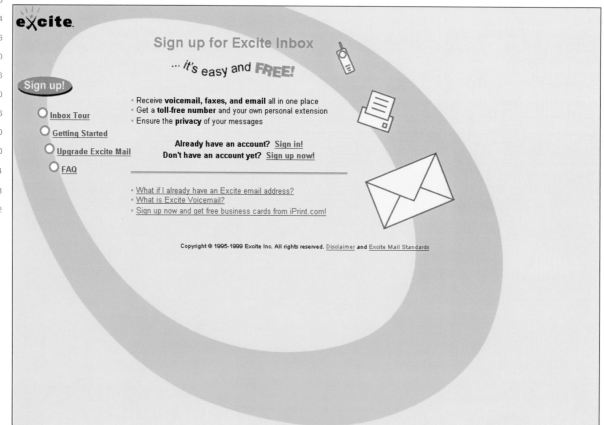

system, too. This lets you color-code your emails into groups. So, if you need to find a specific message you'll be able to search by sender, date, time, subject, or label - for example you might use the color red to signify that a message is urgent.

You will also find that filtering can save you a lot of time. You can program your software - and in some cases your web-based mail - to search for certain words and either delete, or file, the messages accordingly. The reason you might want to delete messages is due to what is known as Spam, or unsolicited bulk email. Most of these junk emails are about get-rich-quick schemes or pornographic sites. These can be deleted by filtering such messages into the rubbish folder. Choose your keywords carefully. I have mine set up for 'nudity' and 'millionaire', and have no doubt missed out on some attractive offers.

Once you've found your way around a bit more, you might want to choose a different email program that suits your needs better than the one you haphazardly started off with. Although the two main browsers come with free email packages, there is a paid-for version of *Outlook Express* that has additional qualities, and the excellent *Eudora Pro* is a firm favorite in the marketplace. Then there are the many web-based services, which are also very good for sending and receiving email if you're traveling about the globe.

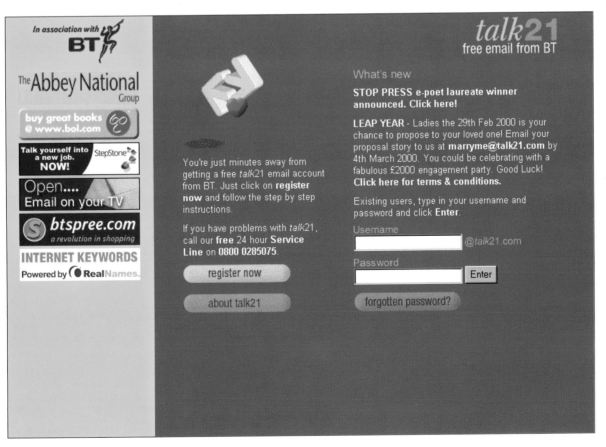

Eudora

Probably the best email software available. Not only does Eudora come in the paid-for 'Pro' version at £34.95 (around $56), and a free 'Lite' version, the company also has a web-based service called **Eudora Web-Mail** (www.eudoramail.com). The Lite and Pro versions are both excellent, with obvious advantages to be had for the £35…

www.eudora.com

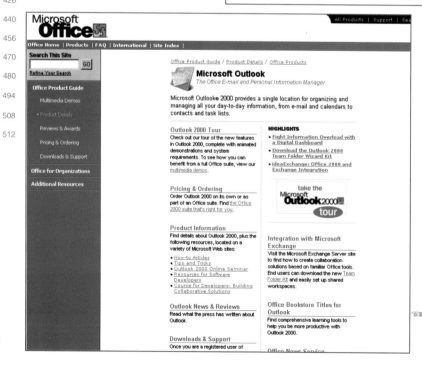

Outlook

The package that comes bundled with Microsoft's Internet Explorer browser, so definitely the most widely used email software. It too comes in free, and paid-for, versions and like Eudora has a free web-mail service in the shape of **Hotmail**. Outlook has its idiosyncrasies, but it and Eudora are pretty much neck and neck for quality.

www.microsoft.com

Another.com

Choose from thousands of funny domains at which to get an address. For example, fashion lovers could go for 'insertname-here@iloveprada.co.uk.'

www.another.com

Care2

If you want to feel good about using free email, Care2 promises to make a donation to an animal charity every time someone signs up with them.

www.care2.com

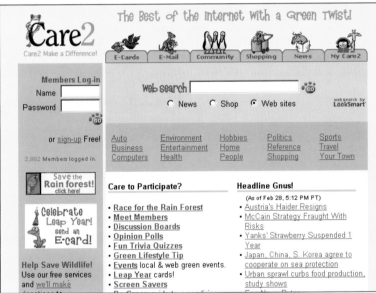

Hotmail

Microsoft's free, web-based email service. Along with **Yahoo!**, probably the best known - although given its recent hacking, not always for the right reasons.

www.hotmail.com

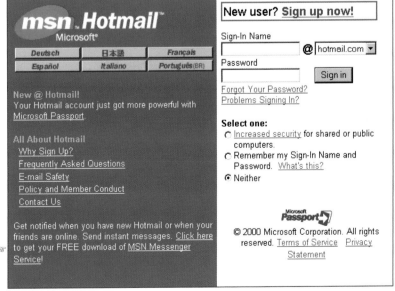

Netscape

Another one of the better known email packages - again because it comes packaged with Navigator as part of the Communicator package.

www.netscape.com

PostMaster

Good web-based email site from Bibliotech, who know about secure email. You get voicemail back up, as well as message filtering and address book management.

www.postmaster.co.uk

Anti-Social.com

You might not get a reply using a name like this, but the domain name alone makes the service worthy of note.

www.anti-social.com

Yahoo!

One of the best known free web-mail services, but this time for the right reasons - good reliability and services.

www.yahoo.com

Angelfire

Although better known for its free web space, Angelfire is powered by Lycos, making it reliable and a good spam blocker.

www.angelfire.com

ApexMail

Although not one of the major players in the free email arena, Apex offers good mail blocking and mailbox flexibility features.

www.apexmail.com

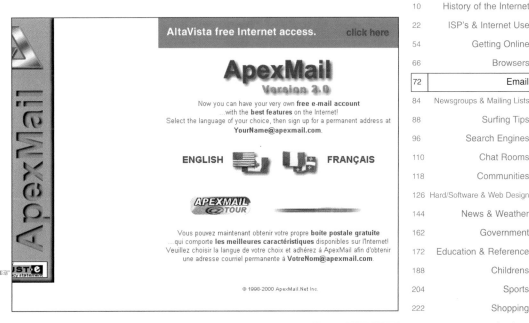

Asian City Web

Targeted at the world's Asian community, the service has high hopes for its explosive market potential.

www.asiancityweb.com

BBoy.com

Hip-hop themed free web-based email system.

www.bboy.com

Bla-Bla

Another domain name designed to get users noticed, those who have signed up also get a news service.

www.bla-bla.com

Catholic Online

Much like Asian City, the Vatican is hoping to net a lot of users given the loyalty it enjoys from them!

http://webmail.catholic.org

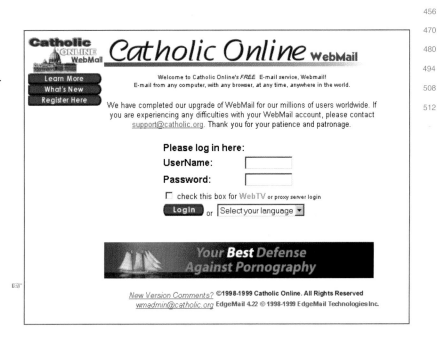

Celtic.com

Probably not quite the user base of Asia or the Church of Rome, but the idea's a nice one.

www.celtic.com

Chickmail

Pretty girl power rules here and, if the rumors are anything to go by, the service is pretty good too.

www.chickmail.com

email.com

Possibly the best name in the free web mail business.

Dog Mail

If email problems have dogged you before, you could try the canine themed Dog Mail.

http://mail.dog.com

Easypost

The UK-based service seems to be offering all manner of free web site related goodies, like 100MB of space and domain name transfer.

www.easypost.com

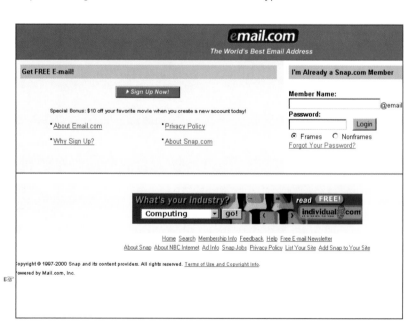

www.email.com

email choice

Unlike so many other free email companies, email choice offers a generous 15MB for email storage and transfer.

www.emailchoice.com

England Online

Another Lycos-backed web-mail system that offers an address @england.com. A must for English football fans.

www.splendiferous.com

Excite Mail

Email addresses are available at '.com' and '.co.uk' domains so take your pick.

www.excite.co.uk

GetMessage.com

Even if you are offline, this service will get the message through with free fax-back and voicemail messages.

www.getmessage.com

Grabmail

Another web-based free email company keen to get the message through via pager or fax.

www.grabmail.com

Graffiti.net

Like Angelfire, this site's more of a community than a simple 'drop in to pick up your messages and push off' service.

www.graffiti.net

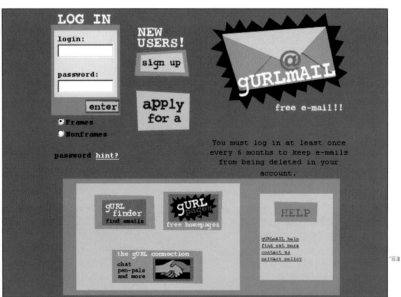

GurlMail

More girl power, this time with added pen pals and a home page to boot.

www.gurlmail.com

Hushmail.com

Claims to be the world's only web-mail service with end-to-end security. This alone makes it noteworthy.

www.hushmail.com

NightMail

Easy-to-use free email service, that offers no extras, but has attracted quite a crowd of users.

www.nightmail.com

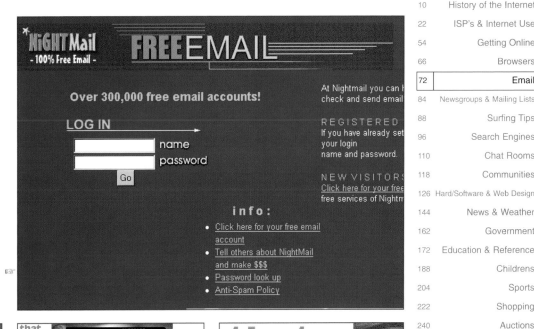

Talk21

British Telecom's web-based email service that also lets you tap into other email accounts you hold.

www.talk21.com

That Web

One of the very simple free mail firms that allows you to get your other email accounts all in one place.

www.thatweb.com

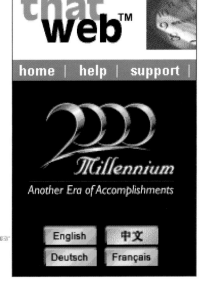

Twigger

Pan-European email service that - like Talk21 and That Web - lets you pick up other email accounts.

www.twigger.co.uk

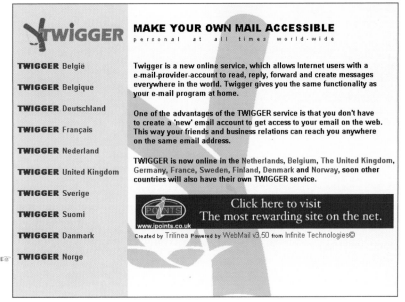

B efore the world wide web, one of the most popular uses of the Internet was the Usenet. It allowed people to post messages on public notice boards, using a similar technology to email. It is still used today, but is not as widely used as it once was. Whereas the web is a more passive experience, like reading a magazine or watching TV, the Usenet is more interactive. It allows you to air your views, and have discussions with others, in areas of the Usenet called '**newsgroups**'.

Newsgroups work in a similar way to a public notice board. On the web, you will find that many sites have forums that work in exactly the same way. Once you 'post' a message on the newsgroup of your choice, anyone else can read it. Not only that, but they can post a reply to your original message, or start another strand of discussion.

The great thing about Usenet newsgroups is that, like the web, they cover a huge diversity of subject matter. It is estimated that there are over 30,000 newsgroups currently in operation, covering any topic you can think of, and quite a few you can't!

These are organised into divisions, which are in turn sub-divided into topics, and then sub-divided again if the topic has different discussion points.

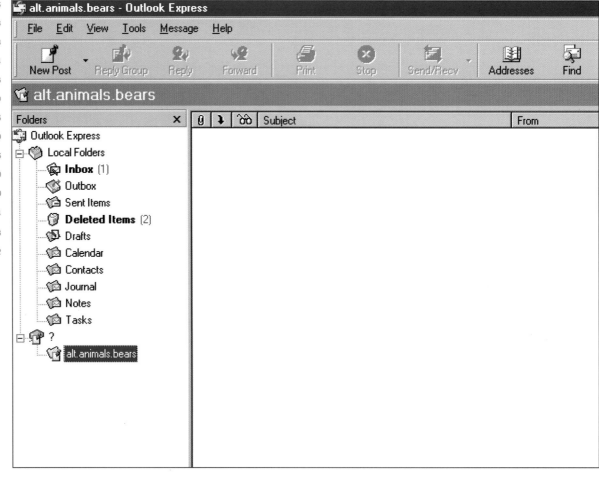

Right: This is what your newsreader will look like when you first begin.

For example, one of the most popular, and largest, newsgroups is called 'rec'. This stands for recreation. It is sub-divided into divisions such as 'sports' and 'arts', and then further sub-divided by topics such as football, films, or even television programs.

There are many others such as the 'biz' newsgroup. As the name implies, this covers discussions of a business nature, from marketing and business strategy, to new products, mergers and job opportunities.

One particularly large newsgroup is called 'comp'. This deals with every aspect of computers from programing languages, software applications, hardware and such like.

The 'info' newsgroup is a relatively small forum, but covers a wide-ranging collection of topics. 'News' does not deal with what you might think; it reports on the newsgroups themselves. For example, new users will find an area called 'news.newusers'.

If you are interested in academic discussion, with an emphasis on the scientific, try 'sci'. You will also find professional scientific forums here, while those interested in culture, religion and the like should try 'soc'.

Another slightly misleadingly named newsgroup is 'misc'. Although this does stand for miscellaneous, the majority of topics are US-based and cover areas of discussion that you might find elsewhere.

If you can't find your pet subject in these, or any of the other newsgroups, your best bet would be to try the 'alt' newsgroup. It was set up to encompass any topic of conversation that the others did not cover, and deals with things that might be considered 'alternative'. Be warned, as this was started as a kind of protest, and the topics and language used in some of the forums may offend you.

Now you know a bit about the thousands of newsgroups out there, you'll need to know how to access them. The email software that comes bundled with both the main browsers - Internet Explorer and Netscape Navigator - has software called a Newsgroup Client that lets you access the Usenet. A great many other email software packages are also newsgroup enabled. Check your software's manual to be sure.

If you are going to be using newsgroups a lot, it would be better to get some dedicated software. These can be found at many of the software download sites, mentioned in the **Software** section of this book. It is also a good idea to download and read a newsgroup's Frequently Asked Questions (FAQs) file. This prevents you asking a question that has already been answered, and will bring you up to speed on what is going on in the forum.

You will need to ask to subscribe to any newsgroups that take your fancy. Your Newsgroup Client will then need to download the newsgroup from the news server on your Internet Service Provider (ISP). There are two drawbacks to this process. First, these files can be very big and take a long time (depending on the speed of your connection). Second, many ISPs do not carry certain newsgroups that they consider to be unsuitable - most of which come from the aforementioned '**alt**' newsgroup.

When you have subscribed to a newsgroup, and read its FAQs, you will need to consider a few points of newsgroup etiquette. Keep your messages short and simple, and try to write clear, obvious subject lines. You will be able to spot any replies to your posting when a new message appears beneath it beginning with the word 'Re:'.

The other main form of mass communication on the Internet is the **Mailing List**. You will find many web sites have mailing lists you can join. To subscribe to a mailing list, you just have to have an email address and email software. Sites that operate mailing lists usually just ask for your email address, although some want other details.

Those web sites that do offer mailing list facilities will want to make them obvious, as it is a good way for them to communicate with you. If at any time you no longer wish to receive a mailing list, you need only unsubscribe from it, by sending the site an email saying as much.

Mailing lists are similar to newsgroups, but differ in several key ways. Instead of posting a message and having anyone look at it, they only allow you to view messages if you have joined that mailing list. Some act as nothing more than newsletters, keeping you informed about your favorite subject. Others do encourage you to join in, but these are few and far between.

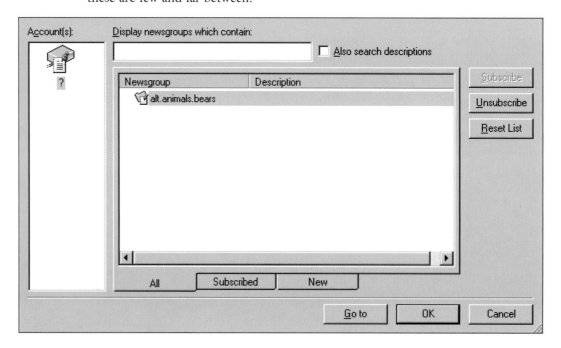

Right: From your newsreader software you can control your newsgroup subscriptions.

FAQs By Newsgroup

[**By Archive-name** | **By Author** | **By Category** | **By Newsgroup**]
[**Home** | **Latest Updates** | **Archive Stats** | **Search** | **Help**]

Big Eight

comp	humanities	misc	news
rec	sci	soc	talk

Other Hierarchies

alt	aly	at	aus
austin	ba	bionet	bit
biz	ca	can	capdist
ch	chinese	davis	dc
de	demon	eunet	fido
fj	fr	gnu	info
it	k12	la	malta
maus	mn	ncf	no
ny	nyc	nz	ping
pl	sac	sat	tue
tx	ucb	ucd	uiuc
uk	usm	vmsnet	yolo
z-netz	zer		

[**By Archive-name** | **By Author** | **By Category** | **By Newsgroup**]
[**Home** | **Latest Updates** | **Archive Stats** | **Search** | **Help**]

Last Update March 13 2000 @ 08:32 PM

Left: More help can be found at www.faqs.org/faqs/by-newsgroup.

The biggest complaints about the Internet are that it is slow and complicated. While the former can be true, the latter need not be the case. Knowing how to get the best from the Internet can take time, but although a steep learning curve, it is a relatively quick process. This is particularly true if you have some help. That is what this section is all about. We'll look at ways in which you can make your experience of the web easier, faster and generally better all round. These tips will concentrate on things you can do to improve your browsing (using the Internet to view web pages and the information they contain). You will find tips on using email and search engines in the **Email** and **Search Engines** sections of this book.

When you are moving from site to site on the Internet you will notice that there are a lot of images, pictures and animations. These can take a long time to load if you have a slow modem, or the Internet is busy. If you think your modem is slow, it might well be! Try setting the connection speed to maximum and see if that improves things. You can do this by clicking on '**Settings**' in your PC's '**Start**' menu. Then select '**Control Panel**' and click on the '**Modems**' icon. Then select '**Properties**'. Under the '**General**' tab you'll find a drop down menu called '**Maximum speed**'. Just click on that and select the fastest speed listed.

Another of the easiest ways to speed up this process is to find the options that control your browser (the piece of software that displays web pages), and switch off these mostly-unnecessary intrusions. This will affect your enjoyment of the finer aspects of web design, but if you're only after text-based information it's perfect.

*Right: Speed up your browsing by setting the Internet options in **IE**.*

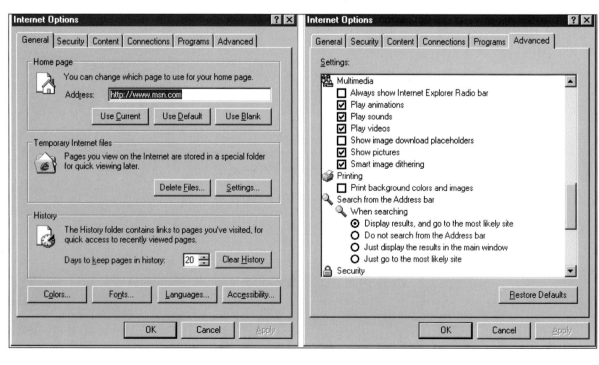

To find the settings in *Internet Explorer* (*IE*) just follow this route: **Tools>Internet Options>Advanced**. Here you will find a list of settings. Just scroll down to '**Multimedia**' and deselect all the settings from '**Always show Internet Explorer Radio bar**' to '**Smart image dithering**' and then click '**Apply**' followed by '**OK**'. In *Netscape Navigator* follow this route: select '**Edit**' from the menu and then click on '**Preferences**' followed by '**Advanced**'. Deselect the box marked '**Automatically load images**'.

When you have images disabled, and you need to see a particular graphic, both browsers allow for this. Simply use the right hand mouse button to click on the space where the image would be, and then select '**View image**' (in *IE*) or '**Show image**' (in *Netscape*).

If the very reason for your visiting a site is to watch a movie or listen to a clip, then try to use streaming media. Most multimedia sites allow you to view video files in several different formats, and if you can, select '**Real Player**', *Window's* '**MediaPlayer**' or '**QuickTime**'. All of these plug-ins (see the section at the end of the chapter entitled *Getting Online*) play back as you download the file, which means you don't have to wait for the whole media file to download before activating it.

dark teen movie, a drama about ballet, a drama about Africa, two clips from a psychotic black comedy, and

"Gossip" Full Trailer (4.5Mb, MOV)
"Center Stage" Full Trailer (7.2Mb, MOV)
"I Dreamed of Africa" Full Trailer (6.2Mb, MOV)
"American Psycho" Clip #1 (Streaming, RealVideo)
"American Psycho" Clip #2 (Streaming, RealVideo)
"Robocop: Mini-Series" Commercial (4.5Mb, MOV)

he Lord of the Rings" will be coming to the Net soon folks according to an NL executive, but before it does everyone to see. According to 9nin, Nine Inch Nails frontman Trent Reznor will apparently be doing the soun irth of Christ. In other soundtrack news, the band Smashmouth has just covered Steely Dan's classic "Do It Goo Goo Dolls and Third Eye Blind will all be doing covers of various Steely Dan songs for the movie accor terday and live in Los Angeles, you can participate as an extra in a major scene from the film (and hopefully e specific details click here. Thanks to Ringzone, 'adandnat', 'JC fan' & 'dAsT'.

le got rave reviews at the recent AICN screening, but was that just a lucky one-off? DH's regular LA corres revved up his engine to look at the Bruckheimer car thriller "Gone in Sixty Seconds":

Review: "Gladiator"   Review: "Gone in Sixty Seconds"
(Positive, No Spoilers) (Positive, Very Minor Spoilers)

Left: If you are in a hurry, always look for downloads you can 'stream' rather than download.

▼

Earlier I mentioned that the Internet may be busy. Just like a real location, such as a shop, some times are more popular than others. But as with everything on the Internet you have to think globally. The US has the biggest number of Net users (some 120 million) so, as you can imagine, things can get pretty slow during office hours there. If you live outside the US time zones, try to use the Internet when the US is asleep, and if you live inside those time zones try to use the Net in the early morning or late evening.

Remember to save the web addresses of the sites you visit most in your '**Favorites**' (*IE*) or '**Bookmarks**' (*Navigator*). This will save time as you will not have to go through the process of finding the site again, or typing in the site's address (known as a URL) again. If you looked at a site a few days ago and have forgotten the URL, no problem, just use your history (a record of most recently visited sites). In *Netscape*, select '**Communicator**', then '**Tools**', then '**History**'. Click on the desired site and hit '**Ctrl D**'. In *IE*, click on the '**History**' icon and then select the appropriate site.

On the subject of typing, always be careful when entering a URL in the address window of your browser. If you mistype it, you will either end up at the wrong site or your browser will spend time looking for an address that doesn't exist. You can also save time by missing out the '**http://**' bit of a web address in the most recent versions of both *IE* and *Navigator*.

Right: Remember you can always find the address of a site you've visited by checking your **History**.

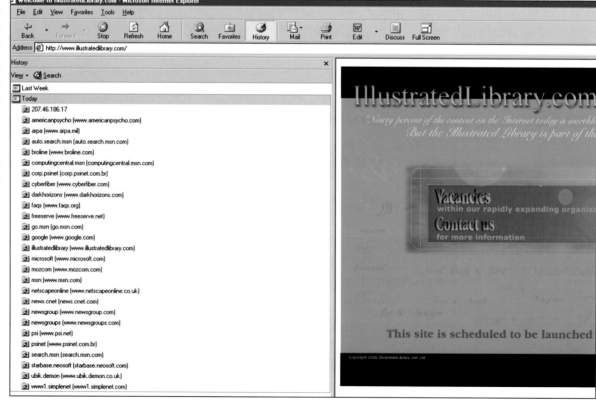

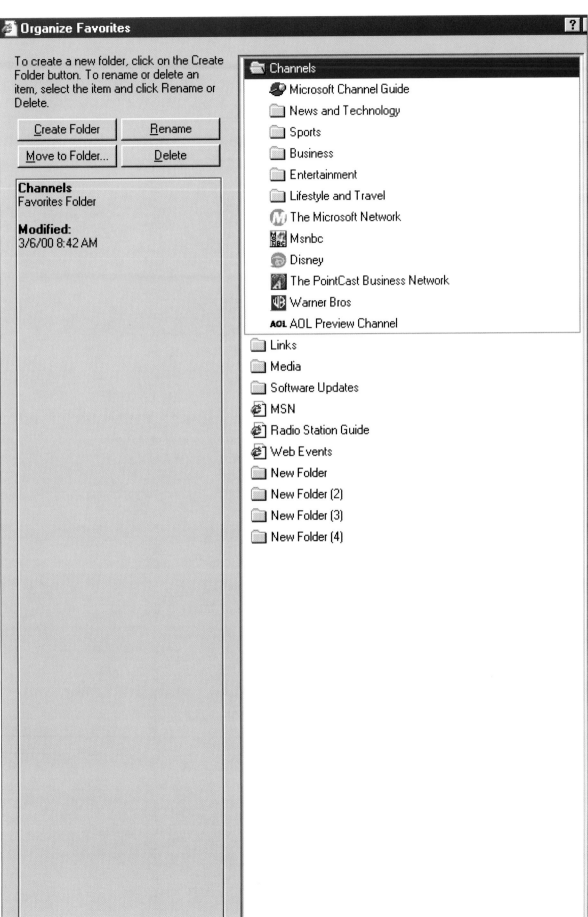

Organize Favorites

To create a new folder, click on the Create Folder button. To rename or delete an item, select the item and click Rename or Delete.

Create Folder   Rename

Move to Folder...   Delete

Channels
Favorites Folder

Modified:
3/6/00 8:42 AM

Channels
🌐 Microsoft Channel Guide
📁 News and Technology
📁 Sports
📁 Business
📁 Entertainment
📁 Lifestyle and Travel
Ⓜ The Microsoft Network
Msnbc
Disney
The PointCast Business Network
Warner Bros
AOL AOL Preview Channel
📁 Links
📁 Media
📁 Software Updates
MSN
Radio Station Guide
Web Events
📁 New Folder
📁 New Folder (2)
📁 New Folder (3)
📁 New Folder (4)

Left: To help you get the best from the Internet, both browsers allow you to **'Bookmark'** *sites. You can arrange them into folders.*

Some sites produce versions of their pages that are designed for slow machines or slow connections, so use them. These will say things such as '**Frames or No Frames**' (click on '**No Frames**') or '**Flash or Non-Flash**' (click on '**Non-Flash**'). And remember that you can use more than one browser window at a time. Just click on '**Ctrl**' or the '**apple**' symbol and '**N**' on your keyboard to bring up another window.

If you need to look at information you have already viewed online, you might not have to connect at all. Your computer keeps a record of all the sites you have visited in what is termed a 'cache'. This lets you launch your browser software and look at web pages you already have in your computer's memory. In *Navigator*, select '**Go offline**' from the file menu, and select '**Work offline**' in *IE*.

In general, it will also help speed things up if you increase the size of your cache. *Internet Explorer* users will find this under '**Internet options**' in the '**Tools**' menu. Select the '**General**' tab and then click on the button marked '**Settings**'. You will be faced with a number of options as to when *IE* should update a page - you should select the '**Every visit to the page**' setting. Those using *Navigator* should follow this route: **Edit>Preferences>Advanced**. Click on the '**plus**' sign (a **triangle** in *Macs*) and then '**Cache**'. You should select the '**Once per session**' option.

Right: For faster browsing, try increasing the size of the cache in your browser's **Settings** *or* **References**.

As an aside, *Navigator* can err on the low side when it comes to using memory, but users of **MacOS 8.1** and above can ameliorate this by increasing the amount of memory that *Navigator* grabs when it opens. Find the icon for '**Navigator**', hit '**Apple-I**', select '**memory**' and increase it to your preferred size.

Both browsers give you the opportunity to check your saved sites automatically. In *IE*, you can choose to '**Make available offline**' a web site when you add it to your **Favorites**. If you want to alter your existing **Favorites** so you can subscribe to them in this way, following this route: **Favorites>Organize favorites**. Then right click on each site and choose '**Make available offline**'. *Navigator* will do pretty much the same thing by checking your **Bookmarks** for changes to location or content. Open the '**Organize bookmarks**' window and select '**View**' followed by '**Update bookmarks**'. Any altered URLs or updated pages will be highlighted.

You can also save web pages without looking at them. Just right-click your mouse on the hyperlink to the page and then either '**Save Target As**' in *IE,* or '**Save Link As**' in *Navigator*. You can then view the file at any time, even when you're offline.

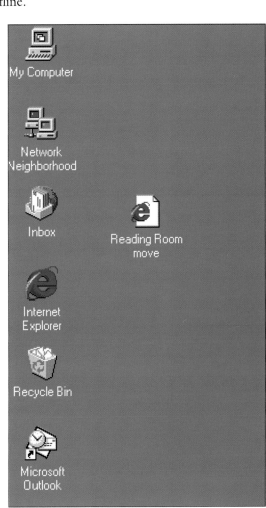

Left: To save a web page without looking at it, just right click on the link (far left), save it, and the file will appear on your desktop (left).

▼

If your connection is slow, downloading freeware and shareware can - quite literally - take hours. One viable option is to buy a reputable Internet or computer magazine that comes with a free CD on the cover. These CDs feature the newest and most popular software you can download. Installing from one of these CDs should take a matter of minutes, thus saving you a great deal of time.

Remember, too, that you don't have to use *IE* or *Navigator*. See the chapter on **Browsers** for where to find alternatives, but it is generally agreed that one of the fastest browsers, that doesn't take up as much of your computer's memory as the two main ones, is *Opera* (**www.operasoftware.com**).

If you really cannot do without your *Navigator* or *IE*, it is often faster to upgrade to the newest version. However, be aware that the newer the browser, the more gadgets and gizmos have been added to it, thus taking up more memory. An alternative is to download the newest patches or fixes for your version.

As a last resort, you can always upgrade your computer. Faster processors (chips), more memory and faster modems, or an even better connection (as discussed in the **Getting Online** section of this book), will improve your Internet experience.

One way of doing this without spending any money is to upgrade your modem's driver (the piece of software that controls how your modem communicates). All you need do is check the manufacturer's web site to see if there is a more recent driver than the one you have, download it and install it.

If you are just connecting to the web to use your email, remember that you need only be online for as long as it takes to send and/or receive your messages. So, if you are sending messages, launch your email software and write your emails offline. You can then queue them to be sent all at the same time once you connect. The same is true of incoming messages. Connect to the Internet, download your emails and then disconnect. You can then read your new messages offline, saving time and, potentially, money.

You can also save valuable time typing in email addresses if you use the address book function that comes in most email software packages. Then you just enter a nickname or select '**Send Message to**' and the name of your recipient. To save more time when receiving email, you can set up 'filters'. So, instead of having one massive in-tray, you can have several themed ones. You can set these up to pick up keywords in the subject line, or specific email addresses. Check your software's help section to find out exactly how to do this, but it is not difficult.

More Information:

Important Notes
System Requirements
Detailed Instructions

---

odate

NT 4.0

1, English Language Version

Read these instructions:

When you click the Next button a dialog box will appear.

To download the software

- **Choose** Open or Run this program from its current location

- **Click OK and setup will begin.**

Click here if you would like more detailed instructions.

Click Next to continue:

Next >   >

Left: Upgrading **IE** *or* **Navigator** *will speed up your browsing, but bear in mind that newer versions will take up more memory.*

▼

Search Engines

After email, the most popular use of the Internet is for finding information and the phrase 'search engine' has become a generic term for any system used to search the Internet. There are two different types of searching device.

The first is the **web crawler** (sometimes referred to as a 'spider'). This is an automated search engine that lets you look for specific pages within bigger sites. For example, there may be a limited number of sites that concern themselves with show jumping, but a web crawler will find individual pages about show jumping within larger sites. However, this type of search engine has one main drawback - it has a tendency to catalog too much information. This means you end up with a larger pile of results from your search.

The second sort of search mechanism is a **directory**, which, as the name implies, is very similar to a telephone book. Instead of the search device going to the site, and then reporting what is there, a directory relies on the site owners to submit information. So, if the site builder forgot to mention an aspect of his or her site, that aspect won't be featured. The directories might not be completely up to date but, if you're looking for specific information, it's usually easier to try a directory before going to one of the web crawlers.

Directories also have the added advantage of categorising their listed sites by topic. This means you use the search engine's database of sites to search for information by clicking on a series of relevant options presented to you. The first list of criteria is very general, becoming more specific the further you follow the search by clicking on relevant words or phrases.

No matter which of the two types of search engine you use, you may not find what you're after immediately. In this case, you'll need to start using advanced searching. Most search engines and directories include advanced options, but their methods vary from system to system.

Check on the search engine's main page for either a help file link or for their list of FAQs (Frequently Asked Questions) to find out what methods it recommends. In general, though, you'll be using two types of advanced searches - **Phrase** searches and **Boolean** searches - and each has its own strengths and weaknesses.

Perhaps the easier of these two advanced search techniques is phrase searching which lets you search on multiple words for one topic. For example, if you are looking for information about OJ Simpson, the typical search engine results will list sites concerning orange juice, the Simpsons animated series, as well as any web site that mentions the name Simpson. The search engine just took your two words and assumed you were looking for sites with references to any of them.

If you want a search engine to do a phrase search, you need to tell it to group these words together. So type the phrase inside speech marks: a search for Bill Gates will return all manner of subjects from paying your bills to fixing rusty gates, but a search for "Bill Gates" should return only information about the Microsoft Chairman. And this doesn't just work on names, but on any phrase.

The other most common method of making a search more specific is to use a Boolean search. This method uses certain keywords. They can differ from search engine to search engine, but the idea is the same. The word 'AND' typed in capitals will let you add terms together, 'OR' makes the search engine look for either word, and 'NOT' excludes words. Sometimes the search engine can handle a combination of these terms. So you could ask for 'breast AND cancer NOT horoscope'.

Boolean searching, with its simple yet powerful capabilities, lets you quickly narrow your searches so the results can quickly pinpoint what you're after. The more terms you can add to the search specification, the more accurate your results will be.

AltaVista

A directory-based search engine, which is good to use if you're looking for recent information or web sites, as any pages submitted to it appear on the service within a few days. Some 25 million people use AltaVista's services every month, including its new portal site content and personalisation service.

www.altavista.com

www.altavista.co.uk

www.altavista.au

www.altavista.ca

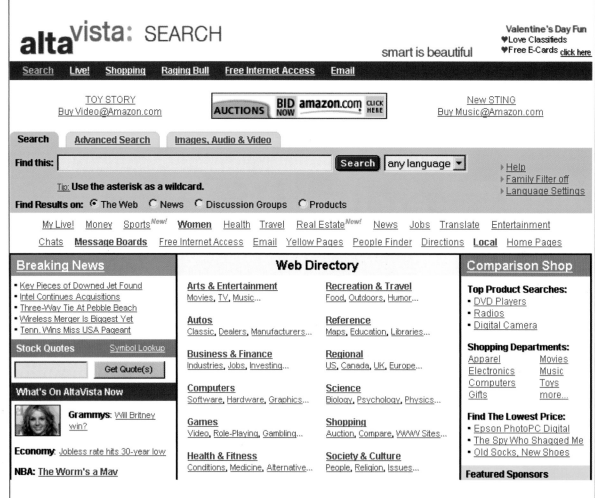

Excite

Over 17 million people use Excite's listings services, which also powers AOL's NetFind, and Netscape's search engine. Excite gives more importance to sites with lots of links listed on them, and has local versions in 12 countries - the US, UK, Australia, China, France, Germany, Italy, Japan, the Netherlands, New Zealand, Spain and Sweden.

www.excite.com

www.excite.co.uk

http://au.excite.com

http://chinese.excite.com

www.excite.fr

www.excite.de

http://it.excite.com

www.excite.co.jp

http://nl.excite.com

www.excite.nz

www.excite.es

http://se.excite.com

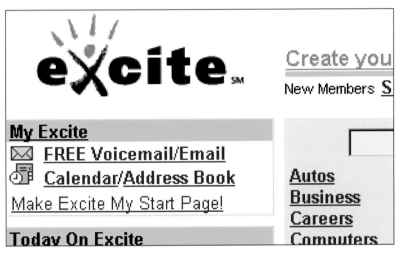

Lycos

Although Lycos creates its descriptions from the first 275 words it finds on sites, you can search for country-specific material on Lycos's 22 sites in the UK, Argentina, Belgium, Brazil, Chile, Colombia, Denmark, France, Germany, Italy, Japan, Korea, Mexico, the Netherlands, Norway, Peru, Singapore, Spain, Sweden, Switzerland, Venezuela and the US (both English and Spanish).

www.lycos.com	www.lycos.co.kr
www.lycos.co.uk	www.lycos.com.mx
www.lycos.com.ar	www.lycos.nl
www.lycos.be	www.no.lycos.de
www.lycos.com.br	www.lycos.com.pr
www.lycos.cl	www.lycosasia.com.sg
www.lycos.com.co	www.lycos.es
www.dk.lycos.de	www.lycos.se
www.lycos.fr	www.lycosch.ch
www.lycos.de	www.lycos.com.ve
www.lycos.it	www-english.lycos.com
www.lycos.co.jp	http://espanol.lycos.com

LYCOS S
Your Personal Internet Guide

My Lycos   Build y

Pictures of the Day

News
Weather

Free Services
Free Email
Lycos Chat
Play Games Online
UK Maps
Free Internet Access
Lycos Radio
Free Home Page

Partners
BT
LOOT
Thomson Directories
Travel service
Books @ BOL.com
Mortgages with John Charcol
Top Jobs on the Net
MP3 @ Vitaminic

Search Services
Business Directory
Classifieds
Buy your Domain
Jobs

h for:

● UK & Ireland ○ The Web

Help
Service

ome Page   Search Options   Safe Search

Discover

Bank for free with First Direct when, where and how you want 24 hours a day

Headlines

Chernomyrdin rules out run for Russian...

Report: Sony chief eyes investment in...

First leg results from a men's...

bguides

s	**Personal Finance**
siness	**Pokémon**
rs	**Property** New!
reer	**News**
ssifieds	**Shopping**
mputer	**Silver Surfer**
ertainment	**Small Business**
ance New!	**Sport**
mes	**Student**
alth	**Technology**
arning	**Travel**
ndon	**UK Roadmaps**
ennium	**Valentines** New!
sic	**Women**
3 New!	**World Travel**

On Lycos Now

New Partners:
Finance from The Motley Fool

New Miniguides:
Instaplay - Shockwave games

New Webguides:
Find what you're looking for in our Classified Miniguide

New on Tripod:
Build your own

EE Internet Access FREE

opping Centre

n't buy or sell until you QXL!

ernet - safe shopping: 6,9% APR

Search Engines

Yahoo!

The Internet's first search engine now claims over 120 million users worldwide. Selectivity makes the content on Yahoo!'s 21 directory search engines very mainstream. Areas covered are: the US, UK, Asia, Australia and New Zealand, Brazil, Canada, China, France, Germany, Hong Kong, Italy, Japan, Korea, Mexico, Norway, Singapore, Spain, Sweden and Taiwan.

www.yahoo.com	www.yahoo.com/r/it
http://uk.yahoo.com	www.yahoo.com/r/jp
www.yahoo.com/r/ai	www.yahoo.com/r/kr
www.yahoo.com/r/an	www.yahoo.com/r/mx
www.yahoo.com/r/br	www.yahoo.com/r/no
www.yahoo.com/r/cd	www.yahoo.com/r/sg
www.yahoo.com/r/cc	www.yahoo.com/r/es
www.yahoo.com/r/fr	www.yahoo.com/r/se
www.yahoo.com/r/de	www.yahoo.com/r/tw
www.yahoo.com/r/hk	

Personalize   Help

Y! Greetings
send an e-Valentine

Search   advanced search

- People Search - Maps - Travel - Classifieds - Personals - Games - Chat - **Clubs**
mpanion - My Yahoo! - News - Sports - Weather - TV - Stock Quotes - more...

housands of stores. Millions of products.

Stores
- Macy's
- FTD
- Coach
- Banana Republic

Products
- Valentine's Day
- Pokemon
- MP3 players
- DVD players

News & Media
Full Coverage, Newspapers, TV...

Recreation & Sports
Sports, Travel, Autos, Outdoors...

Reference
Libraries, Dictionaries, Quotations...

Regional
Countries, Regions, US States...

Science
Animals, Astronomy, Engineering...

Social Science
Archaeology, Economics, Languages...

In the News
- French troops, Kosovars clash
- Loud noise recorded before Alaska Air crash
- Chinese New Year

more...

Marketplace
- Valentine's Day Shopping
- Yahoo! Bill Pay - free 3-month trial
- Y! Careers - resume database, 500,000+ jobs

more...

Inside Yahoo!
- Y! Movies - showtimes, reviews, info
- Play free Fantasy Golf
- Y! Mobile - Yahoo! on your phone
- Y! Greetings - send a Valentine

Search Engines

Ask Jeeves

The first search engine to claim to understand plain English questions using a question-processing engine (semantic as well as syntactic processing).

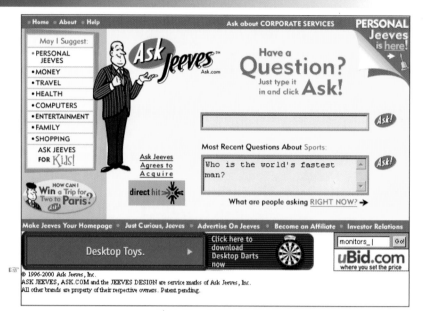

www.askjeeves.com

Bigfoot

The Net's largest directory of email addresses with US, UK, German and French versions. Your first port of call for all email addresses.

www.bigfoot.com

http://uk.bigfoot.com

http://de.bigfoot.com

http://fr.bigfoot.com

Google

Google is a 'next-generation' search engine, which uses an automated method to rank web sites based on the link structure of the Internet itself.

www.google.com

HotBot

Developed by *Wired* (the highly-regarded US computer technology magazine). You can choose to perform Boolean searches without having to type in the terms.

www.hotbot.com

Infoseek

Lets you search within the results of a previous search. Type in 'bugs' and it'll return three million sites. Then enter 'espionage' and you're down to 233.

www.infoseek.com

www.infoseek.co.uk

www.infoseek.nl

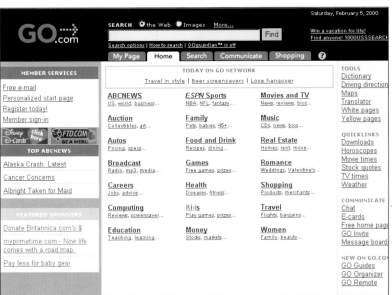

LookSmart

Lists 24,000 different categories and you can even search your home town. LookSmart has sites focussing on the US, UK, Australia, Canada and the Netherlands.

www.looksmart.com

www.looksmart.co.uk

www.looksmart.com.au

http://canada.looksmart.com

http://nl.looksmart.com

Search Engines

Magellan

Part of Excite, but it does let you watch the searches being conducted by other people, 10 at a time in real time in the Search Voyeur section (http://voyeur.mckinley.com/cgi-bin/voyeur.cgi).

www.magellan.excite.com

Metafetcher

Lets you use the search engines peculiar to eight regions (International, UK, Australia, Canada, Netherlands, Germany, France and New Zealand) at the same time.

www.metafetcher.com

SearchUK

One of the two search engines that claims to concentrate on the UK. It's good at updates, but US content does get processed.

www.searchuk.com

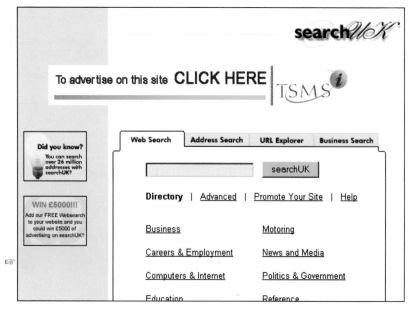

UK Plus

The other UK-specific search engine is from Associated New Media (ANM). Very good at keeping its material UK-orientated and not bringing in US content.

www.ukplus.co.uk

Voila

Deals in thematic searches, so you can narrow your parameters to the specific - such as a name of a city - before the hard work starts.

www.voila.com

www.voila.co.uk

www.voila.fr

WebCrawler

Now part of Excite, but continues as its own brand. Unfortunately, the WebCrawler index is the smallest of any of the major search engines.

www.webcrawler.com

Search Engines

www.about.com

About.com
Standard searching and guides that point you in the right direction.

www.allinonesearch.com

All-in-One Search Page
As the name suggests, employs as many search engines as it can.

www.allwhois.com

Allwhois.com
The place to go to find out who owns what domain name.

www.audiofind.com

AudioFind
Great resource for finding music, lyrics, artists, song titles and albums.

www.buyersindex.com

Buyers Index
US site that searches over 15,000 sources for the best prices.

www.debriefing.com
www.debriefing.com/france

Debriefing
Claims to be the Net's most powerful meta search engine.

www.dejanews.com

Deja.com
Once a great resource, DejaNews is less handy now, but still worth a look.

www.euroferret.com

Euroferret
Search 35 million European pages from Albania to Yugoslavia.

www.euroseek.net

Euroseek
Multi-lingual site covering countries in Europe and beyond.

www.goto.com

GoTo.com
Very basic search engine with no clutter and no fuss.

www.infind.com

InferenceFind
Cuts out duplications to give a better, shorter results list.

www.infohiway.com

InfoHiway
Portal with links to directories, search engines and indices.

Internet Oracle
Great portal sites to every kind of search data imaginable.

www.searchgateway.com

Liszt
The place to go for all your subject-specific mailing list needs.

www.liszt.com

NorthernLight.com
Search the web and get information from 5,400 books, magazines, databases and newswires.

www.northernlight.com

NZ.com
Dedicated to providing online resources for and about New Zealand.

www.nz.com

Onekey
Large database with over 500 categories of sites suitable for children.

www.onekey.com

Ozsearch
Essential web directory and Internet guide for Australians.

www.ozsearch.com.au

Search Engine Watch
The search engine of search engines. Listings, reviews and ratings.

www.searchenginewatch.com

Snap
NBC and CNET's search engine.

www.snap.com

WhitePages.com
Find people, phone numbers, US zip codes or web sites.

www.whitepages.com

WhatUSeek
Add a directory search engine to your own site for free.

www.whatuseek.com

WhoWhere?
Large email directory with 15 main categories and links to other sites.

www.whowhere.lycos.com

Yell
You can find almost any business in the UK with the online version of Yellow Pages.

www.yell.co.uk

Chat Rooms

The Internet was invented to ensure communication could carry on no matter what happened, and to make that communication easier. So there are good reasons why, after email and search engines, online chat is one of the most popular aspects of Net life. In the past, users would have to be content with the newsgroups (see the chapter on **Newsgroups and Mailing Lists** for further information), but with the introduction of real-time chat services such as **IRC** (**Internet Relay Chat**), **Instant Messaging** (**IM**) and **Web Chat**, all that changed.

All are public services that anyone can use, and many sites offer them as a free service. To use these services, all you have to do is log on. This usually entails nothing more than entering a username and password. You then choose a channel, commonly identified as a 'room' or a particular 'conversation', and join it.

If the chat room you have entered has others in it, you will see an electronic conversation being held. This involves nothing more than people typing messages on their computers and sending them. The messages are sent almost instantaneously, so it appears that the conversation is live. Some chat sites require you to download software that will let you use the site. Many **IRC** programs come with a built-in list of **IRC** servers to get you started, but the more specialized, and **IM** software, is peculiar to the site from which you got it.

No matter what software or site you are using, you will need a name to use. It is always better not to use your full name, and some prefer not to use a real name at all, instead preferring to give themselves a 'handle' suited to their character. These are assigned on a first come first served basis, so be prepared to be disappointed if you want to use your given name (e.g. Tammy). However, it is an easy matter to add a number (Tammy159), spell it in an unusual way (Tamii), or use number or punctuation marks (T@mmy or T4MMY).

Many chat rooms and channels are general chat, but hundreds are devoted to specific subjects, and you are bound to find one that suits you. On some sites, you can create your own strand or topic of conversation. And if you are hitting it off with one person in particular, you can go into a private room where you won't be disturbed by anyone else.

Like joining any club or organisation, there are rules and etiquette to be learned about chatting online. You can be thrown off the channel (called 'kicking') for any number of reasons, from swearing to just being rude or a nuisance. The general rule here is: treat the chat room as you would a bar. If you are polite and reasonable, there will be no problem. If there is someone annoying or pestering you, there is often a setting called 'ignore', or similar, that you can use. This will act as a filter so that you won't be able to even see that person's messages.

Finally, a few tips as to the special shorthand used in chat rooms. The most common form is in the use of 'smilies' or 'emoticons'. They are used to indicate people's moods or emotions, and look like sideways faces made up of characters on the keyboard. For example :-) is a smiling, happy face, while :-(is unhappy. The other shorthand used is in the form of acronyms, e.g. LOL is 'Laughing Out Loud', and BRB is 'Be Right Back'. There are many variations on these two forms, but you should find a guide to it on the chat site you join.

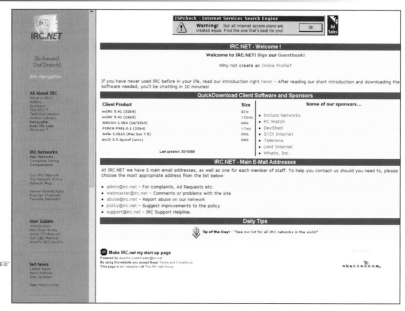

IRC.Net

A very good starting point if you want to find out more about **IRC**, download the software, discover which sites use **IRC** and improve your Netiquette. There is a great introduction to **IRC**, and many sections given over to its history and use, the latest news, and how to get the most from it.

www.irc.net

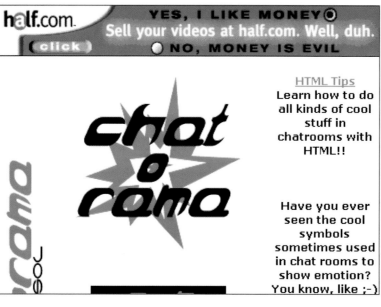

Chat-o-Rama

One of the most comprehensive listings of chat sites anywhere on the web. You can search by subject alphabetically, read about smilies and acronyms, as well as how to use HTML to good effect in chat rooms. A great starting point for web chatters.

www.solscape.com/chat

AbsoluteChat

A multi-forum live chat site with many topics covered. Just log in and away you go. It'll even tell you how many people are in the forums on the front page.

www.absolutechat.com

CU-SeeMe

The leading site for those who have a web cam and so can take part in video-conferencing style chat. In this way you can see who you're talking to, and use your speakers and microphone to actually talk instead of type.

www.cuseemeworld.com

DoBeDo

Great new site from Scandinavia that lets you adopt an online persona and avatar, to help you get over any shyness you might have about chatting online.

www.dobedo.com

Liv4Now

One of the best grown-up (not adult!) chat sites on the web. Aimed at 30-something professionals, the site is split into three main areas, each with its own personality.

www.liv4now.com

Net2Phone

Excellent Voice-over Internet Protocol (VoIP) site that shows you how to chat to anyone on a phone, anywhere in the world, using your PC to get local call rates.

www.net2phone.com

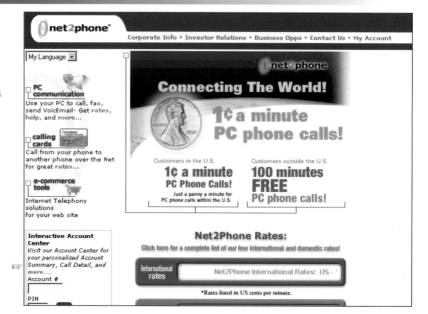

Worlds.com

An amazing virtual reality chat site. You'll need to order the free CD or download the software to make it work, but then you just choose an avatar and a world to live in.

www.worlds.com

Artificial Linguistic Computer Entity (ALICE)

Chat to an artificial intelligence. Can you tell the difference?

www.alicebot.org

ChatBox

Good chat site that concentrates on sport and entertainment.

www.chatbox.com

Chat-Center

Features a variety of chat rooms covering single, teen, adult, college and general topics.

Welcome To Chat-Center.com

ll of our chat rooms and services are totally 100% FREE and supported by our sponsors. Our chat rooms are the most advanced Java based ch the web today offering features like person 2 person chat which allows you to chat privately with a member in a separate window while still be chat in the public room. Profiles allows you to register your nick name so that no one else can use it, while putting in a description of yourself, y mepage url and email address for easy access to you or other chatters wishing to connect with you.

Singles Chat	A place for singles to meet up with other singles online.
Teen Chat	A cool place for teens to meet other teenagers and talk about common intrestes.
Adults Chat	A cool fun, clean chat for adults to meet new friends online.

www.chat-center.com

Chat Connection

Has several sections including live chat, message boards, email and more.

Welcome to The Chat Connection

About Chat-Connection

Welcome to chat connection. We have several chat communities to meet the needs of almost anyone looking for a good chat on the web. All of our chats and services are totally 100% FREE and supported by our sponsors. We bring you a complete online people connection community with chat, message boards, email and more! Our chat rooms are the most advanced Java based chatrooms on the web today offering features like *person 2 person* chat which allow you to chat privately with a member in a separate window while still being able to chat in the public room. *Profiles* allows you to register your nick name so that no one else can use it, while putting in a description of yourself, your homepage url and email address for easy access. *Room Registration* allows all our use to create and manage their own rooms. If you have any thoughts, ideas or suggestions about our site, communities or chat please feel free to contact us at any time.

We Have a chat to fit just about anyone's needs

College Chat	Teenage chat
For college students and college age people. Most people here are between 18 and 27 years of age.	For teenagers and adolescents. Most people chatting here are between 13 and 19 years of age.
Adult Chat	Kids Chat
For adults 18+ Most people chatting here are 25 and up in age.	For a younger crowd. Pre-Teens. Most chatters here are between 12 and 13 years of age.
Singles Chat	Entertainment Chat
For singles looking for the special someone online. The age range in these rooms is very wide.	For music, movies, television, gossip and anything else. Wide range of ages in these rooms.

www.chat-connection.com

ChatNet

Good Mac-only IRC chat site.

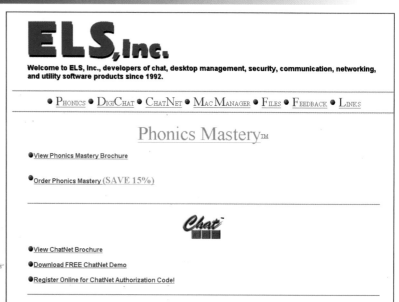

www.elsinc.com

Chat Planet

Very good list of links to chat sites on almost any subject.

www.chatplanet.com

Excite Chat

There are always loads of people using the chat systems so you'll always find someone to chat to.

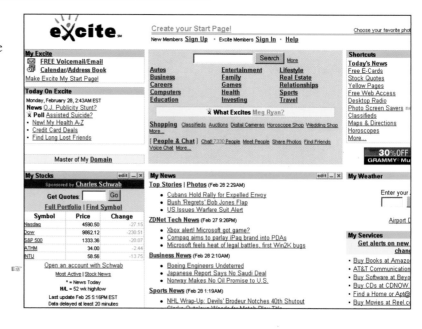

www.excite.com

The Gathering

A simple, easy to use, UK-based chat site with users from all over the world.

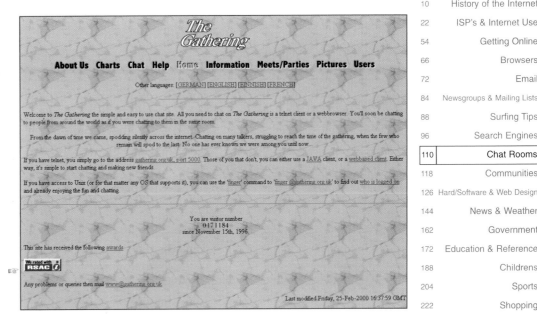

www.gathering.org.uk

Ichat

Offers you the software so that you can set up and run your own chat rooms.

www.ichat.com

Outer Worlds

Enjoy 3D chat in a variety of virtual worlds.

www.outerworlds.com

Webtalker.com

With ten main chat areas and only one rule - no hate - **Webtalker** is a great, easy-to-use site.

www.webtalker.com

Yahoo! Chat

The biggest portal and search engine on the Net also has a wide variety of chat topic areas.

http://chat.yahoo.com

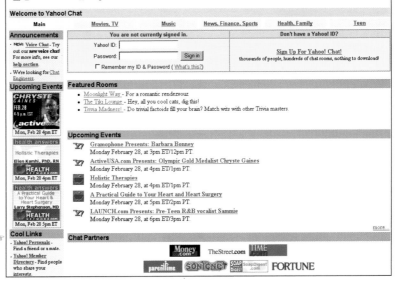

Communities

The idea of communities online is one that has taken on different meanings over the years. A couple of years ago, an Internet community was the collected web sites built, using free web space, that a company - other than an Internet Service Provider (ISP) - had supplied to them in return for taking advertisements. To many, this is still the true meaning of community in relation to the Net, and they refuse to accept that it has taken on new meanings, too.

As with any aspect of language, Internet jargon is forever evolving and moving on. Today, marketing jargon has taken over and any site aimed at a niche calls itself a community - such as **Vavo** (www.vavo.com) for the older sector of the population; the **Rainbow Network** (www.rainbownetwork.co) for gay members of society, and **Handbag** (www.handbag.com) for women. However, in the interests of clarity I will only be using the term 'community' to describe the group of sites built under one virtual roof, free of charge, rather than the marketing niche single web site.

The sources of free web space are many and varied these days, which adds to the slight blurring of the word's meaning on the Net. On top of pure web space offers, you will find that those who offer free, web-based email will usually offer free web space as well. They hand out both for free in an attempt to build bigger online communities, which will in turn generate more advertising revenue. Most of these services can offer you anything between 2MB and 500MB per user.

However, if you are considering creating your own home page and uploading it to a free web space community, you might like to think about the drawbacks of doing so. There not being such a thing as a free lunch, you - and more importantly your visitors - will have to put up with lots of ads, either floating in new windows that open, or on your site itself. You will also be forced to have an unwieldy URL that's difficult to remember. If web page creation is one of your primary reasons for being online, then the format of your address will matter to you. You should also bear in mind that if your site becomes too popular, the community site will remove it and you'll have to find yourself a new home.

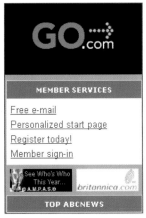

Angelfire

A great community site that not only has free web space (30MB), but also free email, and lets you have a fairly sensible web address. There are helpful features on how to build, improve and promote your site, as well as the chance to be the home page site of the day.

www.angelfire.com

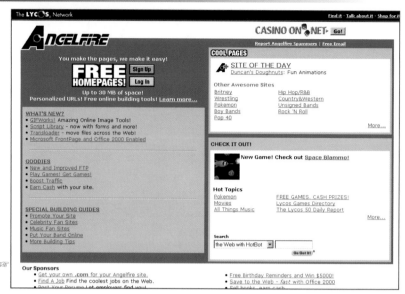

GeoCities

GeoCities was bought by **Yahoo!** last year and the community caused quite a stir when it then claimed to own the copyright of the material on all its users' web sites. That claim has now been dropped, and it is back in the business of providing themed areas (SciFi, sports, 'hometown values', homosexual, and more) in which people can build sites for free.

www.geocities.com

The Express Page

Although slightly less well-known, this very simple site boasts over 3 million pages that have been created using their 50MB of free space.

http://expage.com

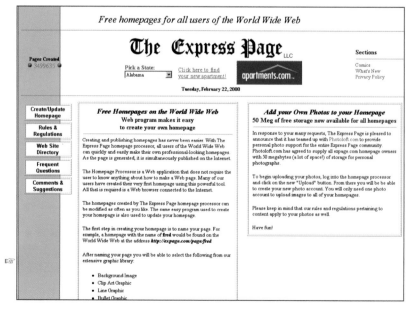

Fortunecity.com

Splits its online communities into 11 sections and offers 20MB of space.

www.fortunecity.com

Free Town

Mainly a massive chat site, but it also offers a limited amount of 'virtual realty'.

www.freetown.com

Theglobe.com

Combines chat, forums, and 25MB of space that will let you "Meet people who share your interests. Debate, flirt, ask questions, get support, speak your mind.".

www.theglobe.com

Tripod

As **Yahoo!** took over **Geocities**, so **Lycos** bought **Tripod**, which offers 11MB of space and a wealth of resource to augment your site.

www.tripod.lycos.com

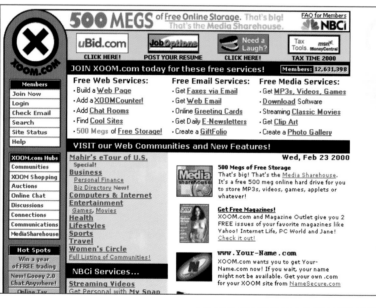

Xoom.com

One of the best community sites, equipped with a wealth of content and services, as well as unlimited web space.

http://xoom.com

AOL Hometown

The free community site from the world's biggest ISP that gives you up to 12MB of web space.

http://hometown.aol.com

Beseen

Good community site from **LookSmart** that offers you the chance to build more than just a single page.

www.beseen.com

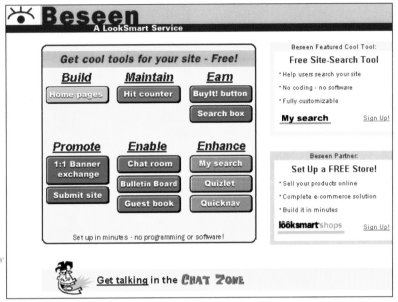

Black Voices.com

Community aimed primarily at African Americans with 5 pages on offer.

www.blackvoices.com

Create uh Page

Very simple 'dart board' site that lets you create a single web page.

www.oe-pages.com

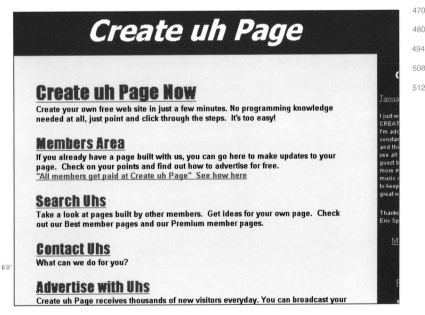

Communities

Go.com

The **Disney**-owned network also offers free web pages.

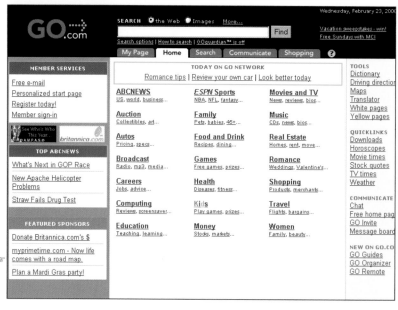

www.go.com

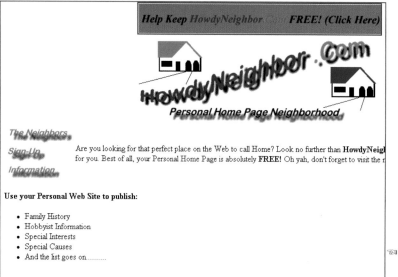

HowdyNeighbor.com

US-centric free email and home page site, but space is limited to 2MB.

www.howdyneighbor.com

iVillage.com

Women's community site that has a wealth of content as well as a free page.

www.ivillage.com

MSN Web Communities

The free web space section of the **Microsoft Network**.

http://communities.msn.com

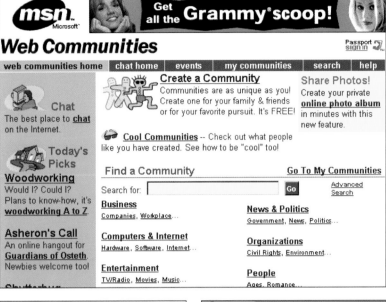

Nettaxi.com

Great little site that offers lots of support and help in building your site, as well as 25MB of space.

www.nettaxi.com

ProHosting

Promises to get you signed up, and your site online, in 30 minutes.

http://free.prohosting.com

ThirdAge.

Aimed at the more mature Internet user, with free email, content, chat and home pages.

www.thirdage.com

Vavo.com

The latest community site for the over fifties has an amazing diversity of content, as well as free home pages.

www.vavo.com

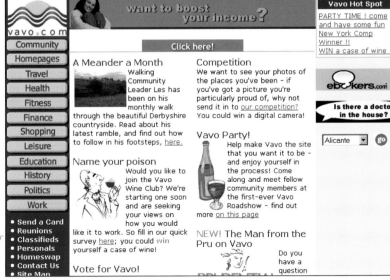

Hardware, Software & Web Design

The Internet has many roles to play when it comes to the subject of software, hardware and web design. You'll find online the manufacturers of whatever hardware or software you use, as well as any number of professional web design agencies. There are also many tutorial style web sites that will guide you through anything, from upgrading your motherboard to getting the best from your word processing software.

You can use the Internet to find out about the latest versions of software you already have, or packages you are considering buying. All the manufacturers are online including Microsoft, Adobe, Quark, Jasc and Sage. In some cases you will be able to get add-ons for software you have registered, or - more rarely - free updates.

There are also many independent sites that carry reviews, and equally as many - if not more - where you can download a trial version for free. If you are going to visit a download site, you'll notice that there are several different classes of software on offer.

Freeware is a program that is free for you to download, no matter how much you use it. You will also find demo versions of software that you would otherwise have to pay for. This type of download will either have a time limit on it - usually about 30 days for evaluation - or will be missing features offered by the full, paid-for package.

You will find the Internet populated with all manner of hardware-related web sites, from the mainstream manufacturers to specialist interest sites maintained by enthusiastic amateurs.

All hardware manufacturers have web sites, but they vary a great deal in quality. Some offer nothing more than glorified catalogs, while others have online help and support or features on getting the most from their products. The best ones will offer you the chance to choose the specification of hardware you want, and then let you buy it online.

You will also find online computer retailers and business re-sellers that offer online purchasing of a wide selection of hardware (and software) products. Complementing these independent sites are those that will help you get the most from your hardware and software with online tutorials, features and walk-throughs.

The same is true for web design. There are any number of professional web design companies out there, but few have any relevant features for the amateur. What you can do is look at the sites you like best, and decide what you like about them design-wise. Alternatively, find out who has designed those sites and see if the person or company has done other sites.

Away from the professional web design agencies, you will find an amazing array of sites aimed at web designers. Some have hints and

tips, while others offer more concrete help in the shape of visitor coun-
ters, animated images, sound files and the like, with which to augment
your site. Rest assured, whatever you're after in the way of hardware,
software and web design, you will almost certainly find it on the web.

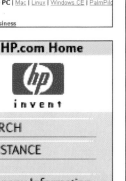

Hardware, Software & Web Design

CNet/Download.com

An awesome collection of computer-related items, including down-loads. Arranged into over 120 sections in 10 areas covering business, desktop, tools, education, drivers, games, home, Internet, multi-media, and utilities. You can also search the huge database by key-word, or simply browse the most popular downloads, the most recent additions, or the CNet team's selection.

www.download.com

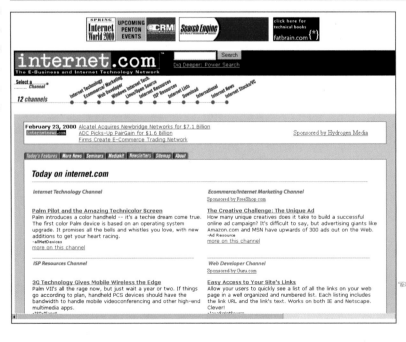

Internet.com

An amazing URL for one of the most impressive sites on the Net. Aimed at web design and Internet/IT professionals, the site covers absolutely everything including software-related mate-rial, Windows, Linux, other Internet technologies, ISPs, downloads, a web developer's area, Internet news, IPOs, stocks, and more.

www.internet.com

Microsoft.com

The biggest manufacturer of software on the planet has a massive selection of updates and trial versions - all of which are free. The company's browser, and various components, are also available for free. You'll find help and support for your Windows operating system, as well as any software from Microsoft.

www.microsoft.com

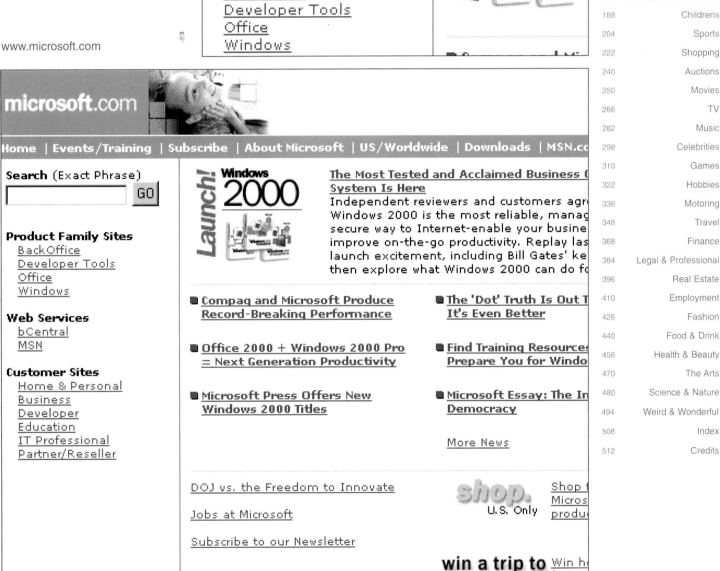

TechWeb

If you're into computers, this is where it's at. Although aimed at the industry, there is a wealth of information here for the enthusiast. You can sign up for specific email newsletters, or just browse through the news or visit one of its many sister sites.

www.techweb.com

TOP NEWS FOR FEBRUARY 23, 2000   last updated 2:38 PM ET

Seagate Makes World's Fastest Hard Drive
The drives will integrate into existing systems and arrays without the need to modify them with extra cooling fans.

Alcatel To Buy Newbridge For $7.1 Billion
Troubled Canadian networking company finds a buyer.

IBM, Lycos, Fidelity, AT&T Create Money App
IBM, Lycos, Fidelity, and AT&T are to test a bundle of financial information services delivered via a broadband appliance.

- 724 In Equity, Technical Link With Motorola
- Gateway Sees $30B In Sales By 2004
- Intel Invests In Cambridge Silicon

➡ Week's Headlines   ➡ More News

Spotlight

Careers & Training
The Internet makes it easier to be an IT free agent.

Windows 2000
Get your PC up and running in a hurry with Winmag.com's Essential Guide to Installing Windows 2000.

Advanced IP Services
Which private IP service provider fits your needs?

Advertisement

FEATURES

TOP DOWNLOADS
1.) StayOn Pro 3.19
2.) My Personal Browser 4.5
3.) Modem Booster 1.0
4.) Internet Answering Machine 1.0
5.) Download Accelerator 3.5

Search

Win (all) ▾   Go

PLANET IT TECH CENTERS   COMMUNITY FOCUS

Tom's Hardware Guide

One of the best hardware resources on the web. You'll find guides to motherboards and CPUs nestled next to both the latest, and a vast archive of, hardware-related news. There are message boards where you can while away the hours chatting about your computer and its peripherals, as well as a selective list of links.

www.tomshardware.com

CNET Shopper

Search for the lowest prices!

[ ] GO!

• Hot Deals
• Most Popular

Latest Tech News

Columns

Tom's Guides
Mainboard
CPU
Graphics
Display
Digital Video
Storage
Business

Archive

Message Board

Links

Contact

Advertising Info

Order Tom's Book

Welcome to Tom's Hardware Guide
Updated: February 23, 2000

Enter Your E-mail: [ ]
Submit

CPU Guide

NEW February 17, 2000
The Race Is On: 1 GHz processors at ISSCC in San Francisco
At the International Solid-State Circuit Conference in San Francisco several companies described designs for microprocessors with 1 GHz clock speed. AMD demonstrated a system with a 1 GHz Athlon from its fab in Dresden, Germany.

• **Transmeta introduces Crusoe**
• **Intel's Frequency ID Utility**
• **Kryotech's SuperG 1GHz**
• **More Releases**

Mainboard Guide

February 14, 2000
The Impact of the AGP-Speed
Does AGP1x vs. AGP2x vs. AGP4x make a significant difference in performance? We tried to find an answer on two different platforms for each, Pentium III and Athlon.

• **Irongate with Super Bypass vs. VIA Apollo KX133**
• **NVIDIA's New NT-Drivers for Athlon on KX133**
• **New Hope For Athlon - The VIA Apollo KX133 Chipset**
• **More Releases**

Tucows Network

Amazing online resource of downloadable freeware, shareware trial version and full version software. You'll find multiple mirror sites on every continent, which means faster downloads, and some great features that will help you get the best from your software. Choose from any software type you can think of - and some you may not know existed!

www.tucows.com

Webmonkey

The best-known and most widely-respected site covering web site design. It has absolutely everything for web designers - from basic tutorials on authoring, through more complex design and programing, to getting a job in the industry.

www.hotwired.com/webmonkey

ZDNet

Hugely impressive network of technology sites, with particular concentrations on software downloads, shopping for software and web site design. You can search the site's product reviews by name or brands, and then go straight to the download section and get the trial version. If you're having problems, you can try the Tech Support section for advice and tips.

www.zdnet.com/downloads

Adobe

Not only does Adobe publish many design and web page authoring tools, it is also responsible for Acrobat reader (a plug-in that lets you read documents online).

www.adobe.com

Apple

Now that Apple's agenda is almost entirely Internet-driven, you'll find lots of information about iMacs, iBooks, G3s and G4s, as well as tools and extra kit for them.

www.apple.com

Compaq

One of the world's biggest manufacturers of PCs offers technical support, and a great area where you can spec up your ideal computer. No online sales though.

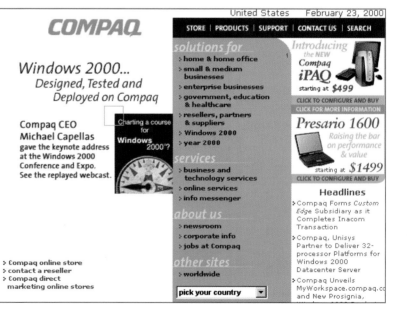

www.compaq.com

Dell.com

Dell - unlike its main rival
Compaq - lets you buy online,
and track your order as it leaves
the warehouse and wends its way

www.dell.com

www.dell.co.uk

Gateway

Lesser-known PC manufacturer
that will build a PC to your own
specification from an order you
make online.

www.gateway.com

IBM

Probably the most famous name
in computers, IBM offers online
PC ordering, and has links
through to the wide number of
services the company offers.

www.ibm.com

Intel

The manufacturer of most of the world's PC microchip processors has a wealth of online services, and its excellent web Outfitter service.

www.intel.com

Internet Magazine

The UK's most respected magazine for and about the Net. Its site has question and answer content on web design, as well as online and downloadable tutorials. There's even a list of useful top software.

www.Internet-magazine.com

MacCentral

Magnificent site for Mac enthusiasts that includes forums, news, features and columns, as well as guides to software, games and hardware.

www.maccentral.com

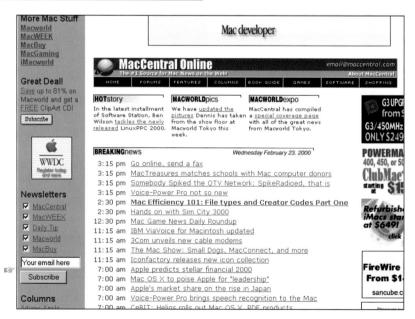

Macromedia

The company that brought true animation to the web with Shockwave, Flash, and Fireworks, as well as top design tool, DreamWeaver.

www.macromedia.com

Redhat.com

The place to go on the Internet for Linux - a free alternative operating system to Windows. Also great on other open source software.

www.redhat.com

Real Networks

This is where you'll find the free, downloadable software that'll let you view movies, subscribe to Internet channels such as CNN, and listen to music on the web.

www.real.com

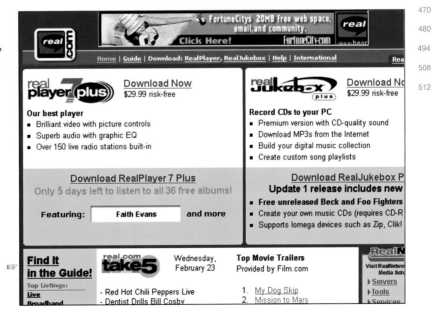

Hardware, Software & Web Design

Action Online

Good UK site covering a very wide selection of cheaper hardware and software.

www.action.com

CommStore

UK online resource that covers a complete range of modem, ISDN and networking solutions.

www.commstore.co.uk

Computers4sure

Great online retailer of all things hardware-related.

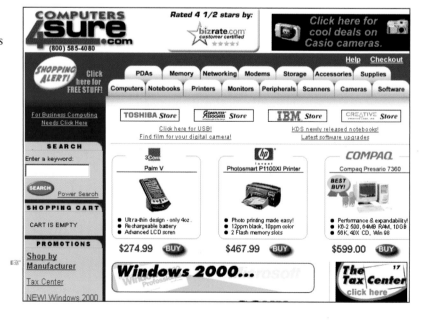

www.computers4sure.com

design.com

An amateur, but worthwhile, site that has a number of resources for web designers, including software downloads.

www.design.com

Eudora

Get upgrades, help, and a free version of one of the best email software products on the market.

www.eudora.com

TheFreeSite.com

Masses of free graphics, fonts, sounds and more for enhancing your web site.

www.thefreesite.com

Hewlett Packard

Browse through all the HP products, and buy product online, if you live in the US.

www.hp.com

Inmac

Not just Macs at all, this site is a comparison shopper site for those after computer hardware.

www.inmac.co.uk

Jasc Software

Publishers of Paint Shop Pro, one of the best image-manipulation programs available.

www.jasc.com

MacInTouch

Keep up-to-date on everything Mac-related, with news and reviews.

www.macintouch.com

MacWarehouse

Very useful UK retail site for Mac lovers who are also fond of bargains.

www.macwarehouse.co.uk

MicroWarehouse

Great US warehouse site offering PCs and other hardware at knockdown prices.

www.microwarehouse.com

Morgan Computers

Morgan is one of the UK's leading dealers in surplus, overstock and close out computer stocks.

www.morgancomputers.co.uk

Quark

Makers of the most popular design software in the world, including Quark Xpress.

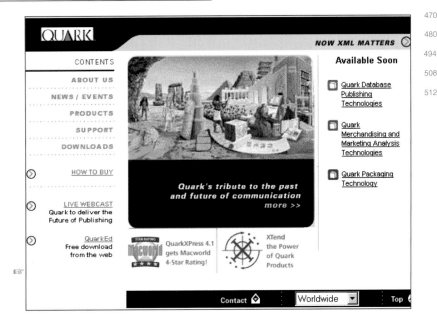

www.quark.com

QuickTime

The latest *Star Wars* trailers were uploaded in QuickTime format. That should say something about its quality and uses.

www.quicktime.com

Reading Room

UK web design agency that, despite a 'business 2 business' portfolio, will build you a site for as little as £1,000 (approx. $1700).

www.readingroom.net

Recreational Software Advisory Council

The place to find unbiased, independent, information about software and electronic media. Also home to the Internet Content Rating Association (ICRA).

www.icra.org

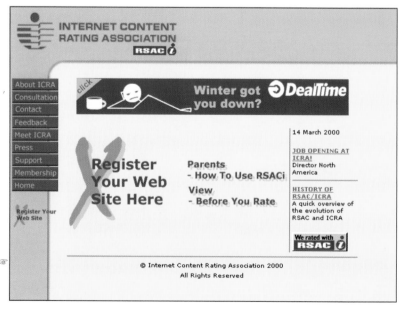

Revolution

Great site of the weekly magazine for the Internet design and media industries, including a web designer's directory.

www.revolution.haynet.com

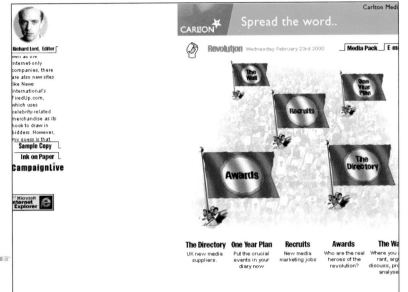

Sage

The world's leading accountancy software publisher has sites for the US, UK, France, Germany, Australia, and New Zealand.

www.sage.com

Sharkyextreme.com

Reports on the latest hardware (and software) technology for the PC enthusiast.

www.sharkyextreme.com

Simply Computers

Good UK site for PC peripherals and accoutrements, as well as software for home and business use.

www.simply.co.uk

Software & Information Industry Association

A site for the software publishing industry with news and details of ceremonies and awards.

www.siia.net

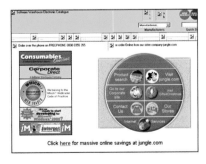

Software Warehouse

Excellent UK and Australian site offering good deals on software, with its own ISP.

www.software-warehouse.co.uk

Versions

Follow the upgrade status of your favorite software via the site, and a free email.

www.versions.com

News & Weather

T he thing about a news story is that, barring developments, it is only news for about 24 hours. Or at least, so newspapers would have us believe. No doubt it was the same back when messengers delivered news. They didn't want to be out of a job. Alas, there is not much hope for the dear old newspaper. Whereas magazines will always survive, the job of delivering breaking news and analysing it in great detail can be done far better by the Internet, than by either the printed or broadcast mediums.

Consider the drawbacks of traditional news mediums. Papers now seem so out of date - when you pick one up it can feel like you're reading yesterday's news, which of course you are. That is the trouble with the newspaper's format. Newspapers cannot be put together and distributed any faster than they already are, so the news will always be out of date. Something else will have happened to move the story along; someone will have made a counter claim or comment, the trial will have moved on a day.

With the Internet, there is no such time barrier. Something happens and it can be written about and be up on a news site in minutes, not hours. The counter argument is that not everyone can access the web at all times. This is true - for the moment. Most people in the developed countries do have access to the web while at work and, with the advent of wireless application protocol (WAP), the Net - and the news on it - will be on your mobile phone. I expect that as a result we'll see the physical newspaper evolve into more of a magazine style pub-

lication, along the lines of *Time* magazine or *Newsweek*. The other great aspect to the Internet news delivery is the space it has. No newspaper can devote too much space to one subject. During the Nato/Kosovo conflict, the papers and television could report on the bombing, but they couldn't go into too much detail on the causes of the conflict; the history of the oppression Nato was trying to stop. But the Internet news sites could. The amount of space a story can take up is virtually unlimited.

So the Internet can not only give you the news as it happens, it can give you as much background information to the news as you want. And being the multi-media network it is, the Internet can deliver live radio and streaming video broadcasts, as well as pre-recorded pieces. You can also interact with people in the news by emailing questions for interviews, or even speak to them live in specially organised chats.

Finally, if you are still not convinced by the Internet's news delivering qualities, consider this. The paper or TV station you watch reflects the culture from which you come.

It also reflects to a greater or lesser extent the political, social and ethical standards of the country you live in, and its government or ruling body. It is said that truth is the first casualty of war, and it has certainly been true in the past. The Internet lets you break those barriers by seeing the other side, and again this was particularly true during the Kosovo conflict.

CNN

Who was there during the Gulf War? CNN, and it's been the top choice for broadcast news ever since. It is also one of the best news sites on the Internet: the depth and breadth of the content has to be seen to be believed, and that's before you get to the broadcast material (including The Larry King Show), and the headline news stories.

www.cnn.com

BBC News

The BBC is known around the world for the quality and impartiality of its reporting, and its web site is no different. The site is divided into sections so it won't take long to find what you're after. If it does, you can try the news ticker of breaking stories, or the search engine which also contains a wealth of archive material. You can even watch the latest news bulletin.

http://news.bbc.co.uk

Press Association

Britain's National News Agency, the **Press Association**, is usually one of the first with the latest news. As with many news sites, the PA is divided into sections to make finding what you're after easier, but no other site has the PA's excellent Storyfinder, which lets you search for current events stories on over 100 UK news sites.

www.pa.press.net

Reuters

The world's biggest name in news is also one of the biggest players online. You can narrow your search for stories by subject matter or continent of origin. There are in-depth pieces to help you get more from the headlines, and special third party links with the emphasis on business.

www.reuters.com/news

abcNEWS.com

A great news resource from the US with live audio, video, and chat as well as pre-recorded pieces, and a lot of great textual content.

www.abcnews.go.com

BBC Weather Centre

Probably the best and most friendly UK weather site.

www.bbc.co.uk/weather

Drudge Report

Very popular news site. It does have the main headlines, but it's loved because it's full of gossip and scandal. It also has some useful links to the world's press.

www.drudgereport.com

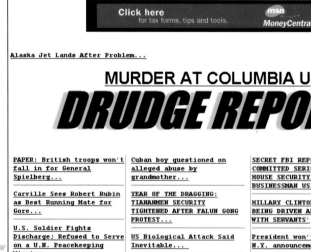

ITN

The UK's other news network is also a world-beater. ITN even make a special news bulletin that is broadcast at the same time every day.

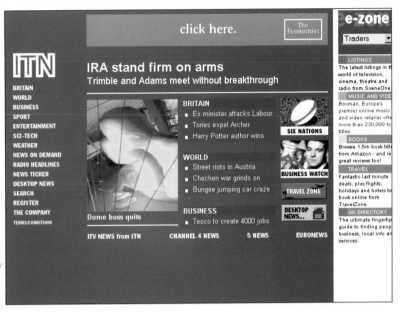

www.itn.co.uk

Fox News.com

Although focused on the US, like the best sites this one concentrates on news not nationality - so no matter where it's happening, it'll be here.

www.foxnews.com

ft.com

The most famous business newspaper anywhere, has one of the best financial sites anywhere. It covers all concerns, from those of the big businesses to those of the small investor.

www.ft.com

MSNBC

The joint effort from **Microsoft** and **NBC** has some great content, but it can annoy you with all the ads that pop up while you move from page to page.

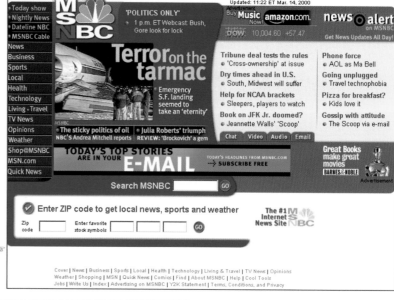

www.msnbc.com

News Unlimited/Guardian Unlimited

Another one of the earliest newspapers online, and still one of the best. There is a whole network here, but these two deal with current events news specifically.

www.newsunlimited.co.uk

www.guardianunlimited.co.uk

The Onion

Classic site taking a very lighthearted (and sometimes rude) look at the news around the world, but with a focus on the US.

www.theonion.com

Sky News

One of the best news sites, with an amazing array of news stories. There is a UK bias, but the rest of the world is well represented.

www.sky.com/news/home

This is Britain

Get away from the headlines, and down to local level, as this site acts as the hub of almost all the UK's regional newspapers.

www.thisisbritain.co.uk

Weather.com

Forecasts the weather for up to three days for anywhere in the world.

www.weather.com

1stHeadlines

Collates all the headlines from the best news sites in one place.

www.1stheadlines.com

7am.com

Where the news breaks first if you live in the US time zones.

www.7am.com

News & Weather

Africa News Online

Non-profit agency that features articles and news from African periodicals.

www.africanews.org

Agence France Presse

The latest news, from the French perspective, in six languages.

www.afp.com

AlterNet

Alternate news stories gathered from the outlying sites on the Net.

www.alternet.org

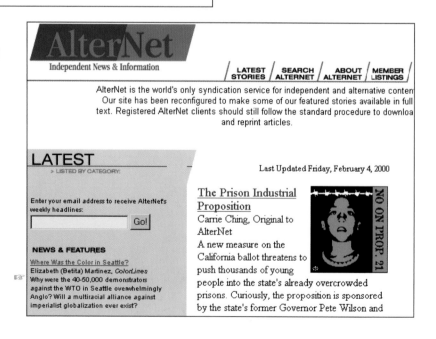

Asia Times Online

One of the foremost news sites for the Asian continent.

www.atimes.com

Automatic Weather Stations

Don't rely on the experts, run a weather station yourself.

www.prodata.co.uk/weather

CBC

The Canadian perspective on the news can be found at **CBC**.

http://cbc.ca/news

CBS News

Great US content; not so great for the rest of the world.

http://cbsnews.cbs.com

Chicago Tribune

The latest news from the Windy City's most famous periodical.

www.chicago.tribune.com

News & Weather

China Internet Information Center

Get the news, in English, from the Chinese point of view.

www.china.org.cn/english/index.html

Crayon

One of the original interactive sites, where you can still 'Create Your Own' newspaper.

www.crayon.net

Disinformation

Digging up the 'news' stories that don't make it to the newspapers or TV.

www.disinfo.com

DowJones.com

The best US business news, from the publishers of the *Wall Street Journal*.

www.dowjones.com

Electronic Telegraph

One of the earliest papers on the web, which since 1994 has been providing quality news.

www.telegraph.co.uk

globeandmail.com

Top Canadian paper *The Globe and Mail* has a site with loads of great content.

www.globeandmail.com

The Hindu

India's top national newspaper delivers all the latest from the sub-continent.

www.the-hindu.com

Index to Online News Agencies from the Middle East

Very useful collection of links to Arabic newspapers and press agencies.

www.rain.org/~maisoui/newspapers.html

Intellicast

Just click the map for global weather forecasts and data.

www.intellicast.com

Internet Magazine Online

Possibly the only site that deals specifically with UK rather than US Internet news.

www.internet-magazine.com

News & Weather

InternetNews.com

Great site for all the major US Internet happenings, primarily aimed at the industry.

www.internetnews.com

The wreckage of a Hizbullah commander's car is removed after it was hit by an IAF missile in the Lebanese village of Barish on Friday.
(AP)

The Jerusalem Post

The top Israeli newspaper available in English.

www.jpost.co.il

Los Angeles Times

Get news, view classified ads, and even customise the paper with an LA twist.

www.latimes.com

Megastories

An amazing resource of world-wide documentaries, all in one place.

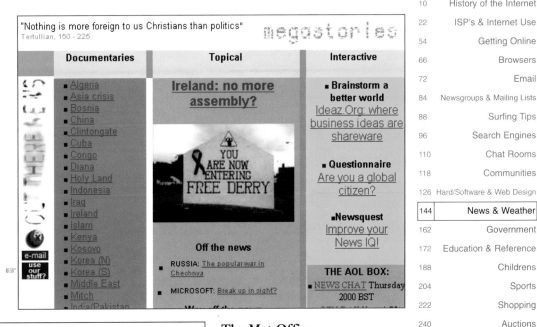

www.megastories.com

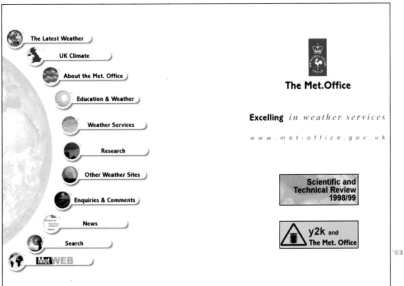

The Met.Office

The UK government site for the UK weather.

www.meto.gov.uk

National Geographic News

Not the latest news, but the most in-depth from the scientific community.

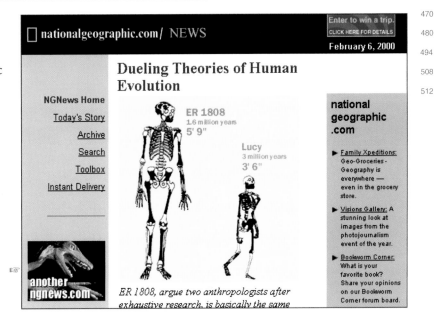

www.ngnews.com

News & Weather

NewCity.com

The alternative news stories coming out of America.

www.newcity.com

News Agencies Online

Practically every news agency on the planet can be found here.

www.irna.com/NewsAG/list.htm

News.com

Part of the **C Net** empire, this is a great site for technology news.

www.news.com

NewsHub

Fully automated news gathering site that updates itself every 15 minutes.

www.newshub.com

NewsNow

Updated every five minutes and tells you how soon the next one is.

www.newsnow.co.uk

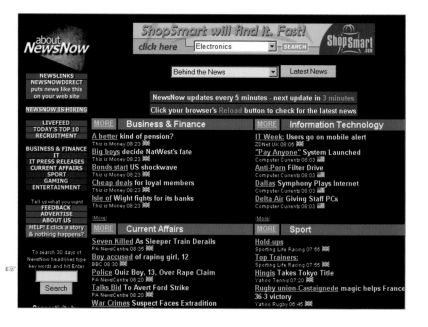

Newsweek Magazine

The second greatest US news magazine has a first-rate web site.

www.newsweek.com

Newsrack

Links to most of the best online newspapers and magazines.

www.newsrack.com

The New York Times

One of the original papers on the web and still going strong.

www.nytimes.com

Online Weather

Concentrates on the UK and Ireland, but also covers the rest of the world.

www.onlineweather.com

The Paperboy

One of the most comprehensive and searchable databases of worldwide newspapers.

www.thepaperboy.com

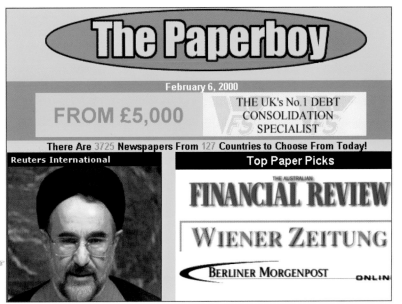

Slate

Once the bad boy of news sites, now a little tamer.

www.slate.com

Tass.Net

Home to the Russian news agency's top stories, newswire and archives.

www.tass.net

Time Magazine

The greatest American news weekly's great web site.

www.pathfinder.com/time

The Times/The Sunday Times

The UK's most famous paper all online.

www.the-times.co.uk

USA TODAY

One of the best newspaper sites in the world, with more sections than almost any other.

www.usatoday.com

The Wall Street Journal

No news here, but you can sign up for a news email.

www.wsj.com

Weather24

Just type in your US zip code and get a weather forecast for the next 24 hours.

www.weather24.com

Weather Forecasts on the Net

A page of links guaranteed to help you find the forecast you're after.

www.advocacy-net.com/fore-castmks.htm

The Week

Good weekly round up of the UK press, with additional content.

www.theweek.co.uk

Wired News

One of the best online resources for technology news.

www.wirednews.com

World Meteorological Organization

For those who can't get enough weather and meteorology.

www.wmo.ch

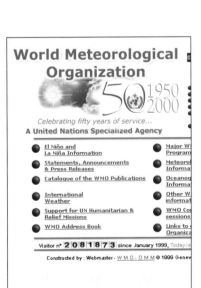

Government

Although developed by a branch of the US government, national and worldwide authorities have been slow to get themselves online. They didn't understand the medium, or how they could make it work for both them and the people they represent. Now, however, some government and international organisations' sites are the best in the world.

The US President's seat of power, the White House, is an excellent site that details the careers, families and achievements of the President and his Deputy. It has links to the most used US government sites, and lets you send the President an email - which is answered very promptly (probably by an automated system).

The UK has arguably the most comprehensive government portal in the world with its all-encompassing Open Government web site. The site has links to all the UK government web sites - from Number 10 Downing Street to the security service, MI5.

According to the latest figures released by Matrix Information and Directory Services, the top 15 most wired (those with the highest proportion of computers hooked up to the web per 1,000 people) countries in the world are, in order: Finland, Iceland, the US, Norway, Australia, Sweden, New Zealand, Canada, Switzerland, Singapore, the Netherlands, Denmark, the UK, and Austria.

All these countries have embraced the Internet and have set up some great governmental sites, but none has achieved the goal of dig-

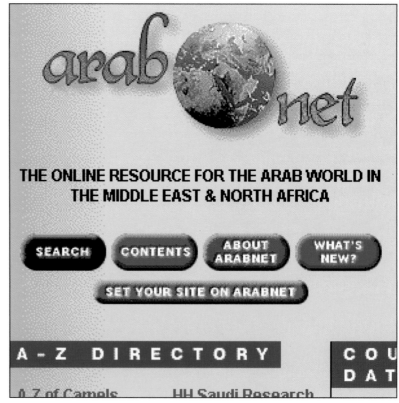

ital democracy. This is the notion of online government taken to its ultimate conclusion.

We will be able to vote online, chat with our elected officials, contribute to debate, and truly become part of the process of democratic government - putting the demos (Greek for people) back in democracy. And this is not so far away. The US plans to have limited online voting in 2000's Presidential Elections. While in the UK, Prime Minister Tony Blair has announced that people will be able to vote online at the next General Election in 2001.

For the moment we will have to be content with government information, once only to be found on the dustiest shelves in public libraries, being readily available on the Net. If you want to know about bills and amendments, white papers and consultation documents, you can now find them on the appropriate government site, print them off and read them at your leisure.

This is not only true of government at local and national level, but also of organisations and bodies that cross international borders. So, you'll find the likes of the European Union, the UN, NATO, and the International Federation of Red Cross and Red Crescent Societies.

Where there are gaps in a country's official presence on the Net, the void has been filled by dedicated amateurs. It has to be said they are sometimes a lot better at giving you the content and links you are after, than their more professional state sponsored compatriots.

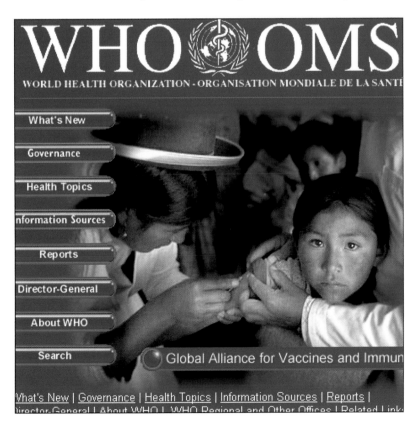

Open Government

Possibly the best government portal anywhere in the world. You can search the site for specific information, or view sites by topic or organisation, visit any of the government departments, and check out the most visited sites that fall under the UK government umbrella.

www.open.gov.uk

Governments on the WWW

If you need details of government and government-related sites encompassing the whole world, this is the place for you. Search by country, heads of state, as well as the world's parliaments, law courts, broadcasting authorities and similar categorised listings. Also has information on multi-governmental organisations, and links to similar sites.

www.gksoft.com/govt/en

Governments on the WWW: Table of Contents

last change: 1999-12-30 -- Gunnar Anzinger <a@gksoft.com>

Additions, corrections, suggestions and other comments are always welcome. Please send an e-mail to me.

Overviews with links to the individual countries:

- Worldwide Governments on the WWW
- European Governments on the WWW
- African Governments on the WWW
- American Governments on the WWW
- Asian Governments on the WWW
- Oceanian Governments on the WWW

Some categories of institutions:

- Multi-governmental Institutions (filesize: 18 kByte)
- Heads of State (filesize: 11 kByte)
- Parliaments (filesize: 44 kByte)
- Law Courts (filesize: 48 kByte)

UN

Although badly designed, this site is a wealth of information concerning world events. Find out about the general assembly, the secretary general, the security council, peace-keeping operations, the many relief and charitable efforts the organisation makes, and international law, to name a few facets of the UN's work.

www.un.org

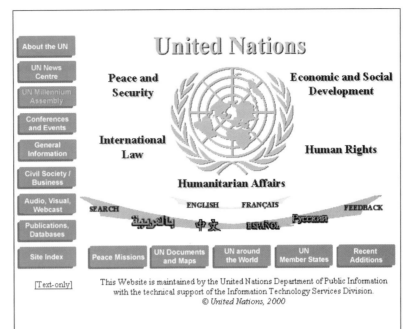

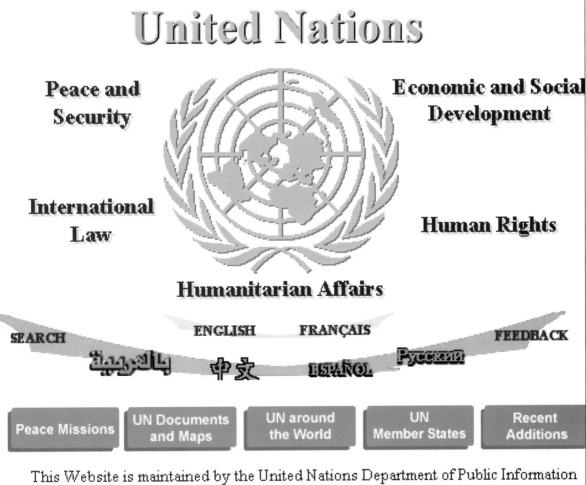

Government

White House

Although called the White House, this site also acts as a US governmental mini-portal with links to the top Federal sites. You can go behind the scenes at the White House on a tour, send email to the President, visit the briefing room or a virtual library, as well as download press statements and speeches.

www.whitehouse.gov

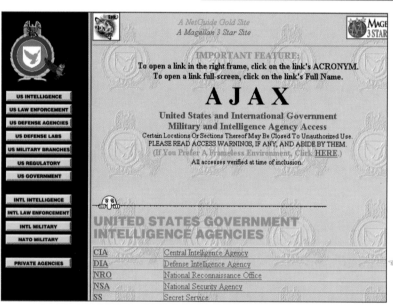

AJAX

A hugely useful listings site. It details and links to every US government agency, from Defence to Justice.

www.sagal.com/ajax

ArabNet

From Algeria to Yemen, all the Arab nations are represented on this site. You'll find links to cultural and government web sites as well as general features on the Arab world.

www.arab.net

Europa

Multi-lingual site with lists of European facts, figures and policy. There are also links to government and, of course, the single European currency.

www.europa.eu.int

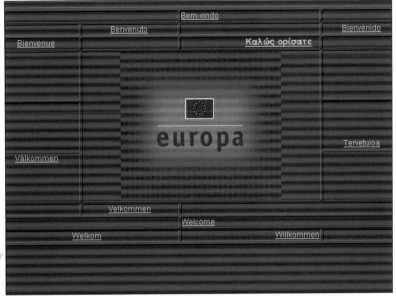

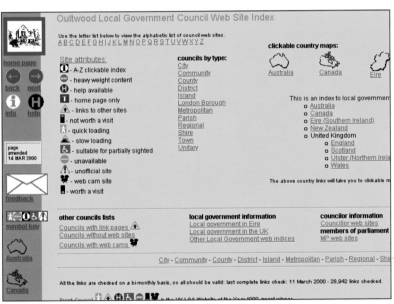

Oultwood Local Government Council Web Site Index

A very long name for a very useful site - it lists all local government in the UK, Canada, New Zealand, Eire and Australia.

www.oultwood.com/localgov

National Websites Official Web Pages

Lists most of the world's governmental web sites, from Andorra to Yugolslavia, but with notable absences.

www.psr.keele.ac.uk/official.htm

G7/G8

Probably the best site for finding out about the Group of 7 (G7) and Group of 8 (G8) geo-political bodies. It's all here.

www.g7.utoronto.ca

www.fed.gov.au

An excellent portal with links to all departments and ministers of the Australian Government.

www.fed.gov.au

The Canadian Government

Not just government in French and English, but maps and other details.

http://canada.gc.ca

The Finnish Council of State

See how the most wired country on the planet does it. You won't find the US or UK government sites in Finnish…

www.vn.fi/vn/english

The Council of State (or Government) consists of the Prime Minister and up to 17 ministers. The term is also applied to the whole formed by the Government and ministries.

The Government of Tibet in Exile

The official site dedicated to the return of independence to Tibet, sanctioned by the Dalai Lama.

www.tibet.com

International Federation of Red Cross and Red Crescent Societies

History, aims, and contact information, for the Red Cross or Red Crescent in 176 countries.

www.ifrc.org

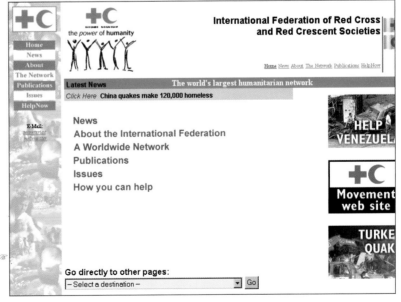

Government

The National Assembly for Wales

Useful site for the new governmental body in Wales.

www.wales.gov.uk

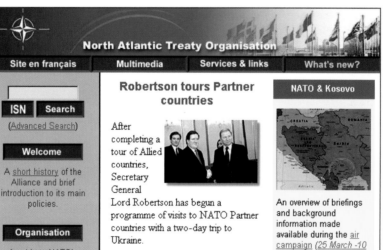

NATO

The latest reports on NATO operations, the history of the alliance, and a virtual tour of its headquarters.

www.nato.int

Number 10

Visit the British Prime Minister at his London residence.

www.number-10.gov.uk/index.html

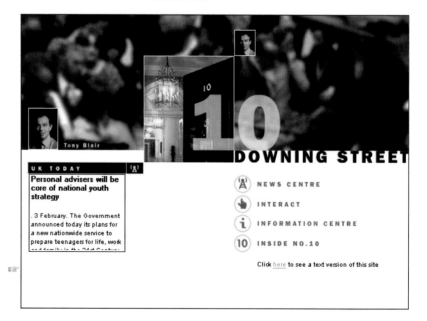

NZ GO

The trendy portal for the New Zealand government and its resources.

www.govt.nz

Saturday 5th February 2000, 11:22 pm

Welcome To New Zealand Government Online

NZGO is the Official Gateway to New Zealand Government. This website provides an overview of New Zealand and its government, access to government services information, as well as government agency contact details.

News in Brief

Click here for a more detailed map

- Hutt Valley Wastewater Project
- Waitangi Day: A History - new exhibition on NZHistory.net
- Commission of Inquiry into INCIS
- Australian Sesquicentennial Gift Trust for Awards in Oral History
- Latest Population Estimates

more...

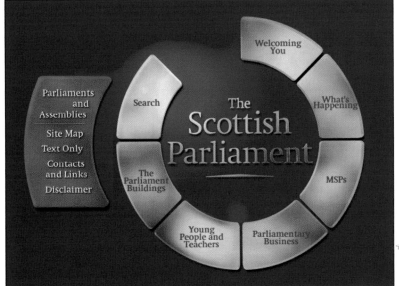

The Scottish Parliament

Online info for the new parliament north of the border.

www.scottish.parliament.uk

World Health Organization

Sources of information about world health, and what the organization is doing to improve it.

www.who.org

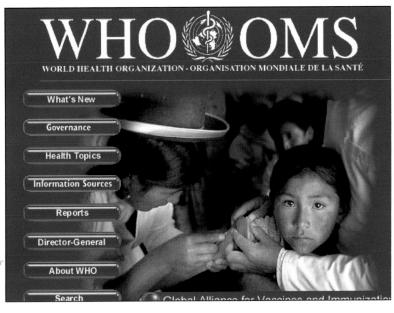

Education & Reference

It is hard to imagine a place that will be more affected by the rise of the Internet than the classroom. The way in which children learn, and the methods teachers use, will change completely over the next few years. Education is always on the agenda for every politician in the western world. The introduction into the classroom of the Internet, and other new technologies, has been seen as a priority by every country to ensure that it is not their children who fall behind in the information race.

As universities were among the pioneers of the Internet, most around the world now have access to the Net and use it for swapping ideas, collaboration on research projects, and keeping others informed of their findings. University students, too, have embraced the web as a tool for targeting the most relevant texts to use in their study, or for making friends around the world and promoting better understanding across cultures and national boundaries.

Slowly but surely, schools across the UK, US, Canada, Australia, New Zealand and Europe have been joining their colleagues in higher education with their own connections to the Internet, email addresses for students, and access to the biggest and most exciting reference library in the world. Generally, the figure for the number of schools connected to the Internet is about 80 per cent. This applies to the total number of schools in Canada (90 per cent) and in the US (75 per cent), and the number of secondary schools in the UK (90 per cent).

Encouragingly, recent research carried out has found that socially, Internet users are held in high esteem by teenagers and children. Not for this generation the name-calling and the term 'nerd' bandied about. The up-and-coming generation understand that the Internet is 'cool' and represents a big chunk of their future.

In the UK, the Labour government has been introducing the National Grid for Learning (NGfL). This will bring teachers up-to-date materials to enhance their skills, and children high quality educational materials. To facilitate this, teachers have been receiving training in information technology (IT). There has even been the promise of an email address for every child in the country.

There are now services tailored to helping children to complete their homework successfully such as the excellent **Homework Solver** (www.homeworksolver.com), and to secure email facilities, such as **SchoolMaster** (www.schoolmaster.net), that allow children to converse confidentially with teachers about problems they are experiencing or things they don't understand. This section also includes resources that can only be accessed by children from a school. Away from the confines of putting education and schools together, the Internet is a fantastic resource for anyone doing research. From looking up a word in a dictionary to finding out the latest data from Mars, the Internet can help you, and most of the time it only costs as much as a local telephone call. You will find stalwarts of the reference world, such as the *Encyclopaedia Britannica*, rubbing shoulders with newcomers to the public information market, such as the Central Intelligence Agency in the US.

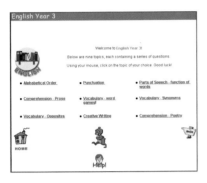

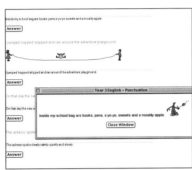

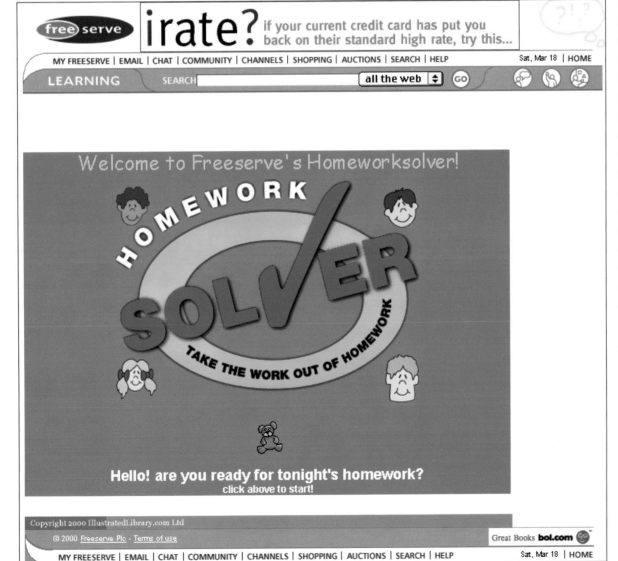

Allexperts.com

This site has been around for a while and is one of the best-kept secrets on the web. If you have any question that you need answering by an expert, just choose your expert, fill in a form with your question, and within a day or so you get an answer. Experts are rated for knowledge and speed of response, so you can pick the best!

www.allexperts.com

The World Factbook

No matter what country in the world you want to find out about, the CIA's World Factbook will have a very detailed entry. You get a map and accompanying text on the geography, people, government, economy, communications, transportation and military capabilities of that country. If you're in a hurry, you can just read the introduction to each nation. The information really has a thousand and one uses.

www.cia.gov/cia/publications/factbook/index.html

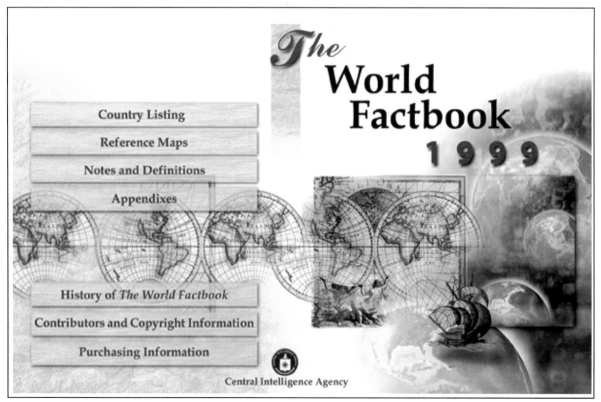

NASA

One of the most amazing sites on the entire web. You can see what images the space shuttle and various satellites are sending back to earth, view databases of astronomical photography, planetary mapping and space exploration. There is a huge educational resource as well as general information for the curious. You can even interact with NASA scientists and sometimes vehicles.

www.nasa.gov

Feb 13, 2000

"NASA is deeply committed to spreading the unique knowledge that flows from its aeronautics and space research...."

Read NASA Administrator Daniel S. Goldin's welcome letter, bio and speeches.

Welcome to NASA Web

Do you dream of exploring space or

NASA Begins to Map the Earth and Receives a Valentine from Mars

The six-member crew of STS-99, the Shuttle Radar Topography Mission, has begun its "21st century mission placing Earth back on the map." The astronauts will make close to one trillion measurements during their 11 days on orbit. For up-to-the-minute status reports, news events, how to

today@nasa.gov

Interested in the latest information NASA has to offer? Then take a look at today@nasa.gov. This on-line newsletter, updated daily, contains the latest news about NASA science and technology.

- NASA Begins to Map the Earth and Receives a Valentine from Mars
- As Shuttle Begins Earth Mapping, Space Station Plans Next Component

Encyclopaedia Britannica

If you need to find something out, this is a great place to start. Not only can you search the whole of the encyclopaedia, but you can also check out the editors' choice of web sites or use the Merriam-Webster's Collegiate Dictionary. There is so much information here that it is well worth exhausting this site's knowledge base before moving on.

www.eb.com

AngliaCampus

A very good UK site with a two-month free trial that really allows you to explore the excellent content that's on offer.

www.angliacampus.com

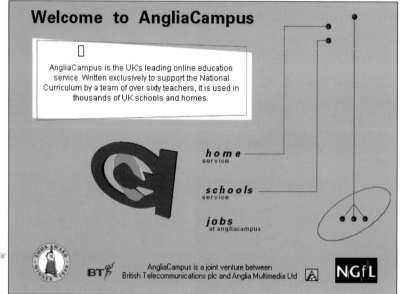

Ask An Expert

Another very good site for getting the opinions of experts.

www.askanexpert.com

The Complete Works of William Shakespeare

Every play that the Bard ever wrote is here for you to print and plunder as you will.

http://tech-two.mit.edu/Shakespeare/works.html

FamilySearch

One of the Net's biggest uses is tracing people's ancestry. This Mormon site is probably the best place to start.

www.familysearch.org

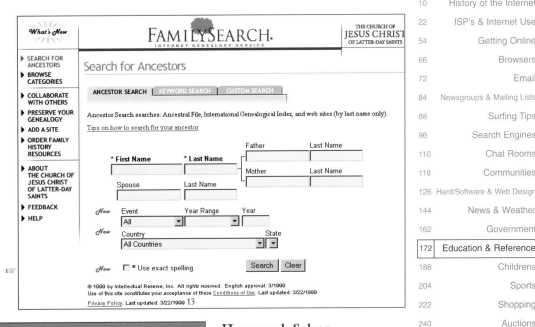

Homework Solver

A great UK resource from the Illustrated Library, developed with the help of teachers, and aimed at younger children.

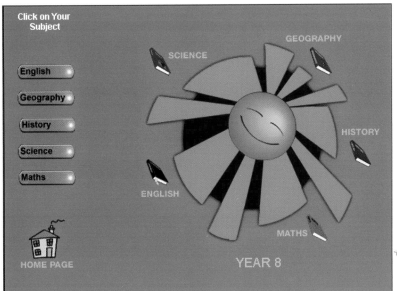

www.homeworksolver.com

The Library of Congress

An archive of practically every document in American history. For many, the Library of Congress *is* American history.

http://lcweb.loc.gov/homepage

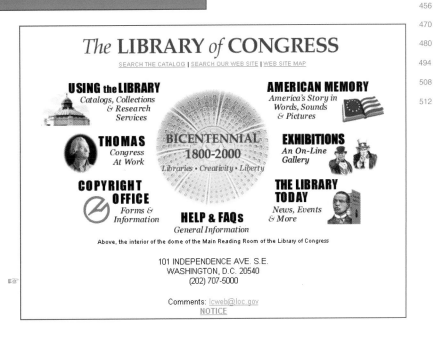

Living Library

One of the best learning resources in the UK from the market leader in educational sites. Unfortunately, this one costs.

www.livinglibrary.co.uk

megaConverter

The ultimate weights and measures site. Take any measurable amount, put it in the MegaConverter and see what it equates to in any other measurable amount.

www.megaconverter.com

Nua

Possibly the world's leading Internet research company, Nua's site carries abridged versions of all the latest reports and surveys concerning the Internet.

www.nua.ie

OneLook Dictionaries

If you need to look up a word, find a synonym, rhyme one word with another, get a famous quote for a speech or even use specialist dictionaries, this is the place to start.

www.onelook.com

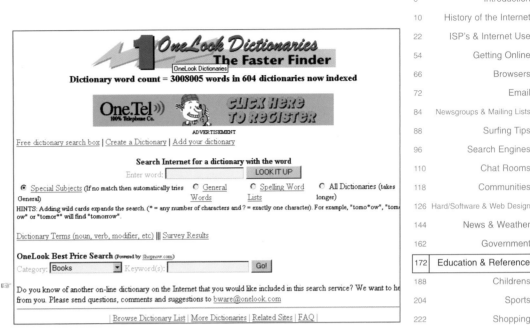

refdesk.com

An all-purpose reference portal with links to almost any subject you can think of, categorised by topic.

www.refdesk.com

Teldir.com

The most amazing resource of telephone directories that covers the globe. Teldir also makes a great place to start tracking down your family, too.

www.teldir.com

www.A-levels.co.uk

Amateur site-cum-portal that covers almost anything about the UK's A-level exams you could wish to know.

www.a-levels.co.uk

American School Directory

Find the best US schools with their profiles and pictures.

www.asd.com

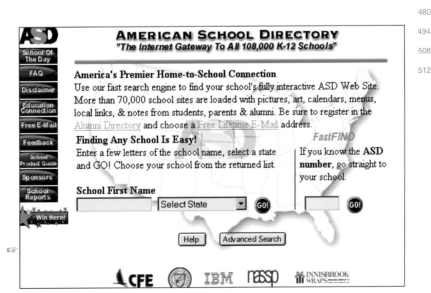

ArgoSphere

A really interactive site, for ages three and above, with learning activities and games.

www.argosphere.net

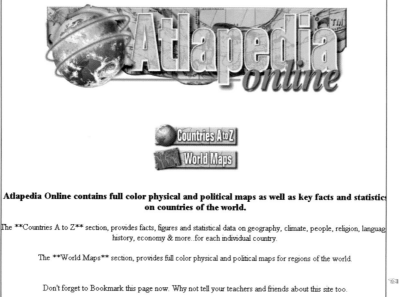

Atlapedia Online contains full color physical and political maps as well as key facts and statistics on countries of the world.

The **Countries A to Z** section, provides facts, figures and statistical data on geography, climate, people, religion, language history, economy & more..for each individual country.

The **World Maps** section, provides full color physical and political maps for regions of the world.

Don't forget to Bookmark this page now. Why not tell your teachers and friends about this site too.

Atlapedia Online

Atlapedia has every kind of map you might want - physical, political, statistical and factual.

www.atlapedia.com

Babel Fish

If you find a site in French, German, Spanish or Italian, just copy the text, paste into the window at Babel Fish and you'll get a translation. Invaluable.

www.babelfish.com

Welcome to the Internet Site of the Babel Fish Corporation

Are you are looking to translate English into either French, German, Italian, Portuguese or Spanish?	Êtes vous regardez pour traduire le Français en anglais?	Sind Sie schauen, um Deutschen ins Englische zu übersetzen?	Siete state osservando per tradurre l'italiano in inglese?	São você está olhando para traduzir o português em ingleses?	Es usted está mirando para traducir a español a ingleses?

Other Sites of Interest

The Babel Fish Corporation	The Alberta Traveller Site	The Babel Fish Virtual Net
Our corporate site with information on	Are you traveling to Alberta any time	Check out the companies that are

BBC Education

Part of the BBC's remit is to produce educational output. This is its online contribution.

www.bbc.co.uk/education

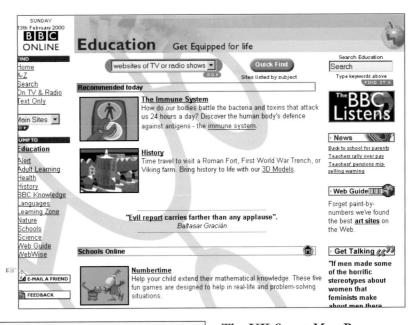

The UK Street Map Page

If you need to find your way about in Britain, look no further.

www.streetmap.co.uk

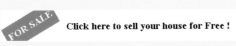

Channel 4 Learning

One of the UK's main broadcasters of programs for schools has augmented its service with this great online resource.

www.schools.channel4.com

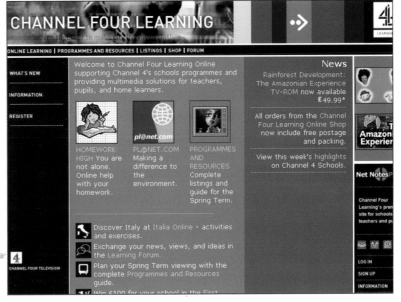

Education & Reference

Dictionary.com

A host of reference including Bartlett's Quotations, Roget's Thesaurus, The Skeptic's Dictionary, and others.

www.dictionary.com

DfEE

You'll find the UK's National Curriculum, special needs links and information, an education guide for parents, and a guide to choosing the best school.

www.dfee.gov.uk

Directory for UK Higher Education Administrators

A great site for finding out places of higher education in the UK.

EduWeb

A great site with links and resources for children and teachers in the UK.

EdViews

Lists over 25,000 sites that have been approved by teachers.

www.mailbase.ac.uk/juga   www.eduweb.co.uk   www.edview.com

Exploratorium

Scientific experience web site for schoolchildren.

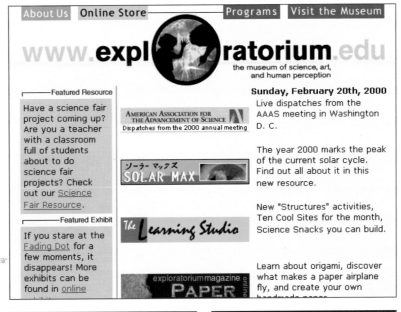

www.exploratorium.edu

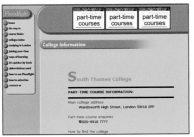

Flood*light*

Every part-time and evening course in London listed, priced and rated.

www.floodlight.co.uk

Free Worksheets

If you need to download or print off some worksheets to help your children, there's no point in paying!

www.freeworksheets.com

Hungry Minds

Great US site for those who need information on courses and places of education.

www.hungryminds.com

Infomine

Party of the University of California web site, InfoMine lets you view university resources as well as suggesting ways you might find what you're looking for.

http://infomine.ucr.edu

Education & Reference

Learn 2.com

No matter what it is you want to learn about, chances are Learn 2 will have a channel or section devoted to it.

www.learn2.com

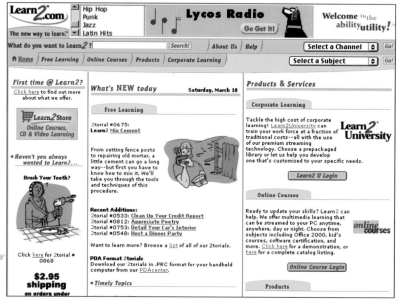

Learn Free

Videos of how to learn various skills such as dog training, teaching children to swim and the like.

www.learnfree.com

LearningStore.co.uuk

If you need to buy books or learning toys for your children, this is where you need to go.

MapBlast

One of the three great map sites on the web with the zoom facility represented by a balloon.

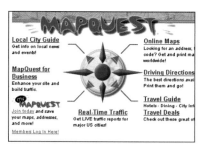

MapQuest

A truly amazing resource. Start at country level and zoom in until you're at street level.

www.learningstore.co.uk   www.mapblast.com   www.mapquest.com

Multimap.com

Another outstanding map site, with links to places of interest included below each map.

www.multimap.com

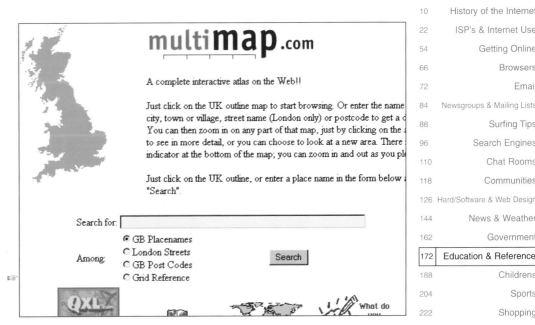

National Grid for Learning

An excellent resource for schools, teachers and parents in the UK.

www.ngfl.gov.uk

Number 1 for Nurseries

A great resource for those seeking a nursery school for their child in the UK, or those working in the business themselves.

www.number1fornurseries.com

Education & Reference

Nursery World

One of the best UK resources for nursery school workers.

www.nursery-world.co.uk

Oncourse

No matter whether you're planning to study in the US, UK, France, Spain, or Australia, On Course can help.

www.oncourse.co.uk

Schoolzone

The UK's best educational search engine.

www.schoolzone.co.uk

Smithsonian Institution

Although difficult to find your way around, this site does house some amazing resources.

www.si.edu

Learnfree.co.uk

Supported by the *Times Educational Supplement*, this site is another place for those who have a question but no answer.

www.learnfree.co.uk

Topmarks

UK educational resource that covers most topics.

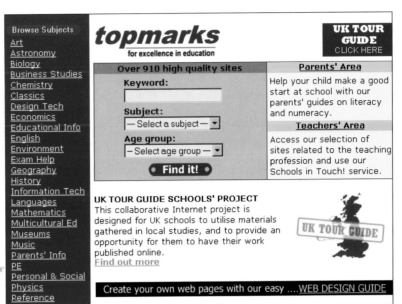

www.topmarks.co.uk

UCAS

The UK's clearing system for higher education.

www.ucas.ac.uk

UpMyStreet

The best guide to property prices, council tax, educational standards and crime rates in the UK.

www.upmystreet.com

US Department of Education

Many links to great content for and about education.

www.ed.gov

World Time Zone

An outstanding site for finding out what time it is in those obscure - and not so obscure - places around the world.

www.isbister.com/worldtime

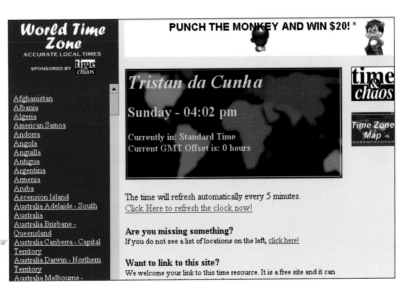

Childrens

One of the major criticisms of the Internet is that it can be a child unfriendly place. Alas, the media has hyped the web to the extent that the uninitiated could be forgiven for thinking that you only have to connect to the Internet to be inundated with images of porn, or instructions on how to make a bomb.

This is not the case. However, anyone who has access to the Net also has access to these, and many thousands of other, sites containing disturbing or unsuitable content for young eyes.

Fortunately there are ways to ensure your children don't see what you'd rather they didn't. The best way is to supervise all Internet use. Helping your child surf the web can be a rewarding and learning experience for both of you. You can pass on your knowledge, answer their Internet questions, and show them the best sites for homework, hobbies or interests.

Unfortunately you may not always have the time to monitor what your children are doing, and anyway it is often impossible to do so. So what *can* you do? The answer is simple. Employ something else to monitor them for you.

In this case you have three options. You could use the **safety settings** on the most recent versions of the *Netscape Navigator* and *Internet Explorer* browsers.

To set *Navigator's* filtering tool, follow the route of:
Help>NetWatch>NetWatch Set Up>New User.
You will then have to set the levels of access manually.
In *Explorer*, take this route:
Tools>Internet Options>Content>Enable.
You can then set the filter for bad language, nudity, sex and violence.

Despite the use of password protection, these systems are not as thorough as they might be, and children are not stupid when it comes to finding ways round the settings on a computer...

The second option is to use an **Internet Service Provider (ISP)** such as *AOL*, which sells itself on its family values and blocks anything that it deems 'unacceptable'. This is fine if you want censored access for yourself, but what if you don't? You could go for two ISPs. There are now ISPs that cater exclusively for children such as *KidzNet* in the UK.

The third and final option is the most popular. Simply get yourself a special piece of **software that will filter** the content your child can view. There are four main brands of this software and while some are free, others you will have to pay for. The four key players in this market are *Cyber Patrol*, *Net Nanny*, *CYBERsitter*, and *Surf Watch*. They all have lists of unsuitable sites and let you control access. Some even tell you when someone in your household has tried to access an unsuitable site.

However you decide to censor your child's access to the Net, there are many sites tailored to his or her needs and wants. As well as the excellent range of educational sites that I looked at in the **Education & Reference** section, there are many that are primarily there for enjoyment. Following is a selection of filter systems, child-centric sites and sites that are just good fun.

Cyber Patrol

Part of the Mattel Toy empire, Cyber Patrol set up a team of parents and teachers to define what is, and is not, suitable for children on the web. Prices start at $29.99 (around £18.75) for home use, and you can download a trial version that lasts for seven days.

www.cyberpatrol.com

Net Nanny

Set up in 1995, Net Nanny is one of the big four popular filtering tools on the web - attracting some 1.4 million visitors every month. As well as filtering, it also prevents strangers communicating via chat rooms, sends warning messages, costs $26.95 (around £16.80), but doesn't offer a free trial.

www.netnanny.com

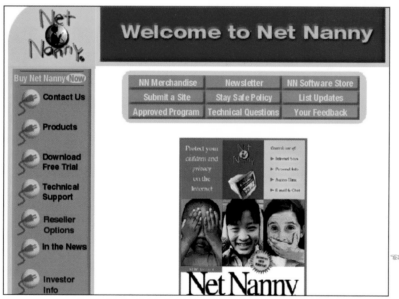

CYBERsitter

Self-proclaimed easiest to use filtering software, CYBERsitter updates itself automatically several times a day, and claims to be very difficult to remove other than by the person who installed it. You can download a trial version for ten days, or pay $39.95 (around £25) for a full copy.

www.cybersitter.com

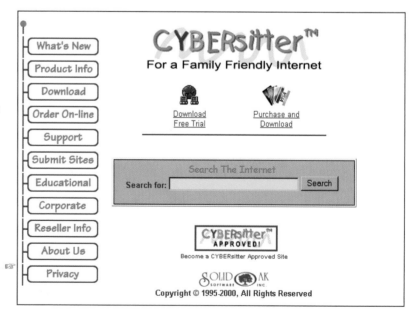

SurfWatch

The original Internet filtering system, and still one of the best, with over 8 million copies of its software sold. Prices start at $39.95 (around £25) for home use, but there is no trial version for you to try. It does have daily updates, is customisable and has blocked over 100,000 sites so far…

www.surfwatch.com

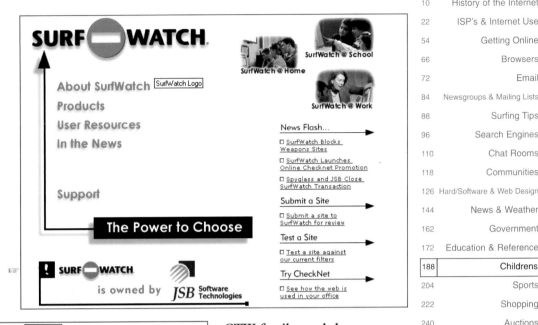

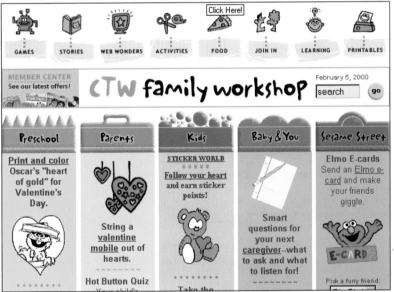

CTW family workshop

Meet Big Bird and Elmo at Sesame Street Central or there are plenty of other things for kids and parents to see and do at the Children's Television Workshop.

www.ctw.org

Cyberkids

Practically everything your child could need for a stimulating online experience. Fun & games, shopping and a learning center.

www.cyberkids.com

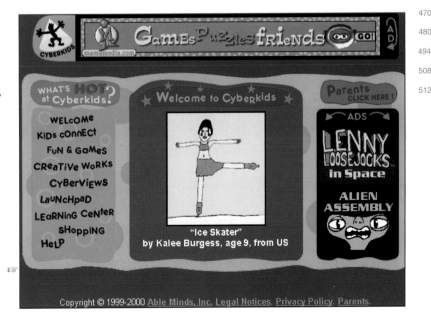

Disney.com

Every child's all-American favorite. As well as material related to its cartoon movie releases, there are also some excellent activities and other content.

http://disney.go.com

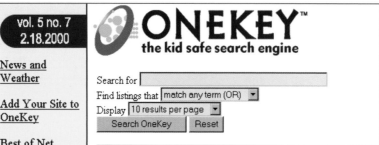

OneKey

The largest searchable database of sites suitable for children. It offers over 500 categories - from sport and technology to lifestyle and business.

www.onekey.com

Surf Monkey

This interesting beast is a newcomer to the filter market, but has the added extra of having its own children's browser, and it's free.

www.surfmonkey.com

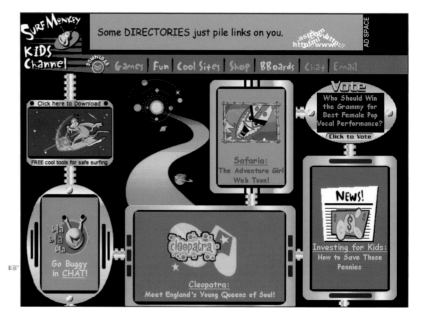

Yahooligans!

From the makers of the original search engine, this directory is for 7-12 year olds. All sites are checked by teachers to ensure both content and links are appropriate.

www.yahooligans.com

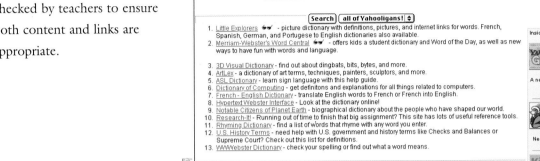

Ask Jeeves for Kids!

The place to go for those awkward questions such as 'why is the sky blue?'.

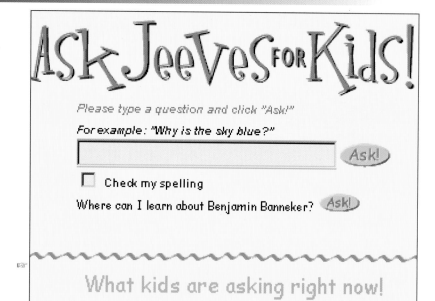

www.ajkids.com

Bolt

A major chat-based site for children, which also has good content and activities.

www.bolt.com

Bonus

A place online for kids to hang out, chat and pursue interests.

www.bonus.com

Babyworld

Expectant parents' online guide to everything about having, and bringing up, a baby.

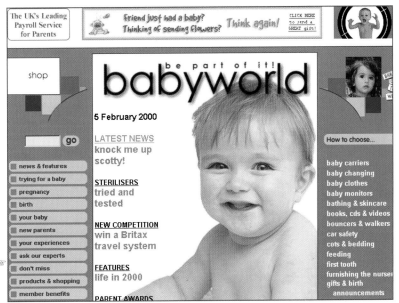

www.babyworld.co.uk

Cartoon Network

The home of cartoons such as *Scooby Doo*, *The Flintstones*, and other favorites.

www.cartoonnetwork.com

www.cartoonnetwork.co.uk

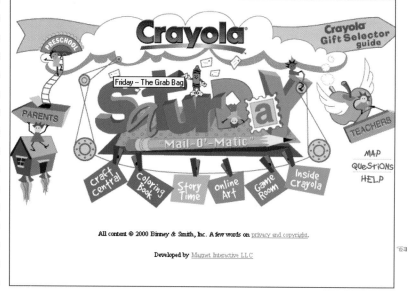

Crayola

The world's most famous crayon company has printable stories and colouring-in activities.

www.crayola.com

Discovery Channel Online

The documentary site for UFOs, dinosaurs, wildlife, history and lots more.

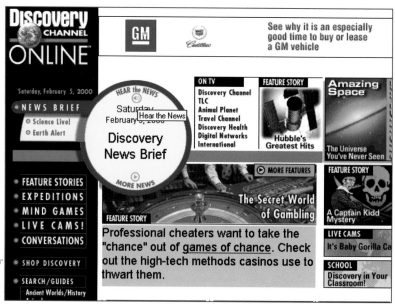

www.discovery.com

eToys

One of the Internet's leading online toyshops. Have your credit card ready.

www.etoys.com

www.etoys.co.uk

A Girl's World Clubhouse

Here teenage girls can enter competitions, get advice, or even keep an online diary.

www.agirlsworld.com

Headbone Zone

Chat, read features and play games on this children's portal.

www.headbone.com

Kidz.net

UK-based ISP that concentrates on content and services for children.   www.kidz.net

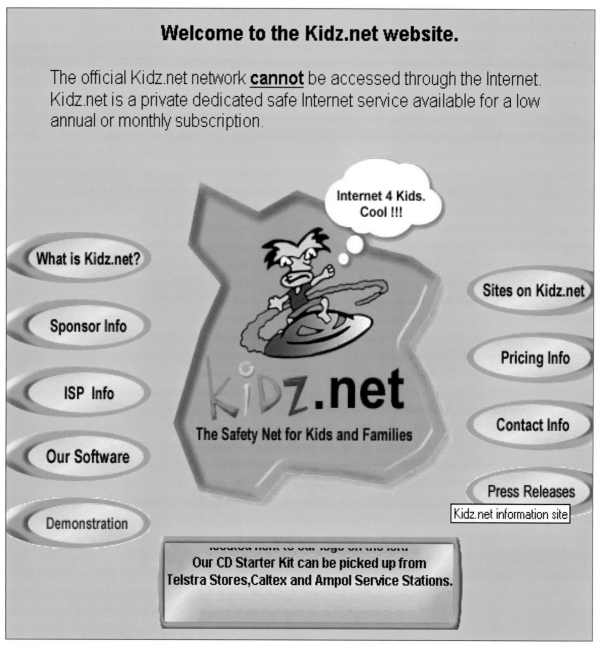

Kids' Space

Games and activities, plus areas for visitor's artistic and literary contributions.

www.kids-space.org

Kids Travel

Excellent advice and tips on transporting your children worldwide.

www.pathfinder.com/travel/klutz

Lego

The world's top building block also has a great site with digital Lego bricks.

www.lego.com
www.lego.co.uk

McDonalds.com

A good community and portal site from the hamburger giants.

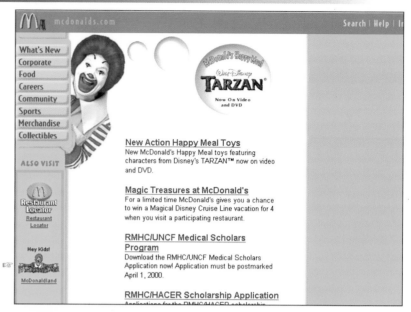

www.mcdonalds.com

Nick.com

All your children's TV favorites and some good extra content such as safety online from Nickleodeon.

www.nick.com

Sportal

For European sports, these sites are hard to beat.

www.sportal.co.uk

www.sportal.de

www.sportal.es

www.sportal.it

www.sportal.fr

Sports Illustrated for Kids

The place to go for all American sports.

www.skids.com

Teen.com

The 'ultimate' place on the web for teenagers with many and varied resources.

www.teen.com

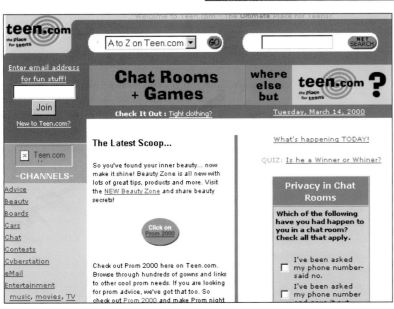

Teletubbies

Visit Tinky Winky, Dipsy, Laa-Laa and Po to play and interact.

www.bbc.co.uk/teletubbies

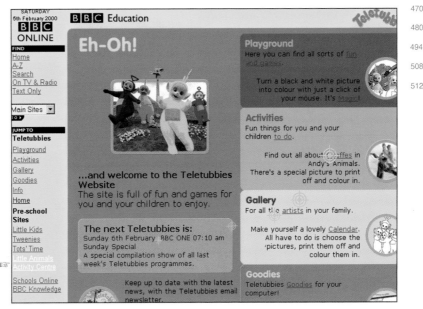

Thunk

Scrambles your text so you can swap emails in code. Great fun.

www.thunk.com

comics.com

United Media site, home to the cartoon strip 'funnies'. Charlie Brown, Dilbert and Garfield all feature.

www.unitedmedia.com

Warner Brothers.online

Bugs Bunny, Porky Pig, Daffy Duck, Pinky and the Brain, the Animaniacs. Enough said.

www.kids.warnerbros.com

Yucky.com

Science and the environment used in fun and yucky ways.

www.yucky.com

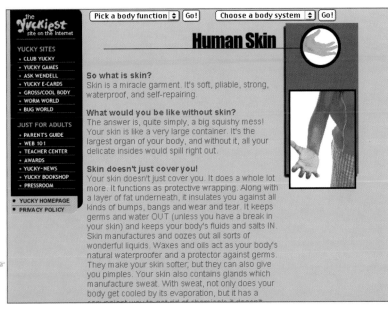

Pick a body function ▢ Go!   Choose a body system ▢ Go!

Human Skin

So what is skin?
Skin is a miracle garment. It's soft, pliable, strong, waterproof, and self-repairing.

What would you be like without skin?
The answer is, quite simply, a big squishy mess! Your skin is like a very large container. It's the largest organ of your body, and without it, all your delicate insides would spill right out.

Skin doesn't just cover you!
Your skin doesn't just cover you. It does a whole lot more. It functions as protective wrapping. Along with a layer of fat underneath, it insulates you against all kinds of bumps, bangs and wear and tear. It keeps germs and water OUT (unless you have a break in your skin) and keeps your body's fluids and salts IN. Skin manufactures and oozes out all sorts of wonderful liquids. Waxes and oils act as your body's natural waterproofer and a protector against germs. They make your skin softer, but they can also give you pimples. Your skin also contains glands which manufacture sweat. With sweat, not only does your body get cooled by its evaporation, but it has a

the Yuckiest site on the internet

the best source for science entertainment

Yuckiest Site on the Internet

Beat THE WINTER BLAHS

Play with your food!

This Week's Poll
You have a sleepover and someone starts telling dirty jokes:

Vote Here!

Check the results of past polls

WHAT'S NEW
Too cold outside? Try these Yucky activities:
- Make ordinary milk turn into slime
- Do you know your "icks" from your "ooze"? Take Yucky's Trivia Challenge
- Go ahead and play with your food! Try Fun and Yummy Science!
- Best Hot Media! picks of Winter

DON'T MISS
- Worm Libs hits the road
- Blast the blahs and send a Yucky E-Card
- Wendell shares his favorite funnies

JUST FOR ADULTS
- PARENT'S GUIDE

YUCKY SITES
- CLUB YUCKY
- YUCKY GAMES
- ASK WENDELL
- YUCKY E-CARDS
- GROSS/COOL BODY
- WORM WORLD
- BUG WORLD

JUST FOR ADULTS
- PARENT'S GUIDE
- WEB 101
- TEACHER CENTER
- AWARDS
- YUCKY-NEWS
- YUCKY BOOKSHOP
- PRESSROOM

- YUCKY HOMEPAGE
- PRIVACY POLICY

Sports

S port is big business. However you view or follow your favorite team or player, you devote a lot of time and probably money to it - travelling to the events, buying tickets, books, magazines, memorabilia, replica kits and videos, subscribing to satellite or cable TV. All so you can get more from your passion for sport.

The Internet lets you do most of the things listed above, but for free. Sport is one of the most popular forms of content on the web, so you can read endless features on every aspect of your sport, from player and game analysis to tactics, fitness regimes and histories. You can find out amazing facts, or memorize complicated statistics (but you don't have to because they're all on the Net). And because there are no space limitations online, the archives you'll find will astound you.

The immediacy of the Internet also means the same for sports news as it does for current events reporting. The Internet is immediate. Site owners can, and do, update their news sections as and when the news happens, not just on the hour or half hour. And because of email, you don't even need to return to a site to get the latest headlines. You can sign up to one of the free email newsletters that abound online.

There's also the opportunity to meet and chat with fellow sports fans online in the many chat rooms and forums you'll find on sports sites. After all, if there's anything sports fans like better than their favorite sport itself, it's sharing their passionate views and opinions

with others. This can even lead to you being given the chance to write a feature or report for one of those sites. The Internet isn't just about text, though. You'll find images of every sportsperson in the world somewhere on the web. And because this is the web, you aren't limited to static images either. You'll find video clips of great sporting moments, highlights from recent games or matches, as well as live or pre-recorded interviews.

The real beauty of the Internet is its diversity. If you follow a major sport like football, baseball, cricket, rugby or tennis, you are already well catered for outside the arena of the Internet. However, you may not be able to get hold of books and magazines about volleyball, lacrosse, dog racing or water polo. This is not the case on the Internet. A quick trip to any search engine or directory will reveal hundreds if not thousands of web sites dedicated to the sport you follow, no matter what it is. *Yahoo!* alone has 100 sports in its categories and each of these lists at least five or six sites. Some of the best sporting web sites have been those that tie in with international tournaments - World Cups, Olympic Games and the like. The Nagano Olympic site of 1998 was one of the most popular web sites ever. The same year, the official site of the Football World Cup in France introduced animation and live match commentary, while 1999's Rugby World Cup site was stunning with long video clips, interviews, and a whole host of other multi-media content. This year's Euro 2000 and Sydney Olympic sites promise even better things.

Sports

CNNSI.com

News channel CNN has teamed up with *Sports Illustrated* to bring you this great sports site. It concentrates a bit too much on the US side of things, but its breadth of coverage, including college football and women's sports, is outstanding.

www.cnnsi.com

CBS SportsLine/Sports.com

An excellent trio of sports sites owned by different companies but joined in one of the best sports networks on the web. CBS covers American sports such as NFL, NBA and NHL, while Sports Web/Sports.com deal in soccer, cricket, rugby and a whole host of other international sports.

http://cbs.sportsline.com

www.sports.com

www.sportsweb.com

Sporting Life

Probably the best UK-based central sporting news site on the web. It is linked to the Press Association for fast updates, and contains such gems as the halls of fame, a sporting quiz, the buzzing zone, an amazing archive and the 'extra' - an area covering every other sport.

www.sporting-life.com

Sky Sports

The British cable and satellite broadcaster provides excellent content on football, rugby, cricket, tennis, golf, boxing, motor sports, basketball, ice hockey and yachting. They don't come much more comprehensive than this and, even if you don't subscribe to the TV channels, the site is a great bonus.

www.sky.com/sports/home

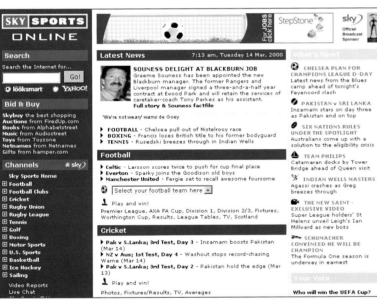

10-Tenths Motorsport

Includes content on Formula One racing, the world rally championship, the touring car championship, motorcycle racing, speedway and karting to name a few.

www.ten-tenths.com

A to Z Encyclopedia of Ice Hockey

UK-based site dealing with ice hockey around the world. Find player profiles, team news, leagues, competitions, events, and a lot more besides.

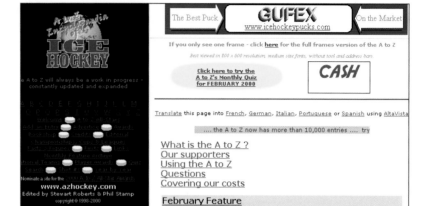

www.azhockey.com

CricInfo

Probably the best cricket site anywhere on the Net. CricInfo has a huge amount of content as well as servers all over the world to ensure fast downloading.

www.cricinfo.com

The Equestrian Times/Horsenews.com

A great site where you can find out almost anything about show jumping, dressage or three-day eventing. It also lets you take virtual course walks, too.

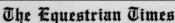

www.equestriantimes.com

ESPN.com

Part of Disney's *GO* network, ESPN covers the major US leagues - NHL, NBA, NFL etc - as well as tennis and soccer. There's online radio and a shop, too.

http://espn.go.com

EURO 2000

One of the two main sporting events of the year 2000 (the other is the Olympics). The site promises much in the way of content and multi-media, so it should be a good one.

www.uefa.com/euro2000

Eurosport

European site with a broad range of sports (including cycling and sailing) in a variety of different countries across the continent.

www.eurosport.com
www.eurosport.de

Sports

Football365

News, gossip, facts, stats, a viewing guide and the great Danny Kelly, making it one of the best soccer sites on the Internet.

www.football365.com

Fox Sports

Comprehensive coverage of major sports (both US and world) is offset by in-depth sections on subjects such as sports business and US college sports.

www.foxsports.com

From The Terrace

With its irreverent but knowledgeable style, and mixture of league and non-league content, this site must be the best for soccer fans who really know their stuff.

www.fromtheterrace.co.uk

Majorleaguebaseball.com

This official site covers every base for dedicated fans. From statistics and standings, to the history of the sport, and player profiles. It's all here.

www.majorleaguebaseball.com

MountainZone.com

A surprisingly difficult to find site that includes details on downhill and slalom skiing. It also has the usual resort reports and an equipment shop.

www.mountainzone.com

Olympics

The official site for the Sydney 2000 Games promises to be a great one. A good site to keep an eye on.

www.olympics.com

Racing Post

The quintessential British racing periodical. The site covers everything from bloodstock and tipsters, to results and betting on horses and greyhounds.

www.racingpost.co.uk

Scrum.com

Covers almost everything a dedicated rugby fan could wish to know, with some great contributors. Scrum.com is probably the best rugby site on the Net.

www.scrum.com

Sports

Sportal

An amazing collection of sites which aims to be the leading global provider of sports content. At the moment, though, it concentrates on soccer.

www.sportal.com

www.sportal.co.uk

www.sportal.net

www.sportal.de

www.sportal.fr

www.sportal.it

www.sportal.se

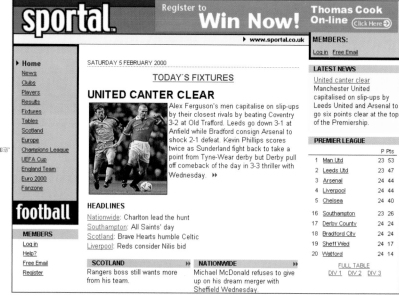

Sportserver

Very clean site with good news content. It also deals in sports outside the US, such as European football and soccer.

www.sportserver.com

Sport Quest

Amazingly useful sports-only search engine. Ideal for when you really can't find that obscure sport on a regular search engine.

www.sportquest.com

1ski.com

This is one for those who want to ski themselves, not just watch others do it.

www.1ski.com

19thHole.com

Irreverent look at golf, with a lot of good content.

http://19thhole.com

Australian Football League

The official site for Aussie rules football.

www.afl.com.au

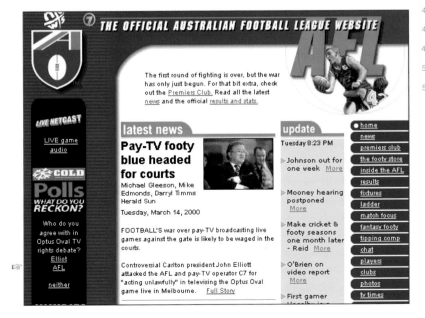

Sports

Baseball.com

Not just League baseball, but the whole thing with the usual mix of news and stats.

www.baseball.com

BBC Sports

Good coverage of a limited number of popular sports.

http://news.bbc.co.uk/hi/english/sport

The Blood-Horse

Very thorough US-based horse racing site with many excellent features.

www.bloodhorse.com

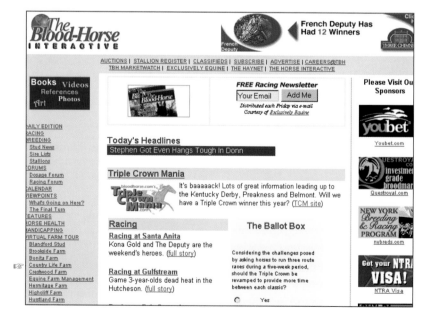

Board-it.com
One of the largest and best snowboarding sites.

www.board-it.com

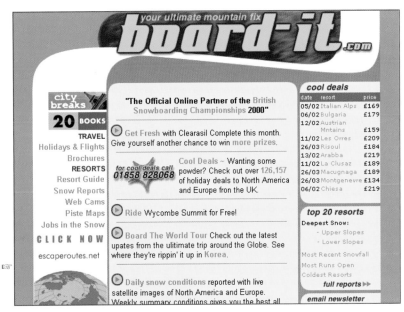

Boxing.com
A great resource for boxers, including Net radio broadcasts of the big fights.

www.boxing.com

BoxingPress.com
UK-based boxing site with news, views, chat, results and forthcoming fights.

www.boxingpress.com

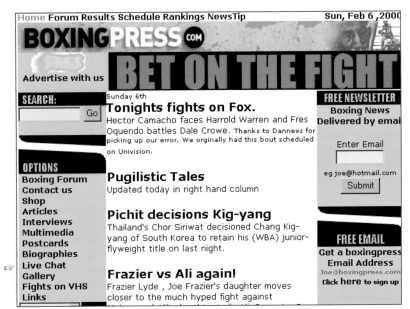

CricketUnlimited

One of the UK *Guardian*'s excellent sites - this time dealing with cricket.

www.cricketunlimited.co.uk

Fastball

Great baseball site encompassing news, features, statistics, chat and a forum.

www.fastball.com

Fish and Fly

Deals with fishing in the UK and Europe, with good links to other sites.

www.fishandfly.com

Fishing

Good fishing portal that includes place to stay when you've gone fishin'.

www.fishing.co.uk

Formula1.com

Unofficial site, but very good nonetheless, with excellent coverage.

www.formula1.com

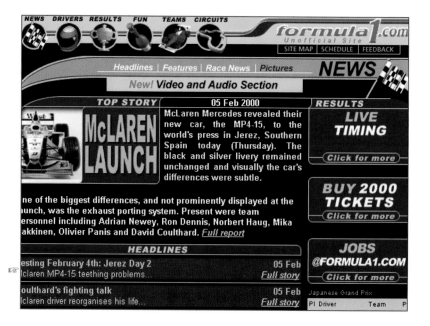

GameOn

Darts news and features from
Embassy World Darts.

www.embassydarts.com

Golf Zone

Golfing search engine, chat
room, scores, news, trivia, betting and even weather reports.

www.golfzone.co.uk

ITTF

The official site of the
International Table Tennis
Federation.

www.ittf.com

ITV-F1.com

Very thorough site belonging to
the official broadcaster, sanctioned by Bernie Ecclestone.

www.itv-f1.com

Major League Baseball Canada

The official site for the Canadian
branch of baseball.

www.majorleaguebaseball.ca

Sports

NHL.com

The official site of the US National Ice Hockey League.

www.nhl.com

NBA.com

The official site of the US National Basketball Association.

www.nba.com

NSSF

Home to the US National Shooting Sports Foundation, with details of range and hunting seasons.

www.nssf.com

Race Offshore.com

A great site for powerboat racing fans, with schedules, results and TV times.

www.raceoffshore.com

Real Tennis

Useful site for fans of the ancient game favored by HRH the Duke of Wessex.

www.real-tennis.com

Rugby365

Brother site of Football365. It covers its topic with equal enthusiasm.

www.rugby365.com

Sailfree.com

Covers everything from racing results to knot tying lessons.

www.sailfree.com

Shotgun Sports

UK site full of resources for those who enjoy shooting.

www.shotgunsports.org

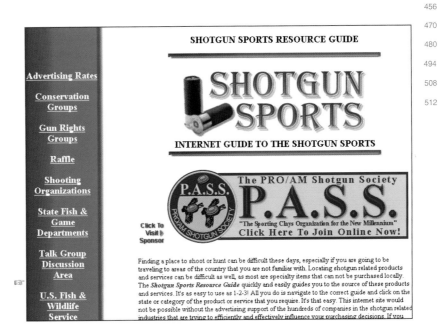

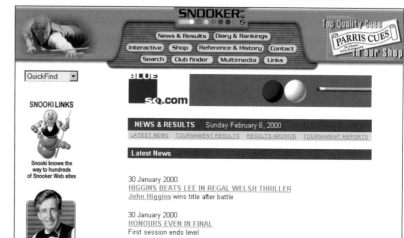

Snooker Net

All the results, reference, features and news a snooker fan could want.

www.snookernet.com

SkiPages.com

Good skiing site with Ski-Search facility, news, resort reports and equipment for sale.

www.skipages.com
www.ski-search.com

Swimmersworld.com

Swimming news and information, meet results, and club pages.

www.swimmersworld.com

TEAM*talk*

The best football fanzine-style site for UK soccer.

www.teamtalk.com

Tennis Corner

Outstanding site for tennis fans that really makes use of the technology.

www.tenniscorner.rivals.com

Track & Field Links

Comprehensive listings of all the best athletics sites.

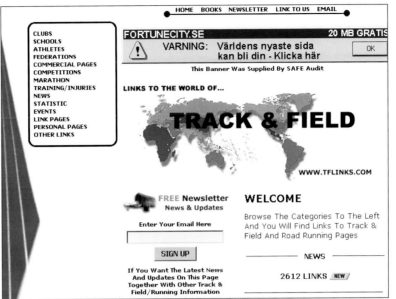

www.tflinks.com

UK Diving

The longest-running UK diving site, with its own shopping mall for underwater gear.

www.ukdiving.co.uk

Wimbledon

The All England Lawn Tennis Championship is not just a sporting event - it's a tradition.

www.wimbledon.org

Worldsport.com

The official home of sport's governing bodies and federations.

www.worldsport.com

Shopping

The possibilities of online shopping have been talked about for almost five years now and, although the Net was reluctant to accept e-commerce, it would be almost impossible to imagine modern life without it. The benefits are plain for everyone to see. Shopping on the Internet is easy, you don't have to wrestle with the crowds in the high street and, to top it all, you could even save money.

Christmas 1999 was dubbed the e-commerce Christmas after it emerged that 25 million people spent a total of $7 billion (around £4.3.billion) at e-commerce web sites. This equates to an average spend of $200 (around £125) per online shopper. According to Jupiter, the company that arrived at the aforementioned figures, the season's windfall was due to an increase in advertising and marketing spend by the Internet companies.

The most popular items for sale on the Internet have been books, videos and CDs, but another beauty of online shopping is the diversity of products on offer. Anything you can find on your main street will be on the Internet - and that's just for starters. The diversity of online products will stagger you. From robot dogs, edible delicacies and sexy underwear, to cigars, top quality jewelry and the latest in home entertainment.

No matter what you're after, you can use search engines and speciality sites, like **Shop Genie**, to compare prices and delivery charges. Those with Macs can use the latest version of the *Sherlock* software to locate the best deals. And when I say deals, I mean deals! You will find almost everything offered online is cheaper because, in most cases, the overheads are smaller and the sites are desperate for your business.

The global nature of the Internet means that you'll find many of these bargains at shops and e-commerce sites outside your country's jurisdiction, with the price differences that this entails - so don't fall foul of the law on importing goods. Excise duty is charged on alcohol, tobacco products, cars and a few other items in the UK, while US sales tax differs from state to state. Check with your local or national government tax web site to see what excise you have to pay for buying your product abroad, or away from home. Even if you don't pay the tax at the point of sale, don't be surprised when you are asked to pay it later by customs.

Many people are hesitant about online shopping due to what they have heard about credit card fraud. As with much that is reported in the media about the Net, there is a kernel of truth to this blanket myth.

Internet shopping is not without its problems, though. Along with the taxation issue, people are scared that either their credit card

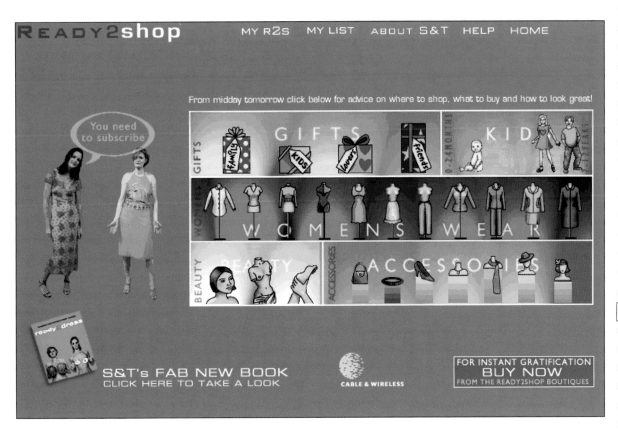

details will be taken and used fraudulently, or that they will pay for their goods but never actually receive them.

If you are uncertain, there are many ways to check that the e-commerce site you are using is a reputable one. First, check that the site has an address, telephone number and email address where you can get hold of someone if things go wrong (an address with a box number is not good enough). When you do enter your credit card details, check that the site is secure. You will usually be alerted when you are moving to a secure part of an e-commerce site by a little window that opens. Another telltale sign will be the broken key, or unlocked padlock, symbol located in the bottom left hand corner of your browser window.

Amazon.com

The king of all online retail sites. Amazon started off as a humble online bookstore in 1995, but now you can buy almost anything - from the usual CDs and DVDs to software, toys, health products, home improvement items to name but a few - in the Z-Shops section. Over 13 million visitors have bought from Amazon in a staggering 160 countries.

www.amazon.com

www.amazon.co.uk

boo.com

The biggest Internet start-up in 1999, backed by some £65 million (around $100 million). This is the first attempt by any site to make the shopping experience as real as possible - you can see the clothing in 3D and spin it to see what it looks like from any angle. Boo.com has suffered teething problems, but it concentrates on popular sports casual clothing, and has active sites in 18 countries.

www.boo.com

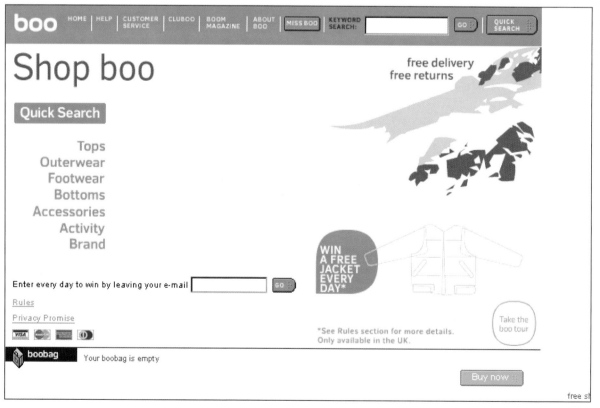

bn.com/Barnes and Noble
This huge US bookstore is impressively comprehensive, and almost rivals Amazon for online kudos.

www.barnesandnoble.com

barnesandnoble.com Affiliate Bookstore

Search for Books at barnesandnoble.com

Visit barnesandnoble.com for millions of titles discounted up to 40-90% off. Great low prices on your favorite books in Bargain Books.

Jeffrey and John thank you for visiting us. for more info click here

Browse barnesandnoble.com for the latest releases in Books in the News, Books in Film, and books in the following areas:

Oprah's Picks	NY Times Books	Art, Architecture, and Photography
Audiobooks	Biography	Business
Children	Computers	Cooking
Entertainment	Family/Relationships	Fiction/Literature
Gay/Lesbian	History	Home/Garden

---

bn.com
BARNES & NOBLE

Books | eBooks (NEW) | Music | eCards | Prints & Posters | Software | Magazines

Browse Subjects | Kids | Gifts | Bargains | Out of Print | Cart | Help | Account

QUICK SEARCH | Keyword | [Search] | Advanced Search

March 20, 2000
Welcome to the new sound of shopping!
bn RADIO

BOOKS GO HOLLYWOOD
See the movie on us.

Special Features
Oprah's Pick:
· Daughter of Fortune
bn.com Live
Award Winners
Bestsellers
Recommended
New Releases
bn.com Editors

Browse Subjects
Art, Architecture & Photography
Biography
Business
Computers
Cooking
Fiction & Literature
History
Home & Garden
Kids!
Sports & Adventure
more subjects...

Specialty Stores
Professional Books
Bargain Books
Academic & Scholarly
eBooks

bn.com Services
· Your Account
· Gift Certificates
· bn.com Insider
· bn.com On the Go

Jerusalem at Center Stage
THE JERUSALEM VIGIL launches the third series (The Zion Legacy) by popular Christian fiction writers Bodie and Brock Thoene. The new series opens in 1948 as the British are withdrawing from the city.

► Previous series: The Zion Chronicles and The Zion Covenant
► Preorder THE INDWELLING by Tim LaHaye and Jerry Jenkins
► More Christian fiction at Barnes & Noble.com

BOOKS IN THE NEWS
The Ramseys Tell Their Story
John and Patsy Ramsey sit with Barbara Walters on "20/20" to discuss JonBenet, the investigation, and their book, THE DEATH OF INNOCENCE.

THE NEW YORKER CARTOON OF THE DAY
Get Your Daily Guffaw
...with a New Yorker cartoon. Also, The New Yorker is celebrating its 75th anniversary with a festival in May. Read all about it!

IN MUSIC
Hail to the Chieftains
It's a St. Patrick's weekend with the Chieftains, who tell us about WATER FROM THE WELL. Also, Irish music collections.
► Top sellers: Steely Dan, Macy Gray, Santana

BN.COM LIVE

Suspenseful Chat
Park ranger/writer Nevada Barr (DEEP SOUTH) joins us in the Auditorium, Monday at 7pm ET.

. **Safe Shopping Guarantee**
. **Order Status**

It's St. Patrick's Day!
Send the luck o'the Irish with our free eCards.

Special Savings
Place an order with us — then save with our partners.
► PETsMART.com
► jcrew.com
► VitaminShoppe.com
► 1-800-flowers.com
► PlanetRx.com

IN BARGAIN
Sentimental Season
Julie Garwood delivers a delightful love story, COME THE SPRING, starring the Claybornes of Blue Belle, Montana.
► More big, BIG books

IN eCARDS

It's Easy Being Green
Especially when you've got our selection of St. Patrick's Day eCards -- all free, all the time.
► Spring!

BlackStar.co.uk

Outstanding video and DVD retail site with excellent customer service. The site lets you build up a wish list of titles, will alert you when your favorite director or star releases a new film, and offers free delivery anywhere in the world. Black Star can be personalized to greet you and set up your payment details automatically.

www.blackstar.co.uk

Yalplay

Formally IMVS, Yalplay is the Net's best-known music retail site. You'll find every type of music and every format as well (including vinyl). Recently the site has branched out into games and videos, and delivers anywhere in the world in 3-5 days. Great content in the shape of reviews boosts this site to one of the all-time greats.

www.yalplay.com

Photoalley.com

The biggest photography super-store on the Internet that covers everything from cameras, film and tripods, to darkroom materials and filters. Unbelievably, it doesn't ship outside the US.

www.accesscamera.com

The All-Internet Shopping Directory

A great resource for helping you find what you're after - fast. Has links to an amazing array of online shopping malls and stores.

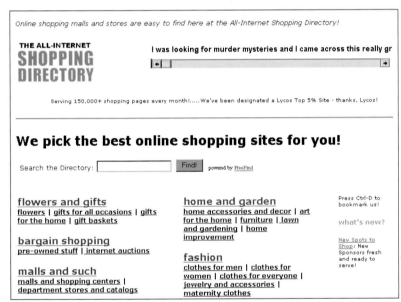

www.all-internet.com

BOL.com

Possibly the second greatest bookshop on the Internet, with sites dedicated to the US, UK, Germany, France, The Netherlands, Spain, Switzerland and Italy.

www.bol.com

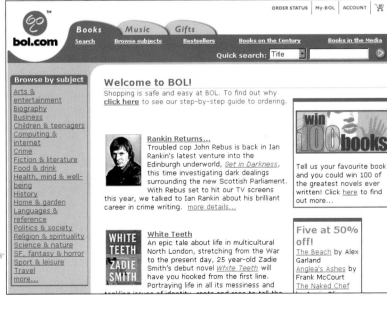

eToys

Possibly the best toy store on the Internet. This wide-ranging site has virtual outlets in the US and UK.

www.etoys.com
www.etoys.co.uk

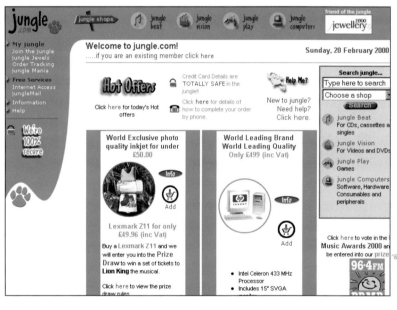

Jungle.com

One of the UK's leading independent retailers on the web. Concentrates on entertainment and home computing.

www.jungle.com

i-Stores

A one-stop-shop for links to hundreds of online stores. The networks cover sites that deliver to the US and UK.

www.i-stores.com
www.-store.co.uk

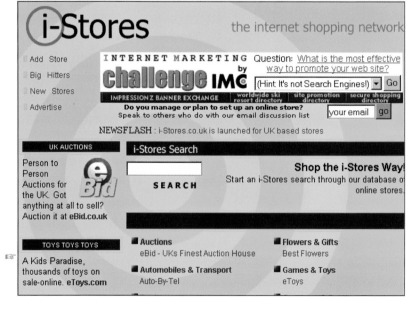

*my*Simon

Truly useful categories, listings and portal site, that'll help you find what you're after online as quickly as possible.

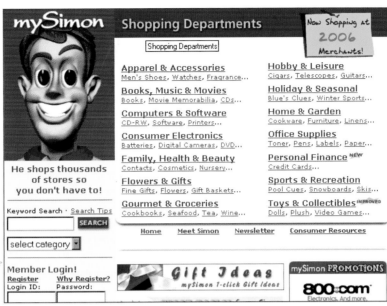

www.mysimon.com

Ready2Shop

Great new site that doesn't actually have online purchase facilities, but has a wealth of advice for those about to hit the streets (or other web sites).

www.ready2shop.com

Think Natural.com

The best natural health site in Europe, if not the world. There's a great range of products, and an amazing depth of content for a shopping site. This represents the future.

www.thinknatural.com

*my*Taxi

Find the lowest possible prices, and build your very own street with favorite/cheapest stores. It's free, it's fun and it saves you time and money.

www.mytaxi.co.uk

Unbeatable.co.uk

A simple site, but one that has truly unbeatable offers on UK electrical goods - home entertainment, in-car stereo, mobile communication and more.

www.unbeatable.co.uk

Shopping

Yahoo!

The biggest company on the Internet is also into shops. A whole section devoted to third party partnerships with high street names, and a thorough serrate facility (naturally).

http://shopping.yahoo.com

101cd.com

Half a million catalog entries that include CDs, books, DVDs, videos and games.

www.101cd.com

800 Hampers

Hampers for every budget and occasion from the heartland of Scotland.

www.800hampers.com

800-Trekker.com

For all your SF and fantasy purchasing needs, look no further than this US-based site.

www.800-trekker.com

Amivin

One of the few online wine merchants, with a great selection of wines, that also offers worldwide delivery.

www.amivin.com

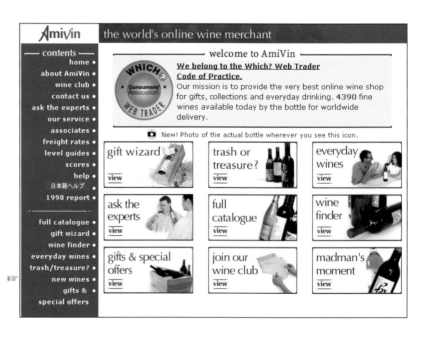

Animail

Great site for all those animal lovers in the UK – 48-hour delivery and lots of products.

www.animail.co.uk

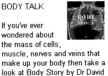

Barclay Square

This online shopping portal has been going almost as long as the web itself.

www.barclaysquare.co.uk

Bigsave.com

Another UK electrical e-tailer offering videos, TVs and computer hardware at knockdown prices.

www.bigsave.com

Bob's Shop Window

Great international listings of the world's shops and online retailers.

www.bobsshopwindow.com

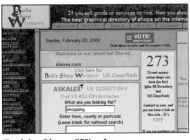

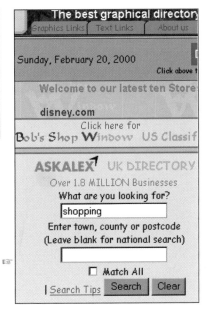

BookBlvd.com

Search through 25 online stores
to find the book you're after -
by price, author, title, ISBN, or
keyword.

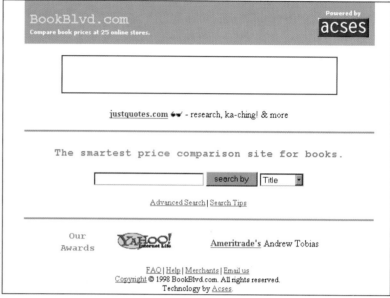

www.bookblvd.com

Bottomdollar.com

US-based site that lets you compare prices on a great range of
products.

www.bottomdollar.com

Borders.com

Another of the Internet's top ten
bookstores.

www.borders.com

British Shopping Links (BSL)

An outstanding listings/portal site of shopping links, targeted at UK residents.

www.british-shopping.com

Buy.com

Easy and secure online shopping, all backed by good customer service and offers.

www.buy.com

Chapters.co.ca

More than just Canada's leading bookseller, the site offers movies, music and software.

www.chapters.ca

Compare Net

A US-based price comparison search engine.

www.compare.net

Condomania

Award winning e-commerce site selling, well, condoms.

www.condoms4u.com

Diesel

A great online fashion network that covers both the US and UK, although you can only purchase online in the latter.

www.diesel.co.uk

Dixons

UK electrical retailer that owns the biggest ISP in the country – it also has a great site.

www.dixons.co.uk

Drugstore.com

US site that covers natural health and beauty, and prescription drugs.

www.drugstore.com

Early Learning Centre

The UK's excellent shopping resource for young children's toys.

www.elc.co.uk

Entertainment Express

A UK-based site offering CDs, videos and games.

www.entexpress.com

EFC Online

Europe's biggest photography site that delivers to both Europe and the US.

www.euro-foto.com

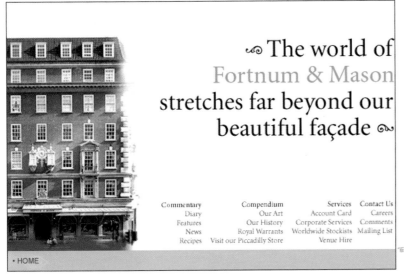

Fortnum & Mason

Online ordering is restricted to hampers, wines, flowers and gifts.

www.fortnumandmason.co.uk

Funstore.co.uk

UK site selling a limited, but popular, range that covers most bases from *Action Man* to *Tweenies.*

www.funstore.co.uk

Games and Videos.com

UK-based site that sells all manner of video games, as well as videos and DVDs.

www.gamesandvideos.com

Game

Every available game, for every available format, for the UK market.

www.game-retail.co.uk

Shopping

GemNet

Very thorough online jewelry store (and ISP!).

www.gemnet.co.uk

Hot Box

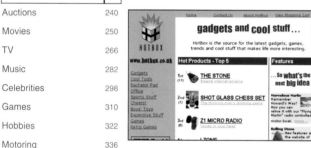

Selective, but very cool, UK gadget and gizmo site with some exclusive items.

www.hotbox.co.uk

Internet Gift Store

Concentrates on the latest fads and trends such as *Star Wars: Episode I* collectibles, *South Park* paraphernalia and *Beanie Babies*.

www.internetgiftstore.com

K2Man

A shopping portal for the man who has everything.

www.k2man.co.uk

Nintendo Direct

Buy your Nintendo games online, and get them shipped to your door.

www.nintendodirect.co.uk

Outlet Bound

Great site for finding expensive items at knockdown prices, with the Locate-A-Store service.

www.outletbound.com

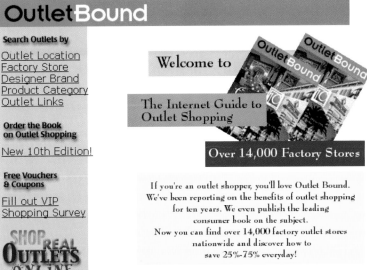

Playstation Direct

A great selection of games for the world's most prolific games console.

www.playstationdirect.co.uk

QVC

The shopping channel's online presence is based in the UK and the US.

www.qvc.com
www.qvcuk.com

Runner's World

Buy your next trainers on the basis of your foot size and type, not your favorite colour!

www.runnersworld.com

Shop Genie

Excellent UK price comparison site that covers books, music, games, films, hardware, and software.

www.shopgenie.com

Shoppers Universe

One of the biggest online department stores, including Great Universal Stores.

www.shoppersuniverse.com

Toy Chest

Traditional UK toy site that deals with pre-school, infants and juniors.

www.toychest.co.uk

Toysmart.com

Well-designed site that lets you search by age (1-12, teenage, and 'kid at heart'). Very good.

www.toysmart.net

Toys R Us

The amazing offline retailer has been very slow to get online - now has US and UK sales sites.

www.toysrus.com
www.toysrus.co.uk

Toy Zone

New entrant to the UK toy market, backed by celebrity Jonathan Ross.

www.toyzone.co.uk

Unbeatable.com/Amdex

The US version of the UK site, also with great deals on home electrical goods.

www.unbeatable.com

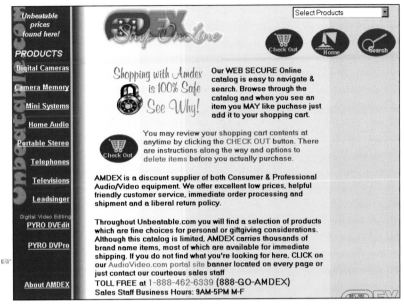

Vinyl Online

Dedicated purely to those classic 38s, 45s and 33 1/3s.

www.vinylonline.co.uk

Whittard of Chelsea

Sells teas and coffees, a colorful range of crockery, and an eclectic mix of CDs, books, chocolate and biscuits.

www.whittard.com

WH Smith

As well as books, the high street favorite deals in music, video, games and magazines.

www.whsmithonline.co.uk

Wine&Co

Will help you with a choice of wine, while telling you more about the subject at the same time.

www.wineandco.com

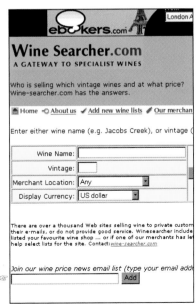

Wine Searcher.com

An excellent wine search engine that'll let you compare price and availability.

www.wine-searcher.com

Auctions

Before the advent of the Internet, the only way to sell your valuables was in a classified ad in the paper, at a car boot sale, or - if you had the money - through a traditional auction house. Now that has all changed. Millions of people are selling their valuable goods, and collections, online at any number of the new auction web sites that have sprung up over the past couple of years.

The established auctioneers were very slow to embrace this new method of plying their trade, so new names - such as **eBay** and **eBid** - have become established as the places to go if you want to auction off things on the Internet. And it's not just the names that are new. The majority of items that you'll find for sale on these sites wouldn't normally turn up at auction. Although you'll find fine art, antiques and the like, most items fall into the 'collectibles' category, with an emphasis on newer collectibles such as *Star Wars* action figures, TV memorabilia, and old computers/computer games.

It is estimated that, in the next 10 years, most dealing in comics will be done over the Internet, and some are making a business of the buying and selling of games, much as experts have done in the antiques and fine art world for decades. It is not surprising when you consider there are over 5 million users of **eBay**, and that the site has more than two and a half million items listed for sale (with an additional 250,000 items added to the site every day) in more than 1,600 categories.

There is no doubt that Internet auctions are hugely popular, but there have been some questionable items on offer over the years including the illegal sale of a human kidney. The auction site intervened to block the sale (which had already attracted bids of up to $5 million).

If you are wondering about the basics of the online auction, they work in a very straightforward way. Whether you are bidding or selling, you need to register with the site. When you do, the terms and conditions tell you that your bid is a binding contract should it be the highest.

Online auctions normally last about a week, and the sites will alert you as to those auctions about to end. Users of **eBay** are rated by how many successful auctions (and therefore truncations of goods for payment) they have undertaken.

At **QXL**, the bidder pays the money to the auction site itself, which in turn pays the seller and ensures the item is delivered. If you are a novice to bidding at online auctions, it is worth considering a few easy rules. First, do research the item you're after, and see what its market value is. Both **Auction Beagle** and **Auction Hunter** will help you with this. You should be able to get some help in auction forums and newsgroups. Always ensure you have the money for something you're bidding for, before you bid for it, and never bid too high.

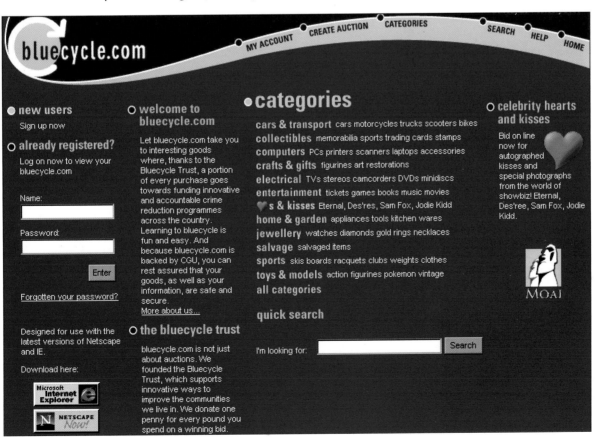

Auctions

eBay

The primary auction site on the Internet. It's big, it's colorful and it's easy to use. Once you've registered, you can bid for almost anything from collectible action figures to antiques. Users are given star ratings for reliability and regular use of the site. You can even check bidders' experiences of sellers before you put in an offer.

www.ebay.com
www.ebay.co.uk

eBay screenshot

home | my eBay | site map | sign in

Browse | Sell | Services | Search | Help | Community

what are you looking for?
[   ] Find it! tips

categorieS

Automotive NEW!
Antiques & Art (111009)
Books, Movies, Music (775704)
Coins & Stamps (162643)
Collectibles (1073967)
Computers (140478)
Dolls, Doll Houses (71583)
Great Collections NEW!
Jewelry, Gemstones (170479)
Photo & Electronics (87072)
Pottery & Glass (237573)
Sports (528913)
Toys, Bean Bag Plush (390387)
Everything Else (431990)
all categories...

Shop by photos in the Gallery

Check out this Interest page

BMW
Asian Antiques
Hello Kitty
Boating
Waterford Crystal

featurEd

Box CRAMMED FULL of Baseball Card Wax Packs!
Drain Buster! The easy way to Un-Clog Drains
Beatles 1964 tour coin in original wrapper !
Golden Retrievers-Raising, Picking, Breeding
No Prescription Steroids Valiums Xanax Viagra
e-f-l-o-w-e-r-s . com

more! see all featured....

greAt colleCtions

welcomE new uSers

New to eBay?
How do I bid?
How do I sell?
Why eBay is safe
Register, it's free!

fun sTuff

Cool Happenings
Charity Auctions

Bid on items for Rosie's For All Kids Foundation.

Get $$$ when you open an E*TRADE account today!

eBay Visa — Apply now!

eBid.com

The UK-only auction site that's very similar in style, if not appearance, to **eBay**. It's a popular site with a good choice of categories covering everything from electrical goods, computers and collectibles, to music, office goods and even tickets.

www.ebid.com

eBid.com screenshot

join the auction revolution

Welcome to the Future of Buying and Selling Online
Allow eBid.com to put Buyers and Sellers together!

eBid.com Welcomes 2 New Auctions

Enter Ubid Auction Here!
Ubid Auction!! Brand Name Bargains from $7
Click the banner Below to enter! 6th smash month!!

All your Sporting Good Needs.
Click Here

QXL.com

Another excellent auction site. Unlike **eBay** and **eBid**, no money changes hands between buyer and seller. Instead, buyers pay a central service and then **QXL** pays the seller, while at the same time arranging for the item to be safely delivered to you.

www.qxl.co.uk

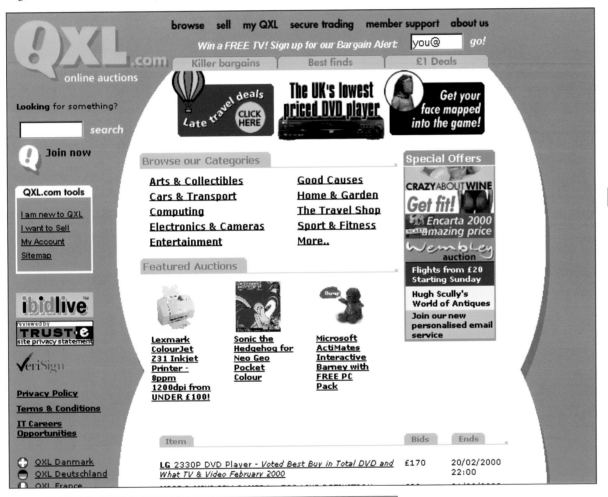

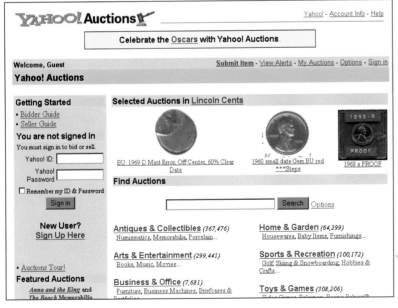

Yahoo!

Divided into sections in much the same way as the company's main web site, it offers a directory accompanied by a search facility. **Yahoo!** has an auction site on both its UK and US web sites. The system is easy to use and boasts an impressive range of auction categories.

http://auctions.yahoo.com
http://uk.auctions.yahoo.com

Auctions

Amazon.com Auctions/ Sotheby's Amazon Auctions

Two auction sites for the price of one. The **Amazon** site deals with the usual wide-ranging content of online auctions, while the **Sotheby's** site covers fine arts and antiques.

http://auctions.amazon.com

http://sothebys.amazon.com

Auction Insider

Get the lowdown on almost every US auction site. You can find out the top items on sale, look at what's on offer in a choice of popular sections, or get a comprehensive list of the auction sites covered.

www.auctioninsider.com

Auction Hunter

User-friendly UK auction site. It offers features about collecting, as well as an 'ask the experts' section that helps to make sure what you're buying or selling is worth the price.

www.auctionhunter.co.uk

Bluecycle.com

An idea from the UK police to offer unclaimed stolen goods for sale online. There are some interesting items to be had here.

www.bluecycle.co.uk

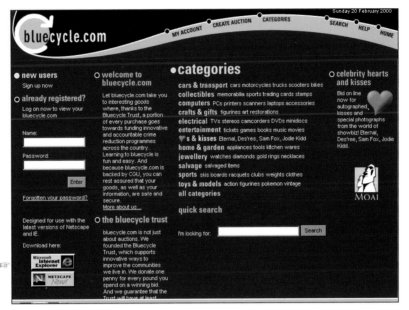

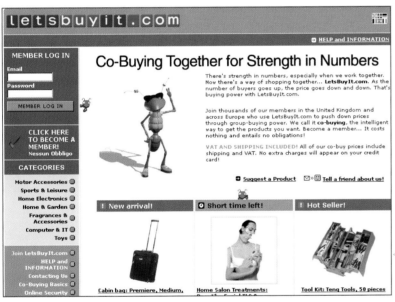

LetsBuyIt

European network of sites that groups buyers together to combine their buying power, and thus lower the price on new goods.

www.letsbuyit.com

uBid

Similar idea to **LetsBuyIt** - to get cheaper goods by buying in bulk - but based in the US and covering a wider selection of items.

www.ubid.com

Auction Beagle

Search four key US auction sites (**Amazon**, **eBay**, **Golds**, and **Yahoo!**) all at once.

www.auctionbeagle.com

The Auction Channel

Live web casts and TV broadcasts of auctions you can join in with from all over the world.

www.theauctionchannel.com

Auction-Sales.com

Great site primarily for computer-related items, but also covers electronics, home entertainment and more.

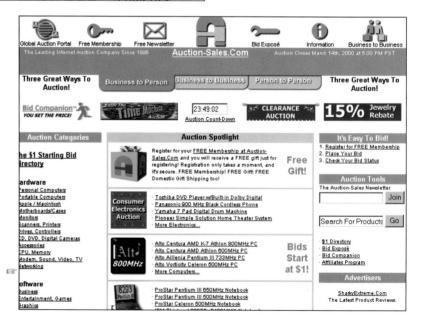

www.auction-sales.com

Auctions.com

What used to be Auction
Universe, now bigger and better.

www.auctionuniverse.com

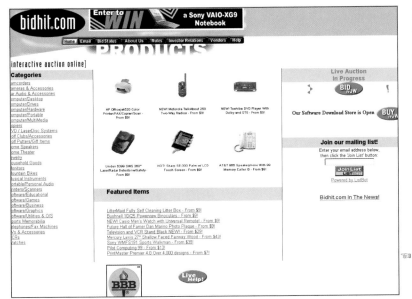

Bid Hit.com

Very good, immediate auction
site that requires no pre-
registration!

www.bidhit.com

DealDeal.com

US site that concentrates on
home entertainment and computer products.

www.dealdeal.com

First Auction

Very good, live auction and bargain site that covers computers, electronics, gift items, collectibles, office equipment, photography, and more.

www.firstauction.com

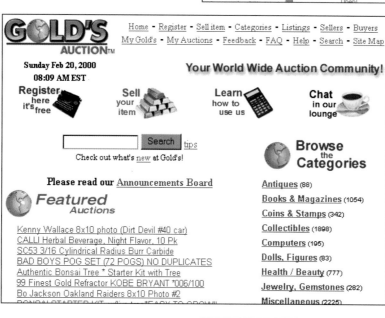

Gold's

Smaller US auction site that you can personalise.

www.goldsauction.com

The Internet Auction List (IAL)

International portal of auction site links covering countries from Antarctica (!) to Venezuela.

www.internetauctionlist.com

Phillips

Traditional auction house that covers the US, UK, Switzerland and Australia, but has no online bidding.

www.phillips-auctions.com

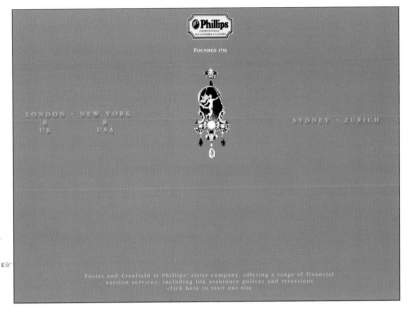

Sothebys.com

The home of the most famous auction house in the world and it has a lot of online auctions.

www.sothebys.com

UltimateBid.com

Great US site that offers once in a lifetime experiences, with most of the money made going to charity.

www.ultimatebid.com

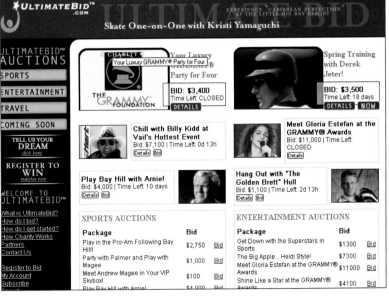

Movies

There's something about the nature of the Internet that means many of its devotees are also fanatical about movies. This makes for as many sites on the subject of films as there have been films made. And then some.

You can argue theory with both directors and students of film, read reviews of classic movies from the era before talkies, or get the latest gossip on the script for films such as *Star Wars: Episode Two*. There are sites with which you can register if you are a struggling filmmaker in need of help hiring crew, and sites to visit if you want to know who played an obscure character in a straight-to-video flop.

If you are interested in film schools, award ceremonies, film festivals, behind the scenes, scriptwriting or soundtracks, there will be a site for you. Even if you cannot find a site that specializes in your pet subject in this section, there will be links from the main four sites that will help you.

The nature of the medium means you will be able to watch trailers, clips and special features, listen to title tracks, snippets of dialogue, sound effects, or even interact with your favorite director, producer, special effects master or actor in live chat forums.

It's not hard to see the appeal of the web's ever-blossoming supply of film content. After all, why wait for that recently announced hot film deal to be rehashed in tomorrow's paper, or next week's movie magazine, when it'll turn up online within minutes? And it's hard to remember a time when the summer blockbusters, Oscar favorites, and everything else in between, hit the cinemas without an accompanying array of online footage.

Now, a warning. There are a lot of personal web sites out there devoted to specific films, genres, actors, or directors. As with any other subject on the Net, some of these personal home pages are subjective, fanatically blind to the opposite opinion, or downright inaccurate.

That is not to say that there aren't hundreds of thousands of personal sites with which you will identify, come to trust, and maybe even add to your bookmarks or favorites. Indeed, many of the sites listed in this section are so good that they have become online film legends, either under the control of the individuals who started them, or now under the control of huge Internet companies who have bought them.

Two cases in particular are those of **Ain't it Cool News** and the **Internet Movie Database** (IMDB). The former was started in the mid-Nineties by one Harry Knowles. The little home page grew both in size and importance (much like its owner) until Harry even got to make a cameo appearance in Robert Rodriguez's *The Faculty* alongside Salma Hayek. It is said that his early, positive reviews of *The Blair*

Witch Project in 1999 led to its phenomenal success. Harry is still in charge and most of Hollywood certainly read, if not worry about, the reviews that appear on his web site.

The Internet Movie Database was started by two British movie fans in a similar fashion back in 1990. This time, the subject matter concentrated on was not news and reviews of the latest films (a topic that marginalizes anything else under the 'movies' heading). Instead, the site set out to be an archive of all movies. It became so successful that it was bought by online book behemoth, **Amazon**.

So there is an amazing array of film resources on the Internet - perhaps even the best. These days not only every studio, whether major or minor, has its own web site, but every movie has one too. *The Blair Witch Project* web site went online in July 1998, acting as a teaser for the hype that followed. Even movie series, such as the James Bond films and the Star Wars phenomenon, are online. I challenge any film fan to use the Internet and still be happy with books, magazines and TV specials.

Ain't It Cool News

The mother of all gossip sites. **Ain't it Cool** is the site to check out if you want news and gossip on upcoming films. The site has inside sources on film productions all over the world, which gives it the ability to confirm or deny rumors ahead of official sources, and post the first review of a new movie.

www.aint-it-cool-news.com

Popcorn

A great British entrant into the film site category, Popcorn delivers the works. From news and gossip, trailers and reviews, through to longer features and competitions. Being a UK site, the full film listings only deal with cinemas in Britain, but the content is excellent, and international versions are in the pipeline.

www.film.co.uk

www.popcorn.co.uk

Mr. Showbiz

From the Disney-owned **Go Network** comes this excellent resource for film fans of both classic and modern movies alike. Over 30,000 film reviews, information on celebrities, the latest news, and a host of links to other relevant sites make this one of the best film-related sites on the Internet.

http://mrshowbiz.go.com

Cinescape

For the very latest news, rumors, and reviews of the best action movies and TV series, **Cinescape** is hard to beat. It's updated at least twice a day by some of the US's top film journalists.

www.cinescape.com

Dark Horizons

This is an excellent independent resource, dealing in reviews and snippets of news from the sets of the latest blockbusters. It also has an extensive archive of films from the mid-to-late Nineties.

www.darkhorizons.com

Empire

The online version of the UK's best film magazine is a treasure trove of news, gossip, reviews, polls, forums, and competitions. A must for all film fans.

www.empireonline.co.uk

Film.com

Run by film critic Lucy Mohl and owned by Real Networks (the company behind one of the Net's major movie players, **Real Player**). This site offers film criticism, reviews, trailers and news on the latest movies.

www.film.com

FilmUnlimited

Run by the UK's *The Guardian* newspaper, **FilmUnlimited** has an excellent resource of reviews, features and star profiles of the last few years' films.

www.filmunlimited.co.uk

The Greatest Films

Although it does not include any foreign language films, this is an excellent site that lists a top 100 that is in-depth, and well-argued too.

www.greatestfilms.org

www.filmsite.org

Movies

Movie-Page.com

All the latest reviews, trailers, posters and news as well as chat rooms, articles, and even complete movie scripts for you to download. Well worth bookmarking.

www.movie-page.com/main.htm

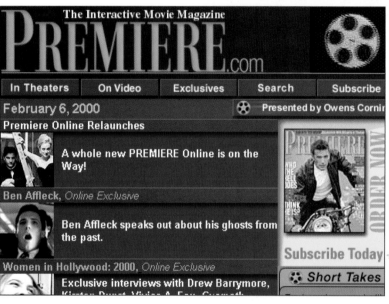

Premiere.com

The leading US movie magazine's online persona has limited its content to brief reviews and news stories, but a great archives section.

www.premieremag.com

Reelscreen

As well as having reviews and news of independent and mainstream movies, this site also offers extensive services to filmmakers, musicians, film fans, and the film industry for free. Well worth checking out.

www.reelscreen.com

Script-O-Rama

Download and read almost any film script - mostly for free. The impressive list includes the classic, the modern, those that never made it to the silver screen, and some that are still in development.

www.script-o-rama.com

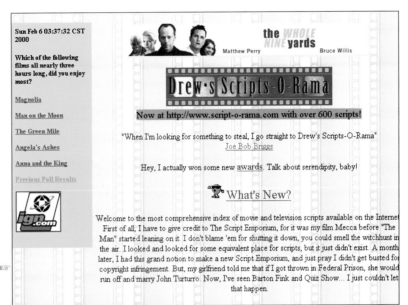

Trailervision

It is often said that the best bit of a modern movie is its trailer. This site takes the argument to its logical conclusion. Ideas here are bound to turn up in Hollywood sooner or later…

www.trailervision.com

Ultimate Movies

If a movie does not have its own official web site, then it won't appear on this definitive listings site that covers more recent releases.

www.ultimatemovies.com

Movies

007.COM

The ultimate behind-the-scenes look at *The World Is Not Enough* and the past Bond movies.

www.007.com

20th Century Fox

The latest movies, forthcoming attractions and past favorites.

www.foxmovies.com

At-A-Glance Film Reviews

This one's a good, if incomplete, alternative to the Internet Movie Database.

www.rinkworks.com/movies

BAFTA

The British Academy of Film and Television Arts awards are second only to the Oscars. Arguably.

www.bafta.org

Bollywood World

All the news, reviews, features and star power from India's answer to Hollywood.

www.bollywoodworld.com

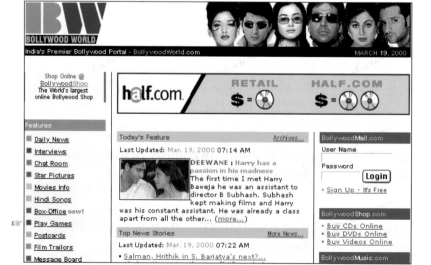

Cannes

The biggest and best-known film festival has an equally impressive web site.

www.festival-cannes.org

Cinefex

For those who love special effects more than any other aspect of movie making.

www.cinefex.com

Cinema Confidential

For two years, this site has been providing news and gossip on the hottest forthcoming films.

www.cinecon.com

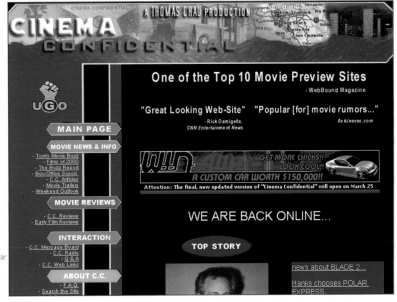

Movies

Dimension Films

The home of *Hellraiser, Halloween, From Dusk Till Dawn*, and *The Crow.*

www.dimensionfilms.com

DreamWorks

Get the lowdown on Spielberg's new films, games, and music.

www.dreamworks.com

Fox Searchlight

The thinking person's division of 20th Century Fox.

www.foxsearchlight.com

Golden Globes

The much sought after film awards' official site.

www.goldenglobes.org

Hollywood.com

Another very good general site, that concentrates on the latest releases.

www.hollywoodonline.com

www.hollywood.com

InLineFirst

Much like **Ain't it Cool News**, but without the clout.

www.inlinefirst.com

MCA Universal

Find out about Universal's films, theme parks, concerts and even jobs.

www.mca.com

Miramax Café

From the people behind *Shakespeare in Love*, comes a very trendy film site.

www.miramax.com

Movies.com

A simple site of what's showing, and what's to come, from Buena Vista.

http://movies.go.com

MovieGuru.com

If you've ever wanted to be a film critic, this site gives you the chance.

www.movieguru.com

Movies

New Line Cinema

Find the latest releases, and where they are playing, or join the mailing list.

www.newline.com

Oscars

The awards, the ceremony, the dresses, the speeches. It's all here in glorious technicolor.

www.oscar.com

Paramount Motion Pictures

A portal to the film company's movies such as *Sleepy Hollow* and *Mission Impossible 2*.

www.paramount.com/motionpictures

Pathe

The European entertainment company with operations in cinema and television.

www.pathe.co.uk
www.pathe.com

Polygram

A wacky site that brings together PolyGram Films, Gramercy Pictures, and PolyGram Video.

www.reellife.com

Sony Pictures

A full listing of what's currently playing, as well as what's coming soon, from Sony.

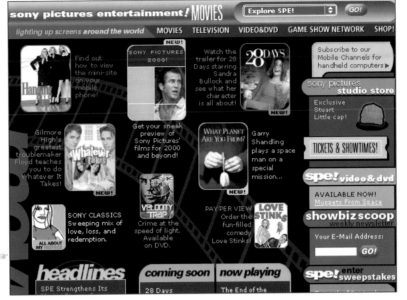

www.spe.sony.com/movies

SoundtrackNet

Interested in the music behind the movie? This is the site for you.

www.soundtrack.net

Star Wars

Need I say more?

www.starwars.com

Sundance Institute

The best-known festival, and organisation, for independent filmmakers.

www.sundance.org/index.htm

Troma Studios

The weirdest bunch of sci-fi films since Ed Wood, all under one roof.

www.troma.com

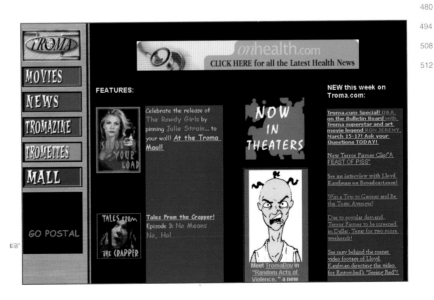

UIP

A very simple site of links to other sites concentrating on specific movies.

www.uip.com

Universal Pictures

Links to the studio's latest fare, as well as some useful info on the company.

www.universalstudios.com/
universal_pictures

Walt Disney Studios

What's new from Walt? Find out here.

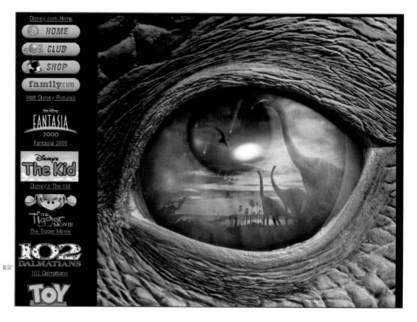

http://disney.go.com/disneypictures

Warner Brothers Movies

The latest releases, and a better representation than most of the studio's older movies.

www.movies.warnerbros.com

WavCentral.com

Download and listen to clips of dialog from over 120 films.

www.wavcentral.com/movies.htm

Variety.com

Only for the true film devotee, or those in the movie business.

www.variety.com

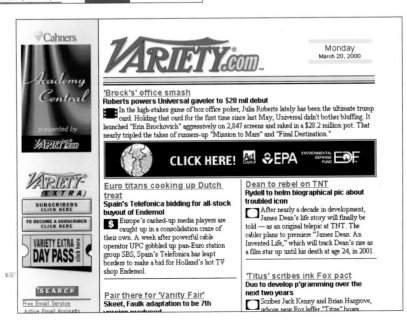

One day the plastic and metal box that you use to 'surf' the Internet will be the same as the one you use to watch television. I don't think you will be surfing on your TV, or watching programs on your PC, although that does already happen. There will be a new device that has the screen size of a television, with the memory and download capacity of a PC. A new breed of consumer electronics will have been born. But, for the moment, what can we do on the Internet with regards to television?

For one thing you will notice how every broadcaster has a web presence. This is partly because the Net will be a mode of distribution for them in the future, and partly because there's a lot for them to get out of being online right now. You can email the relevant departments or TV programs, find out the latest gossip on your favorite show, and even interact with stars, producers, directors, and writers. And, of course, you can check what time those programs go out on air.

Many of the world's favorite shows have their own official web sites and then there are the thousands created by fans. On these sites you will find episode guides, plot lines, character profiles, actor biographies, behind-the-scenes features, and such like. It is often the fan-based site that delivers the best news, as the official site cannot release certain news items or rumors.

As with sport or hobbies, no matter what program is your all-time favorite you will find a site dedicated to it. But what if the show is no longer broadcast, and for which there are no official sites? No trouble, there will be at least one like-minded person out there who has put a site together about it. That's the beauty of the Internet - its diversity. You will find clips, interviews, reviews, and possibly new fan fiction on the subject.

If you are after a complete TV listings service, the Net has them too. You can check out what's on TV anywhere in the world, so if you're traveling and just cannot do without the telly, don't worry. You can also download a listings service for your neck of the woods. This will keep you abreast of that day's programs and let you highlight some, so that you don't forget to watch or record them. You can find out about the complicated science of ratings and audience share. No matter where you live, advertisers are trying to establish the best time to target you with their ads. You'll find all the data on rating you could wish for on the Net, and then some.

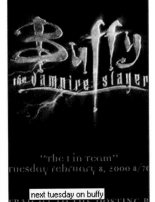

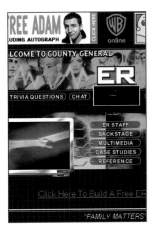

TV Guide

Americans need look no further than here for all their TV needs. A huge site that covers all of the broadcast, cable and satellite output in the US. You can browse through news, gossip, TV and movie reviews, soaps and stars, chat online or view the listings.

www.tvguide.com

Radio Times

Britain's longest-running listings magazine has a great web site. It identifies the best shows on TV in 14 categories every day, and has an outstanding array of sections that includes film, comedy, sci-fi, and a shop. You can search for programs or just plan your viewing schedule.

www.radiotimes.beeb.com

TV Show

Exhaustive site that covers every aspect of television from all around the world. From stars and shows to a search engine and television technology. All subjects are covered and in surprising depth. There are some minor exclusions, but given the ambitious nature of the site, these can be forgiven.

www.tvshow.com/tv

Ultimate TV.com

The biggest and most diverse web site for US TV. As well as the obligatory listings (augmented by clips and promos), there are the Nielsen ratings, a thorough database of shows, full listings of broadcasters, and networks, as well as genre by genre sections.

www.ultimatetv.com

- GAMES
- UTILITIES
- PALM PILOTS
- SCREENSAVERS
- BUSINESS
- GRAPHICS
- INTERNET
- MAC
- AND MORE!

TVShow.com: All About Television, All A

| shows | people | news | what's on | stations | produ |
| home | search | newsletter | random page |

TV Show: Television Worldwide

Welcome to TV Show, the ultimate human reviewed links site for everything related from all around the world! This is the home of the original Television

▶ **TV Shows**
All your favorite shows from around the world. Over a thousand popular and the obsessively obscure.

▶ **TV Schedules**
Guides to what's on where and when, worldwide. All the program

▶ **TV People**
Mad about Melinda Messenger? Keen on Kevin Sorbo? Look no fu list of links for your top television personality!

▶ **TV News**
Daily news, gossip and updates about celebrities and TV shows. wanted to know (or didn't!).

▶ **TV Stations**
Find television stations online. See the official websites for the B to live TV on the Web!

▶ **TV Production**
All about behind the camera, from finance and funding, to script associations and distributing

▶ **TV Technology**
From the first moments in TV history right up to digital technolog out about television's technical side.

UltimateTV.com Your Guid to What's On.

Live from Los Angeles
Sunday February 6, 2000

UltimateTV
Click on the 33 to win $1,000,0
5 42 66 32 52

Get Personalized TVListings. NOW! enter zip

99-00 TV SEASON
TV News-Ratings
TV LISTINGS
TV PREVIEWS
SHOWS
CHAT/BOARDS
NETS/STATIONS
THE TV STORE
TV INFO
EVENTS
- Spotlight On...
TV JUMBLE

SITEWIDE SEARCH

[Search]

Movie Quest
Ultimate TV Channel
INTERVU

What's On Tonight

Malcolm in the Middle
Malcolm takes on the school bully. -- FOX

- "The Practice" ABC
Real: ▶28-56+
MPEG: ▶250+
▶450+

TV News Daily

Top Story:

"God" Takes On "Millionaire"

Other Stories:

- "The Rock" Gives ABC Solid Saturday Win; "The Others" Debuts on NBC
- Charlie Sheen "Spinning" To TV?
- Emmy Founder Syd Cassyd Dies
- "Star Trek's" Scotty Beaming About Fatherhood

What's On Today

- NHL All-Star Game: From Toronto - ABC
- NFL Football: AFC-NFC Pro Bowl - ABC

Shows

- SELECT A TV

BBC

The UK's best-known broad-caster has a site that covers all aspects of its remit. Find channel information, program details, and timings, as well as excellent news, sport, education, health, and history sections.

www.bbc.com
www.bbc.co.uk

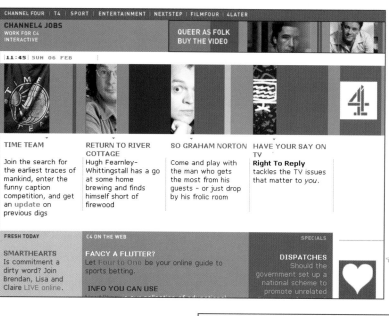

Channel 4

One of the stalwarts of the Internet, Channel 4 has been online since the beginning (almost). A great site with ever-increasing levels of interactivity.

www.channel4.co.uk

The Emmy Awards

The Academy of Television Arts & Sciences rewards the best shows on US TV, and the people who make them, with an Emmy.

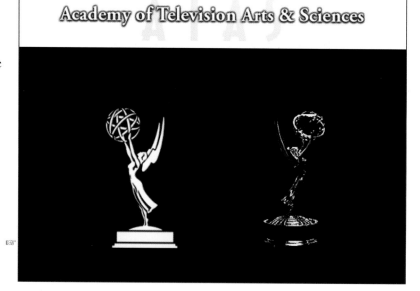

www.emmys.org

EPguides.com

If you need to find out the name of the last episode of *Star Trek* or which episode of *Friends* is 'The One with the Ick Factor', check here first.

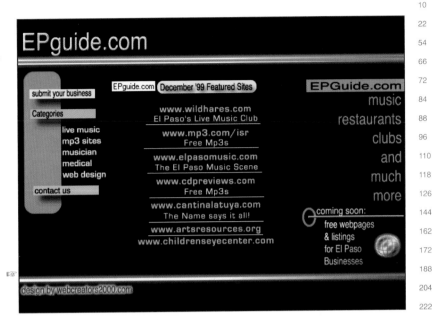

www.epguide.com

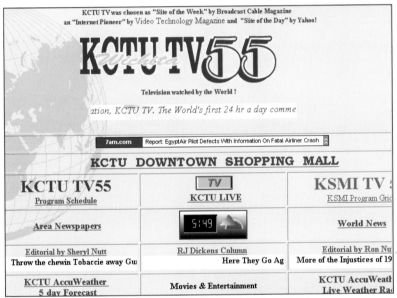

KCTU TV 55

An astounding site that not only broadcasts 24 hours a day online, but also has a great range of other content.

www.kctu.com

The Meldrum Homepage

An amazing collection of British broadcast material made up of test cards, fault transmission pages, classic announcements and the like.

www.meldrum.co.uk/mhp

www.mightybigtv.com

Mighty Big TV

Excellent service for those who have missed any episode of the biggest, mainstream US TV shows. Never fear, their plots are all written out for you here.

www.tvbroadcast.com

TV Broadcast.com

The online version of the US TV industry's weekly journal. Not much good for couch potatoes, but good if you work in TV.

http://tv.cream.org

TVcream

If you had a favorite UK program as a child, this site will give you the nostalgia fix. Includes defunct sweets and drinks, magazines and newspapers.

www.tvparty.com

TVparty

Offbeat TV site that's crammed full of gems such as the most outrageous TV commercials, and long-forgotten shows from *The Virginian* to *Holmes* and *Yo-Yo*.

www.tvthemesonline.com

The Ultimate TV Themes Web Site

Fantastic resource that must contain some 10,000 TV theme tunes on file. You could be here for hours.

http://abc.go.com

ABC.com

Uninspired site of the American Broadcasting Company, which is now part of the Go Network.

BARB

The UK Broadcasters' Audience
Research Board. Does what
Nielsen does in the US.

www.barb.co.uk

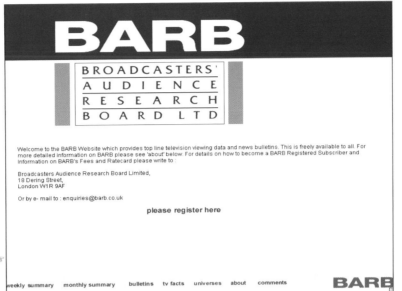

Beeb.com

The controversial site of the
BBC's commercial arm.

www.beeb.com

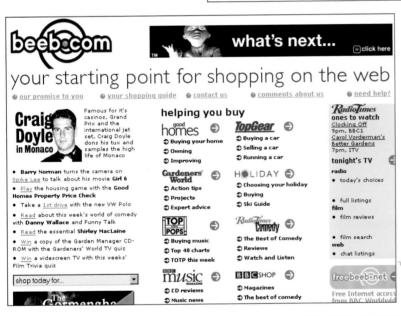

The Bill

Popular UK police drama's
official home on the web.

www.thebill.co.uk

Yahoo! Broadcast

Live broadcasts of TV and radio interviews.

www.broadcast.com

Brookside

Get all the news and the story so far on the UK's Liverpudlian soap.

www.brookie.com

CBC

Very good site from the Canadian national TV corporation.

www.tv.cbc.ca

Buffy the Vampire Slayer

Rather poorly designed official site that covers most of the bases.

www.buffy.com

The-Bullet

Online 'ammunition' for people employed in the UK television industry.

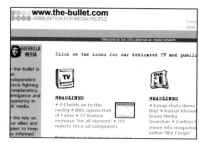

www.the-bullet.com

CBS.com
Interesting and diverse portal site for the popular American broadcaster.

www.cbs.com

Channel 5
Slightly Spartan web site of the UK's fifth terrestrial broadcaster.

www.channel5.co.uk

The Classic TV Database
Great US resource of classic TV programs, especially the Top 100 shows list.

www.classic-tv.com

Cult TV
Great and long-standing online web 'zine covering all things cult.

www.culttv.net

The Daily Script
Immense database of TV scripts site. If you want to write for your favorite show, check this out first.

www.dailyscript.com/tv/main.html

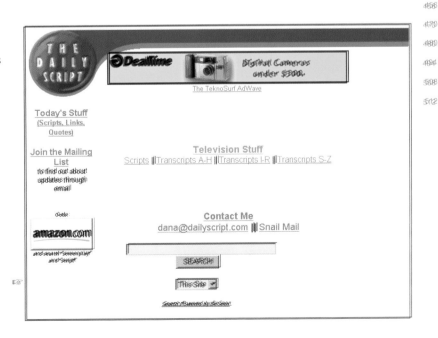

DigiGuide

Free, downloadable listings guide to UK TV.

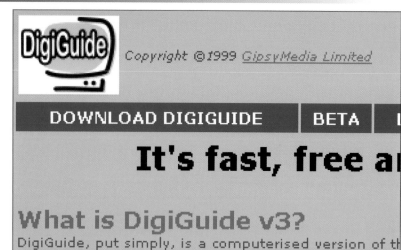

www.digiguide.co.uk

Digital Television: The Site

Everything you ever wanted to know about digital TV, but were afraid to ask…

www.digitaltelevision.com

Doctor Who News

Unofficial site for the latest news from the world's longest-running SF series.

www.whonews.fsnet.co.uk

EastEnders

Official site for one of the UK's two most popular soaps.

www.bbc.co.uk/eastenders

ER

Fun site with a medical feel for the official site of ER.

www.ertv.com

EuroTV

Find out what's on anywhere in Europe - from Austria to Switzerland and beyond.

www.eurotv.com

Fox

Broadcaster of *Ally McBeal*, *Futurama*, *The Simpsons* and *The X-Files*.

www.fox.com

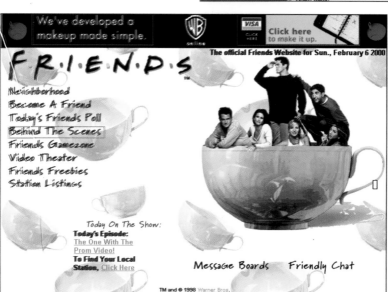

Friends

Official site with everything a true fan could want, and a lot more besides.

http://friends.warnerbros.com

Granada (G-Wizz)

Central hub for news and information on Granada TV programs such as *Coronation Street*.

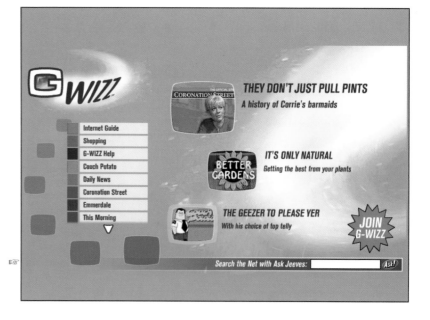

www.g-wizz.net

ITV

The full Independent Television network site with links to all syndicated programs.

www.itv.co.uk

Danny's Jerry Springer Show Page:
Good pictures on the big show and a well written biography on Jerry. If you are interested in chatting about Springer with other fans, Danny has a great chat room as well.

The Life of Jerry Springer:
A nice selection of information and other good links. This guy put in alot of time into his Springer page and the finished product is terrific.

Hour Three- Jerry Springer:
This page is updated daily to inform you about the latest topic on today's episode. Direct quotes from the shows and some behind the scenes info about each episode.

Jerry Springer

The official site is not very good, so here's the best unofficial site on the web.

www.players.iperweb.com/springer

PBS

American public service broadcasting.

www.pbs.org

The Simpsons

Episode guides, character bios and more. Not to be missed.

http://thesimpsons.com

Screen Network Australia

From here you can get to most Australian TV shows and films.

www.sna.com.au

Sky/SkyRocket

UK's leading satellite broadcaster with ground-breaking interactive section.

www.sky.com
www.skyrocket.co.uk

Star Trek

An online home for all trekkers, be they followers of *TOS*, *TNG*, *DS9* or *Voyager*.

www.startrek.com

Time Warner

Owners of CNN, Warner Brothers Network, Cartoon Network and The Comedy Channel.

www.timewarner.com

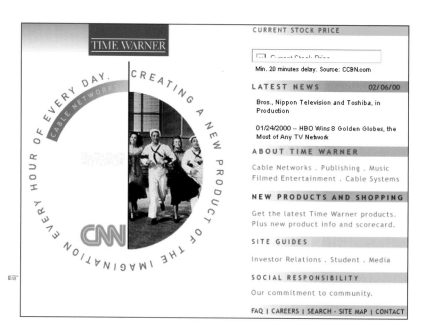

Tubeworld

Amazing labor of love, detailing all TV cross-overs and characters' back-stories.

http://members.aol.com/Tubeworld/index.html

TV Shows Which Debuted From 1976-1996

If you just want to stroll down lack-of-memory lane, try visiting this oddity.

www.mindspring.com/~paprwrk/tvshow.htm

UPN.com

Home of the *WWF* wrestlers, *Star Trek: Voyager*, and *Dilbert*.

www.upn.com

The X-Files

Very thorough site that makes the unofficial sites almost unnecessary. Almost.

www.thex-files.com

Whoosh!

Almost everything you need to enjoy *Xena: Warrior Princess*.

www.whoosh.org

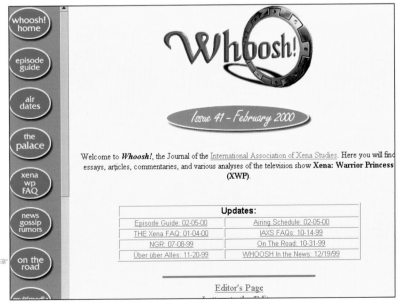

Music

usic is the most popular and controversial sector on the Internet after pornography. Sound files have been on the web for a good while now, and there are several formats out there. The two big ones are **wav** and **mpeg**. Over a year ago, though, mpeg released the third version of its format and the world of music on the Internet has never been the same.

Some search engines claim that searches carried out for this newest digital music format, MP3, have now overtaken the requests made for the word 'sex'. This is quite an achievement when you consider that MP3 is just a compression/decompression standard for downloading audio files. However, there is no 'just' about MP3. The format allows songs to be compressed into small audio files that retain their CD sound quality.

You can download free software that will copy songs from any CD you place in your computer, and turn them into MP3 files. This process (called 'ripping') means that you can store your entire record collection on the hard drive of your PC or Mac, and you can play them at any time without the need for the CD.

You can even buy MP3 players so that your digital music is portable, and these players are very small. Most are not much bigger than a packet of cigarettes, and the newest ones can even be found on watches. Considering the ease of use and the minimal cost (only the portable, hardware players cost anything), you can begin to see how attractive MP3 is to the world's vast number of music devotees.

As you can imagine, the big record companies are not happy about the mass copying of their product and, as the MP3 format can be readily distributed to millions on the Net, there is the matter of illegal piracy involved too. So far the music industry has been very slow to embrace the technology and it is only now, a good year after the initial boom, that Sony has released an MP3 player.

The music industry has been looking for an alternative to MP3, and the major record labels have banded together under the Secure Digital Music Initiative (SDMI) to work on this problem. Another alternative is for digital watermarks to be added to MP3 files, so that only official files can be played. Whatever the outcome, many in the music industry have already made the move to MP3s, if for no other reason than the 17 million MP3 files that are downloaded from the Net every day.

However, there is more to music on the Internet than just MP3s. Being a cheap place for promotion, the Net has attracted a truly huge number of 'wannabe' bands and solo artists. These sites list the artist's latest performances, and forthcoming gigs, as well as either whole tracks or previews of them in - you guessed it - MP3 format. Some stars have fully embraced the web – special mention must go to *The Beastie Boys*,

Jamiroquai and *David Bowie* - while some industry bigwigs have jumped ship to offer up-and-coming bands space and technology to promote themselves online.

You will also find some excellent music news and features sites that cover everything about the industry - from new releases and the charts, to live web casts of music festivals, live web chat with the stars, reviews of concerts, albums and singles, as well as interviews and features.

CREDITS   JAPANESE VERSION

🇬🇧 Brit Awards nomination for Jamiroquai

Jamiroquai have been nominated in the Best Dance Act category of the 2000 Brit Awards, to be held in London on March 3rd. Since the awards begun, Jamiroquai have been nominated a total of 13 times, but have yet to walk away with a prize.

🇬🇧 Jamiroquai back in the recording studio

After the return of Derrick McKenzie from his honeymoon, the band will be back in the studio to record several new tracks. Nothing's been recorded as of yet so we've got no idea what to expect. But if its anything like the rest of the album, it's going to be....supersonic!

Dotmusic

Probably the best UK-based music site that offers a wide number of charts including singles, album, Indie, dance, jazz, and rock. You can also join the community section of the site for a chat with fellow music fans, get the latest music news, or read from the amazing array of features, interviews, and song/album/gig reviews the site has in its archive.

www.dotmusic.com

Click<Music>

Excellent music portal that covers almost everything to do with chart music. **Click<Music>** has a dedicated search engine, and an outstanding web guide of other music sites including artists' official and fans' pages. You will also find some great content such as gig dates, charts, MP3s, CDs, and more.

www.clickmusic.co.uk

Lycos MP3 Search Directory

Very straightforward search facility. Just enter the song or artist name and away you go. The search engine will pull up a list of sites where you can find legal MP3s for download, sorted by reliability. This is supposedly the world's largest MP3 directory with over 1 million files. There are also some great guides on getting started with MP3s, and how to get the most from them.

http://mp3.lycos.com

MP3.com

A great domain name, but nothing to do with the developers of MP3. The site is an outstanding MP3 portal, with over 100,000 free songs for download. You an also personalise the site and add your own 'ripped' CD tracks. MP3.com is one of the busiest music sites on the Net with some 200,000 visitors a day.

www.mp3.com

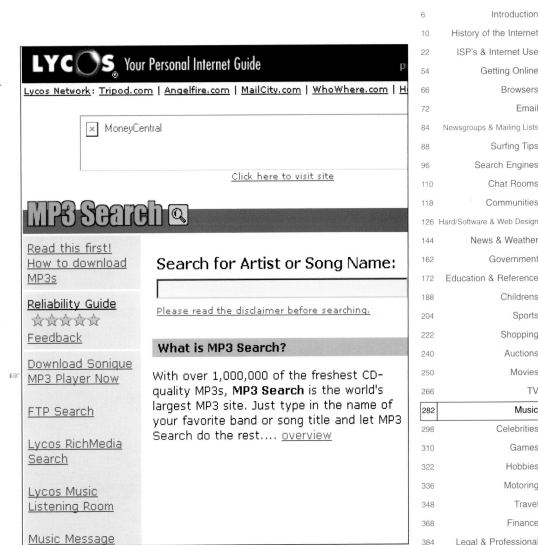

Music

AMG All Music Guide

Amazing resource of music information that includes biographies and discographies, as well as very detailed information on each track such as style, genre, credits, and songs/albums that are similar.

www.allmusic.com

Billboard Online

America's number one chart listing has a great online presence with content from its magazine, music news, and even *Billboard* radio web casting online.

www.billboard.com

Crunch.co.uk

Although most of its content comes from independent dance labels, this UK-based site is one of the best MP3 resources in the UK.

www.crunch.co.uk

Eatsleepmusic.com

Up-and-coming bands can put their tracks on this site, while visitors are invited to download songs for free. The full CDs are available for purchase online too.

www.eatsleepmusic.com

EMI:Chrysalis

Recently merged with Warner Brothers Music, to form a super company, but the EMI suite remains a great resource for fans of Robbie Williams, Kate Bush, Diana Ross, Louise, Geri Halliwell and the like.

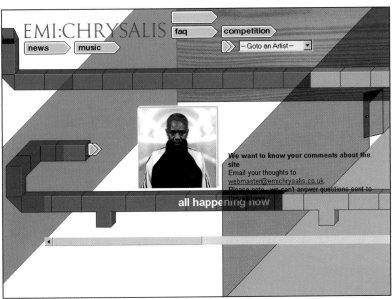

www.emichrysalis.co.uk

Listen.com

Directory of downloadable MP3s organised into different types of music. You can review tracks yourself, or read those written by others, and a 'sounds like' facility helps you find other tunes you might like.

www.listen.com

Music365

Another great UK-based one-stop shop for music. You can read news and reviews, features and interviews, as well as interact with others in the community section. There's even a link through to Yalplay.

www.music365.com

www.Music.com

Amazing music portal that is divided into over 25 sections covering everything from 80's disco and blues, to country, classical, and religious.

www.music.com

Peoplesound.com

Innovative site that brings together music fans, unsigned bands, record labels, and talent scouts, to make an amazing new music experience for all concerned.

www.peoplsound.com

Pollstar

If you need to find out when your favorite artist is playing, and at what venue (almost anywhere in the world), this incredibly detailed site will help you out.

www.pollstar.com

Real Jukebox

Real Jukebox is one of the most popular pieces of software that plays and records digital music. The software also lets you take tracks from your audio CDs and turn them into MP3 files.

www.real.com/realjukebox

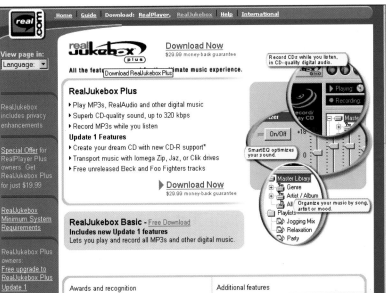

Internet Underground Music Archive (IUMA)

Site for unsigned bands, run by music fans not the music industry. As such, over 4,000 independent musicians are members of IUMA, all of whom have free **mpeg** and **RealAudio** versions of their music.

www.iuma.com

AMP3.com

For more obscure music genres and songs.

http://amp3.com

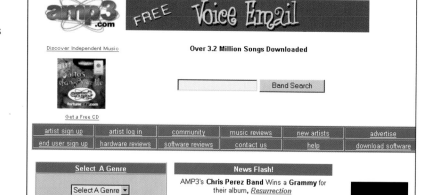

Audible.com

Produces an MP3 player called the MobilePlayer, and has over 15,000 hours of downloadable content.

www.audible.com

AudioCatalyst

Now owned by RealNetworks, you can get ripping and encoding software all in one.

www.xingtech.com/mp3/audiocatalyst

AudioGalaxy

Unsigned band site that offers 25MB of free web space for them to promote themselves (and even use the space to sell merchandise).

www.audiogalaxy.com

The Beastie Boys

One of the few famous bands to take digital music seriously.

www.beastieboys.com

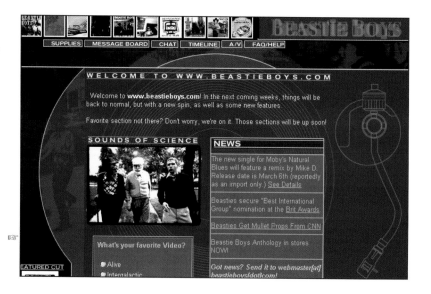

BMG Classics

Good classical, folk and jazz reference site.

www.bmgclassics.com

Daily MP3.com

Excellent resource for the latest MP3 software updates and news.

www.dailymp3.com

David Bowie

One of the greatest icons of rock and roll has an extensive web presence with a UK ISP, online albums and tracks, a comprehensive biography and much more.

www.davidbowie.net

Emusic

Good US-based MP3 site of independent record labels, where you can download a song for 99 cents, and an album for $8.99.

www.emusic.com

Findsongs.com

Great site for finding anything to do with music.

www.findsongs.com

Hitsquad
Great site for music software and links to other sites.

www.hitsquad.com

HMV
Good review and online purchase site.

www.hmv.com
www.hmv.co.uk

Jamiroquai
One of the earliest bands on the web, but one that has concentrated on design, rather than technology.

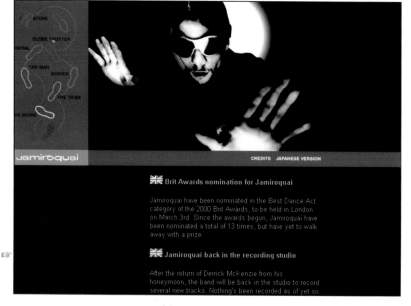

www.jamiroquai.co.uk

Liquid Audio

Record companies' free open
architecture that supports AC3,
MP3 and Windows Media formats.

http://www.liquidaudio.com

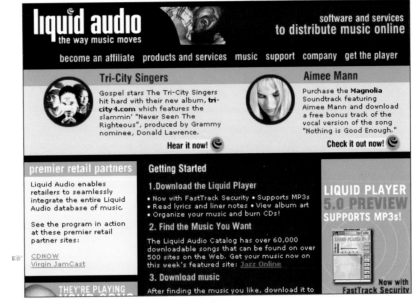

MP3meta

Has the top 200 MP3s and com-
piles the results into one report,
with the files rated by relevancy.

www.mp3meta.com

MP3 Now

Good starting point for anyone
new to MP3s, who wants to get
the most from the technology.

www.mp3now.com

MTV

Outstanding sites, covering every continent, from the king of music channels.

www.mtv.co.uk

www.mtv.com

Music Match

Make your own MP3 files from your CD collection with this free 'ripper'.

www.musicmatch.com

Music Research/RPM Research

UK site that lets people register to take part in official market research for the UK music industry.

www.music-research.co.uk

MusicSearch.Com

Claims to be the only search engine dedicated to music.

www.musicsearch.com

Net Radio.com

Great US site where you can listen to one of over 120 radio stations purely online.

www.netradio.com

NME

Great site from the famous music magazine.

www.nme.com

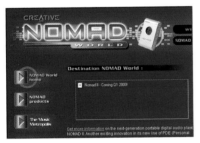

Nomad World

Dedicated to Creative's Nomad digital audio player with an artists' section for downloads.

www.nomadworld.com

Radio Spy

The latest gossip and news from the music industry.

www.radiospy.com

Radio Waves.com

No matter where you are in the world, listen to your favorite music station, or tune into one on the other side of the globe.

www.radiowaves.co.uk

Riffage.com

One of the best sites for unsigned bands, which get 85 per cent of any revenue generated from the site.

www.riffage.com

RioPORT.com

Home of the best-known MP3 player, the Diamond Rio, and a database of all things MP3.

www.rioport.com

Rolling Stone.com

Very good US portal site from the famous music publication.

www.rollingstone.com

SHOUTcast

Lets you broadcast MP3 files from a server.

www.shoutcast.com

Songplayer

Amazing site that will help you play your favorite tracks on piano or guitar.

www.songplayer.co.uk

The Sonic Spot

Useful search facility and web guide dedicated to music.

www.sonicspot.com

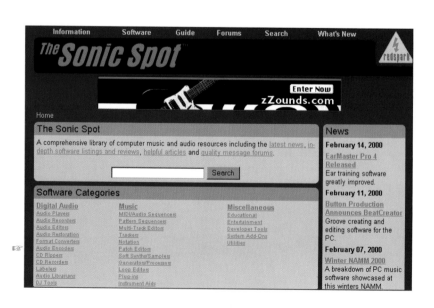

Sony Music

Not only its main music site, but also its new music hub.

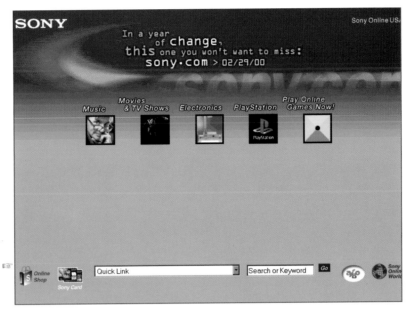

www.sony.com

www.uville.com

Star Gig

Brand new music portal created by co-founder of Chrysalis, Terry Ellis.

www.stargig.com

Tunes.com

Comprehensive music site that covers most bases.

www.tunes.com

Ultimate Band List

Far more than the name suggests - a great site for music.

www.ubl.com

Warner Bros./Entertaindom

Warner Bros. now has its own dedicated music portal called Entertaindom.

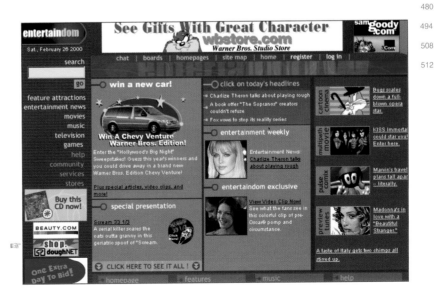

www.music.warnerbros.com

www.entertaindom.com

Celebrities

The one thing celebrities want is to achieve more fame, and the Internet gives them the perfect medium to achieve this. The clever ones have commissioned their own home pages, while the majority are quite content to let their fans do all the hard work, setting up sites as shrines to the favorite stars of stage, screen, music, sports or the catwalk.

As love and hate are two sides of the same coin, there are also some hate sites out there, but these are generally limited to well-known concepts, ideas or companies, rather than people. There are exceptions though, and it seems to be media company bosses that come in for most criticism. Celebrities also fall foul of those with a sense of irony. Thus we have guides to celebrities' graves, their driveways, and their criminal records, to name but a few of the stranger offerings from celebrity sites.

Although I have not listed individuals' web sites in this section, there are many who have set up excellent and innovative sites. The type of celebrity who has a site doesn't seem to follow any pattern, but covers all areas of fame - from comic book guru Stan Lee who has set up a site purely for his new creations (www.stanlee.Net), to supermodel Cindy Crawford (www.cindy.com).

Be they official, or created by fans, celebrity sites tend to have many things in common. They both tend to be very positive about everything the celebrity has done. They have biographies, and pages of stunning color photography. You can usually email your hero, while some fans have gone the route of providing a postal address in the physical world as well.

Fortunately, not only are there fans who put sites together about one celebrity, but also those who make it their life's work to ensure that finding those individual sites is as easy as possible. What you will find here is primarily a collection of the best celebrity portals and search engines, which will enable you to find your favorite celebrity's home page as quickly as possible.

The Internet has even produced its own celebrities. Probably the most famous 'Netizen' is Jennifer Ringley of the famous JenniCAM (www.jennicam.org). What started off as a one web cam site, now has a bi-weekly webcast show, and is reputed to have made Ms Ringley very rich. There have been many imitators, of many people, although AmandaCam (www.amandacam.com) makes a better stab at being online 24 hours a day.

There are even sites on the Internet that will help you to become a celebrity. Just follow their suggestions and you'll soon have the paparazzi peering over your garden fences, and trailing you as you go jogging. Or that's the idea. Some are more serious than others, but there are no guarantees. Whatever your interest in celebrities on the Internet, you will be able to find the person, or the information you're after. No matter how much individual taste you have, there will be someone on the web who shares it.

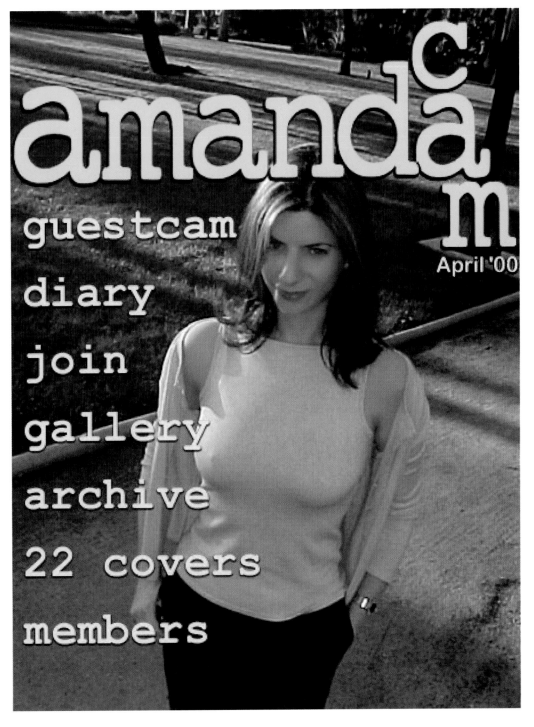

Watch me live in my home 24 hours a day,
7 days a week on my **SIX** webcams.

Celebhoo

Probably one of the best celebrity resources on the Internet, **Celebhoo** lets you find fan and official sites for almost anyone famous - from film stars to pop stars, authors to sporting heroes. You'll find email lists, the latest entertainment gossip, and where to purchase photos and posters of your favorite stars.

www.celebhoo.com

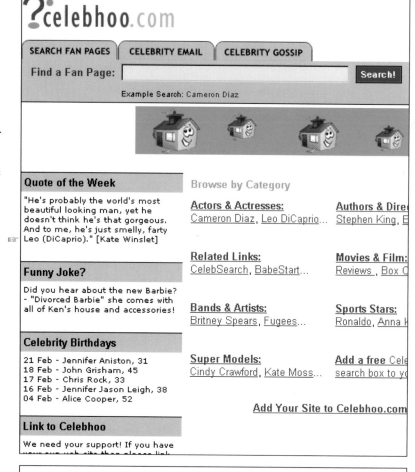

Celebrity Link

An extensive directory of links to over 5,000 sites, devoted to over 2,000 stars. **Celebrity Link's** features include a celebrity site of the day, and a search facility for actors, actresses, models and musicians. You can chat about being a fan in the forum, or check birthdays, or even add your own site to the database.

www.celebrity-link.com

OneWorldLive.com

Community for you to share with celebrities from the worlds of film, television, music, sports, health, personal fitness, beauty and self improvement. You can find out everything you need to know about stars, where they live, where they were born, star signs, education and romantic interests. You can even find out what charities your favorite star supports, and help them with a donation.

www.oneworldlive.com

Star Seeker

As the site says, with all the web pages out there, you can spend a lot of time downloading some pretty useless information. **Star Seeker**, though, is very targeted. Your search results will bring up why the person is famous, links to official and fan sites, as well as resources where you can find out information more objectively.

www.starseeker.com

Celebrities

The Association of Theater Artists

Comprehensive site, listing information and reviews of directors, playwrights, composers and actors.

www.theaterartists.com

Celebrities @ MTV

Stories, interviews and information on a variety of musicians and pop stars.

www.celebrities@mtv.com

Entertainment Sleuth

Great search facility listings site that tries to list as many details about celebrities as you would want to find, including the latest news and multi-media.

www.entertainmentsleuth.com

MovieActors.com

A good resource for pictures and life histories of movie stars, from the 1930s to the present day. Also has information on the latest awards.

www.moviactors.com

The Star Archive

Amazing site with a vast number of stars' addresses and contact details - checked by the site's owner - and includes some scanned-in autographs.

www.stararchive.com

Who2?

Search engine designed just for stars and celebrities. There is a lot of content here, but it also searched **Lycos** for celebrity entries.

www.who2.com

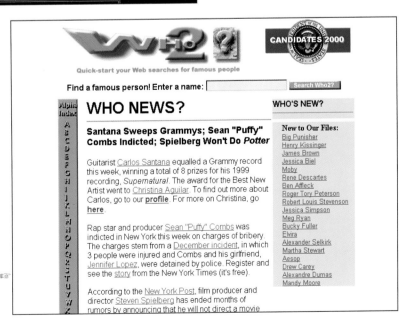

Autographs For Sale.com

Signed photos and artefacts from sports stars, models and celebrities.

www.autographsforsale.com

The Bikini World

If you're a fan of models, here they are in swimwear. Not porn.

www.bikinisworld.com

Biography.com

Great resource for the slightly older or more obscure stars.

www.biography.com

Celebrity 1000

A US site where you can vote for your favorite actress, pop/sports star, movie etc.

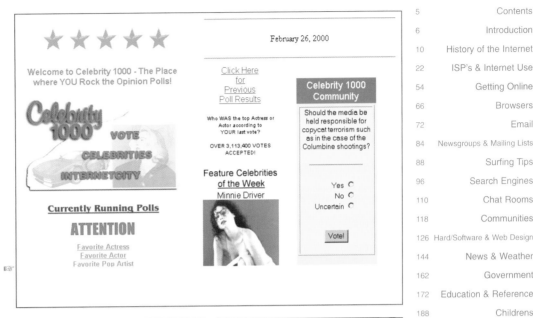

www.celebrity1000.com

Celebrity Addresses of the Famous & the Infamous

Great site for finding the physical addresses of your favorite stars or icons.

http://celebrity.virtualave.net

CelebrityEmail.com

Doesn't actually give you the email address, but forwards your messages to the stars, thus protecting their privacy.

www.celebrityemail.com

Celebrity Merchandise

If you want to buy memorabilia to do with your favorite star, this site will help. Also look out for the free photos.

www.celebritymerch.com

Celebrity Sightings/Alloy

Pictures of people embracing their heroes, stories of close encounters with the rich and famous, and more.

www.celebritysightings.com

Celebrity Stars

A comprehensive list of features which include news, pictures and celebrity chat.

www.celebritystars.com

Celebrity Web

Outstanding site with tasteful photos of many stars, as well as links to their sites, and even associated theme tunes.

www.celebrityweb.com

Driveways of the Rich and Famous

Odd site that has photos of stars' driveways, and interviews with the stars' gardeners and neighbors.

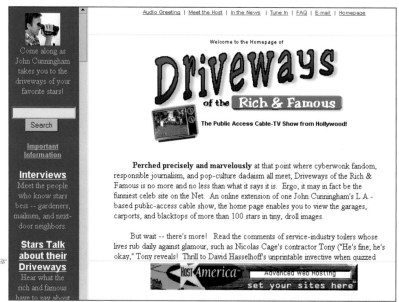

www.driveways.com

Famous Mugshots

When stars go bad - they have grainy photos taken of them by the police.

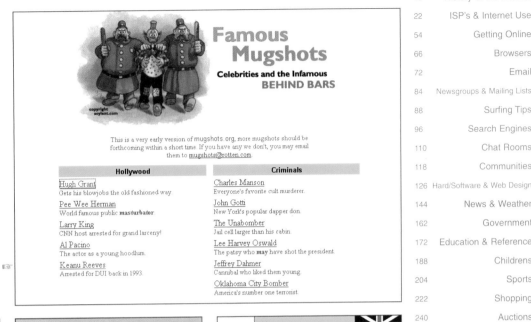

www.mugshots.org

Find a Grave

For those tracking down dead celebrities, this is the place. It has a searchable database of celebrity graves.

www.findagrave.com

Great Life Network

A fee email publication of the lives of 'great people'. Includes entertainment, history and trivia.

www.greatlifenetwork.com

Internet Movie Database

The best film site on the Net is also very good at film star biographies, filmographies, and a photo collection.

www.imdb.com

Muzi.com/Gallery/ Entertainment - Actors and Actresses

A Chinese site featuring stills of actors and actresses and a 'What's New' section.

www.muzi.net

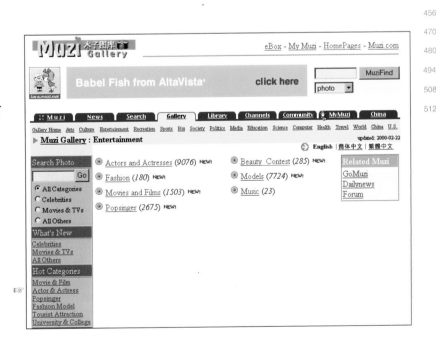

NETrageous

Become a celebrity yourself by learning how to manipulate the media - especially the Internet.

www.netrageousresults.com

Rodeo Drive

Check out latest celebrity events and get a look at individual 'style gurus'. It also offers a brief history of Rodeo Drive.

www.rodeodrive.com

Starbuzz

Information on nearly 2,000 stars and over 4,000 web sites.

www.starbuzz.com

Who Is That?

Great site for if you've ever wondered where you've seen that character actor.

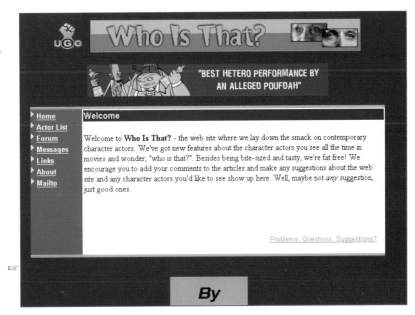

www.who-is-that.com

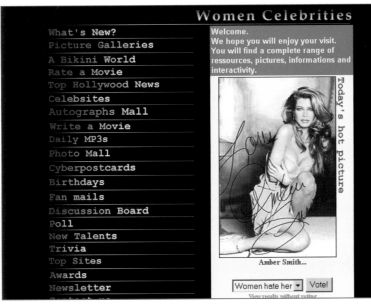

Women Celebrities

A site dedicated to the female of the species.

www.women-celebrities.com

Yack.com

Keep track of the stars you love by seeing if they're going to appear in a live web cast.

www.yack.com

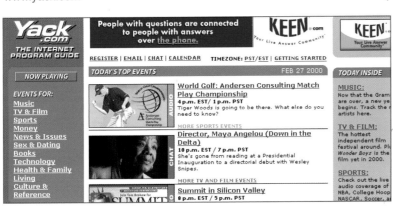

The Zone

Email anyone from Bill Clinton to Madonna, or find out all you wanted to know about individual supermodels, musicians and the like.

www.thezone.pair.com

Games

There is very little more absorbing than a good game. Whether it's an enthralling game of Monopoly, the latest Playstation release, or just a good hand of cards, we al like to play. As is fast becoming the motto for this book - you name it, you'll find it on the Net. And games are no different.

Most traditional board games are still represented by their manufacturers - a mark of just how popular those games were. Waddingtons has sites dedicated to its top selling murder mystery, Cluedo/Clue. And that it is not to mention the hundreds of fan or tribute sites these greats of yesteryear have. The Internet being a bastion of nostalgia (albeit for the sixties, seventies and eighties), if you can remember a game, you'll find a site about it. Escape from Colditz, the Game of Life, Buckaroo - they're all online somewhere.

The Internet has even breathed new life into the real oldies of chess, chequers/draughts, and all manner of card games. At **Yahoo!** you can play most of these classics in real time with complete strangers from around the globe. This might seem quite an eerie experience, but no more so than playing chess via post.

The idea of having the whole world to play against or with is certainly an intriguing notion, and one that the marketing team at Sega were quick to pick up. When it was announced that their new console would come equipped with a modem, allowing game play over the Net, the number of potential players was the same as the world's population - or so we were told in the ads.

There not being such a thing as a new idea, Quake players had known the potential for Internet game play for years. Even lesser games companies, such as Wireplay in the UK, had started to capitalise on this amazing facet of the Net at least a year before the appearance of the Dreamcast.

One of the biggest sales areas on the Internet is in console and PC games. Not only will you find a vast number of gaming sites offering tips and tricks beside the hard sell of the newest title, there are also some outstanding sites belonging to games developers and publishers. Players have even emailed games' creators direct for help when stuck.

For those who still prefer the idea of man against machine, there are plenty of sites where you can download PC games online. There are sites where - thanks to the interactivity of Shockwave and Flash - you can face the computer in any number of far-fetched or down to earth scenarios.

Away from the flashing lights and sharp sounds of electronic wizardry, there are sites that aim to pass on what they have learned after a lifetime of playing chess, backgammon, or chemin de fer. If you like to play, you'll find the game of your choice in the ultimate house of fun - the Internet...

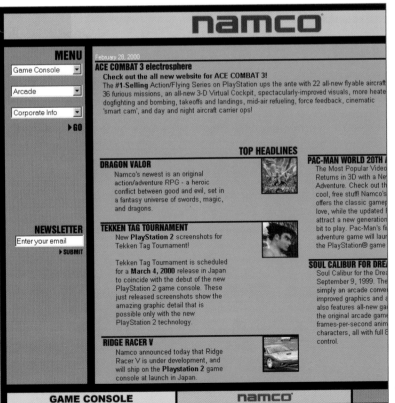

Jamba

An excellent site for word and trivia-based games. Darts, dominoes, solitaire, and poker can be played here as well as lesser known titles such as Friday Frenzy, Jamba Jumble, and Codebreaker. Anyone who has a passion for sixties' and seventies' music should definitely visit here. There are also chances to win substantial amounts of money…

www.jamba.co.uk

Planet Quake

For those who have ever fragged or been fragged. The ultimate site for the Quake addict – or the person who's heard so much and is just plain curious. Get tips and trick, discover all the versions of the game, and learn about new characters, skins, and Quaking on the Net.

www.planetquake.com

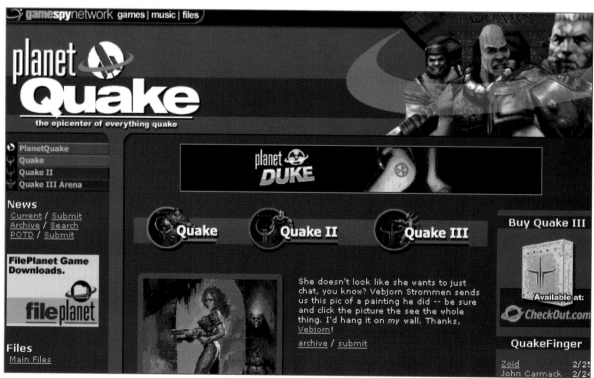

Shockwave.com

A great resource of online games, puzzles, and cartoons that you'll need the shockwave plug-in to play. Choose from action, arcade, puzzles, sports, and adventure. The sports section features a selection of games including pool, ice hockey and golf. While you'll also find the ever-popular **South Park** and **King of the Hill** here too.

www.shockwave.com

Yahoo! Games

Play a wide range of board and other traditional games with complete strangers across the Internet. As this is **Yahoo!**, there always seem to be opponents, but if there aren't you can always play a single player games, such as card games or crosswords. And they're all free.

http://games.yahoo.com

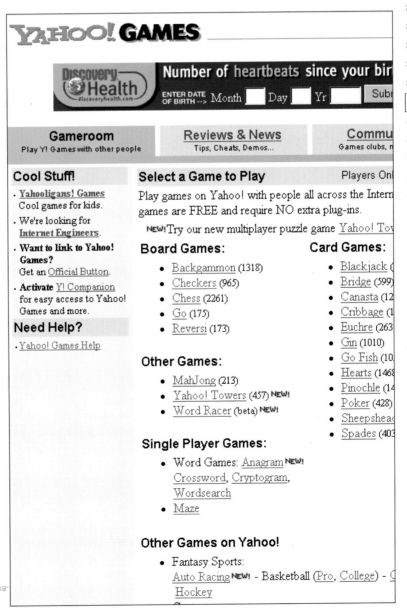

Games

Boardgames.com

Every type of board game from Pokemon, Monopoly, to plain old Rummy are covered and on sale here.

www.boardgames.com

Ezone.com

A good range of games can be played here. Meet plenty of cartoon characters including Lenny Loosejocks and his faithful dog, Donga. Many can be downloaded and sent to friends.

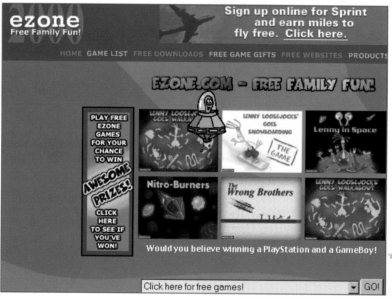

www.ezone.com

Future Gamer

Get awesome game news delivered weekly via e-mail or read it on the Web. Your call.

www.futuregamer.com

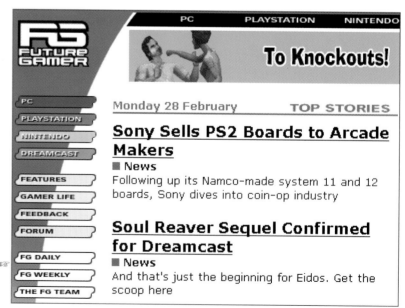

Gamecenter.com

A great site for downloading add-ons for your favourite PC games. You'll also find tips and tricks, news and reviews here, too.

www.gamecenter.com

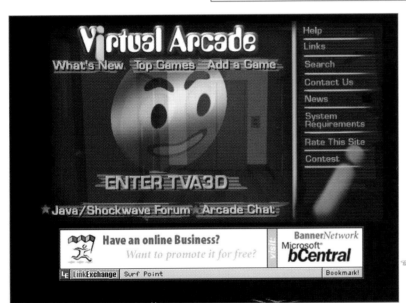

Virtual Arcade

A place to come and play all your favorite games or just hang out in the chat area. Find out the latest games news and you can even win prizes.

www.thearcade.com

Waddingtons/Hasbro

Not only home to Monopoly and Scrabble, but with some online games to lay, too.

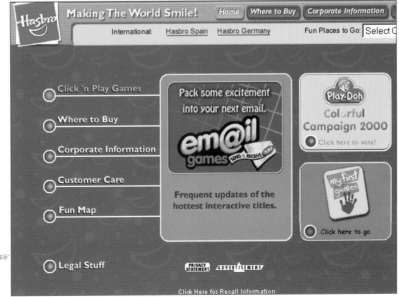

www.waddingtons.com

Monopoly for DOS

Computerised version where you can play against up to five other people.

www.fartoogood.com/monopoly/docs.htm

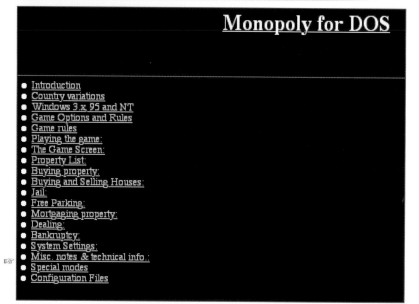

Backgammon Galore!

Rules, software, and tips on improving your game.

www.bkgm.com

Cluedo

Classic murder game in both its US and UK guide.

www.cluedo.com

ChessCentral

Has an online chess store, information on upcoming tournaments, competitions, and links to other sites.

www.illawarva.net.au/chesscentral

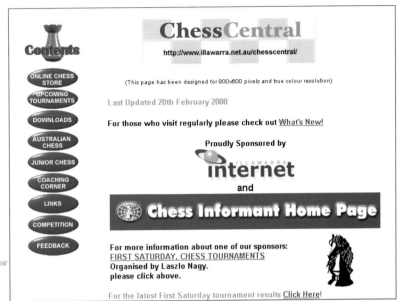

Classic Gaming.com

Under the title, gaming the way you remember it, this site looks forward as well as back.

www.classicgaming.com

Decision Games

Mainly based around the theme of battle, these games were the precursor to Command & Conquer.

http://decisiongames.com

Eidos

The makers of Lara Croft's Tomb Raider series have a useful little homepage, too.

www.eidosinteractive.com

Family Game Night

Dedicated to encourage families to have an evening of fun without involving the television.

www.familygamenight.com

Five by Five Poker

Score high with ten good poker hands and be the envy of five by five players all over the world.

www.serve.com/poker

The Games Kids Play

A whole site dedicated to what children play in the playground.

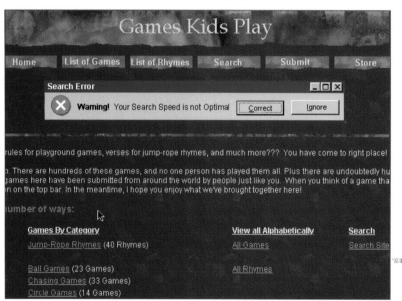

www.gameskidsplay.net

Game-Land

Very good site covering all aspects of games, including those you can play online.

www.game-land.com

Gamespot

Every aspect of computer console games is covered by this thorough site.

www.gamespot.co.uk

Hexits

Chess meets Lego meets cards. Sort of. It claims to be the ultimate board game.

www.hexits.com

Mahjong Online

View the tiles and learn the rules, you can also play if you register

http://games.coolconnect.com/mahjong

Myst

Home to one of the most popular games in history and its sequel.

www.myst.com

Medieval & Renaissance Games Home Page

How did they pass the time before books, let alone TV? Rules for and information about games played before 1700.

www2.lglass.com/~justin/game-hist.html

Medieval & Renaissance Games Home Page

Free Speech Online
Blue Ribbon Campaign

Welcome to a page specifically dedicated to Really Old Games. This page is intended to cover anything and everything pertaining to games in the Medieval and Renaissance periods. All are welcome to contribute; I am particularly looking for relevant sites to point to.

What's New: New files and changes to this site:

- 2/2/00: Noted the current controversy over Tablero: it looks like the main secondary source used for the game is full of strangely ahistorical information.
- 1/31/00: Added all of the individual Ace's Boke articles to the general Rules page. Added a Tafl article to the Ace's Boke.
- 1/26/00: Massive update, as I officially move to the new URL. Added pointers to all of the game descriptions on the Alfonso site. (That site is starting to get very useful!) Killed lots of dead links, and moved pointers to moved sites when I could find them. Reformatted the Rules page to be easier to read and understand. (The original style made sense when there was only one description of any given game, but it had gotten to be a mess.) Put direct links to the relevant chess variations on Hans' Chess Variant Pages. Put direct links to relevant pages on James Masters' Traditional Games site. Added a link to Board Games Studies. Added a whole lotta chess sites. Added lots of related sites and such.
- 12/30/98: Catching up on page-hunting. Added pointer to article about Spain's part in origins of chess. Added a pointer to Dragonsspine's SCA games pages. Added a couple of descriptions of tafl, and some Poch illos. Added pointer to Y Cam's article on Towlbwrdd. Moved Dagonell's page with all the other collections of rules. Put in direct links to rules articles by Dagonell and Modar, on the theory that a single comprehensive index is probably useful. (More is needed on this.) Added description of Rounders. Fixed pointer to Tara Hill, and added their rules page. Added a bunch of assorted alternate descriptions of games. Added description of Celtic knucklebones. Added pointer to Breughel picture.
- 12/17/98: Many additions to my personal bibliography.
- 9/22/98: Added pointer to Robert fitz John's Alquerques page.
- 9/2/98: Added several hnefatafl links. Added pointer to Ravensgard's Norse Games page.
- 8/31/98: Added link to the Alfonso illustrations project. Added a pointer to ShadowWolf's nice, concise History of Tarot. Added a pointer to James Masters' History of Traditional Games. Added a pointer to Kadon Enterprises.
- 5/5/98: Moved all refs to the Landsknecht pages over to their new site. Added pointer to David Levy's Trictrac page under Rules. Added pointer to The Merry Gamester page, under Bibliographies.
- 2/23/98: Lots of additions. Added Wulfgar's games page to the Collections list on the Rules page. Added pointer to a Geocities page under Related Sites. Added pointer to Ambush under Game Software. And added a beefy new collection of Rythmomachia links on the Rules page.
- 2/17/98: Added pointer to The Compendium of Common Knowledge.
- 2/12/98: Added pointer to a new Java implementation of Tablut.
- 2/4/98: Several updates to the listing of Vendors of Period Games, below.

Descriptions of Period Games, and Research Materials

Games

Namco

For all the latest news and reviews – no matter what you play on.

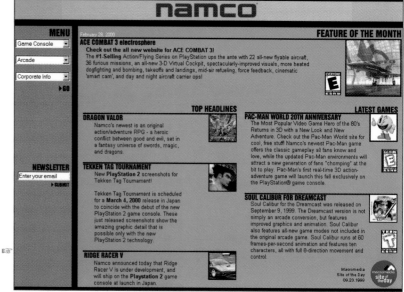

www.namco.com

www.nintendo.com

Where you'll find the latest info on the N64, Game boy and SNES.

www.nintendo.com

North American Tiddlywinks Association

You name it, you'll find it here if it has anything to do with tiddlywinks.

www.tiddlywinks.org

Play Bridge Hand Generator

Practice makes perfect, and this site will keep giving you new bridge hands to figure out.

http://playbridge.com

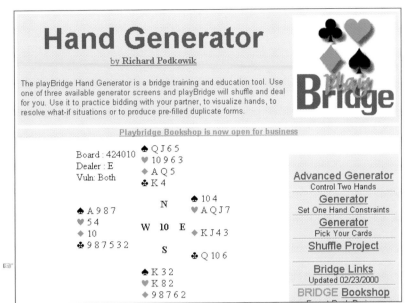

Sega

Home to the good old MegaDrive and now the Dreamcast.

www.sega.com

Thinks.com

Incredible selection of brain-teasers, puzzles and games.

www.thinks.com

University Games Web site

More online fun, this time in the from of brain teasing questions.

www.ugames.com

Wild World of Wonka

Most games from here can be downloaded to play offline.

www.wonka.com

As has often been pointed out, the Internet equates to the world's largest library of information, but due to the number of people that make up the Net, it is also a community of super-power proportions. That means that no matter how off-beat or little heard of your hobby is, there will be tens if not hundreds of people who share that interest. Elsewhere in this book we have examined the huge diversity of sites dedicated to **Motoring**, **Science and Nature**, **Movies**, **TV** and **The Arts**. Now it's the turn of the hobbies and pastimes that are not so globally popular.

Rest assured, you'll find what you're looking for. There are sites out there dealing in every subject you can imagine from aardvarks to zymurgy and, quite literally, everything else in between - including a lot you'd never think existed. Some of those particular topics turn up in the chapter on **Weird and Wonderful** sites so, if you're curious, you know where to look...

The great aspect of the Net often overlooked is its interactivity. This is not a magazine or a TV programme. This is immediate communication. What this technology means is that, unless you prefer it that way, pursuing your interests needn't be a passive experience - just reading material on web pages. The Internet excels at providing news,

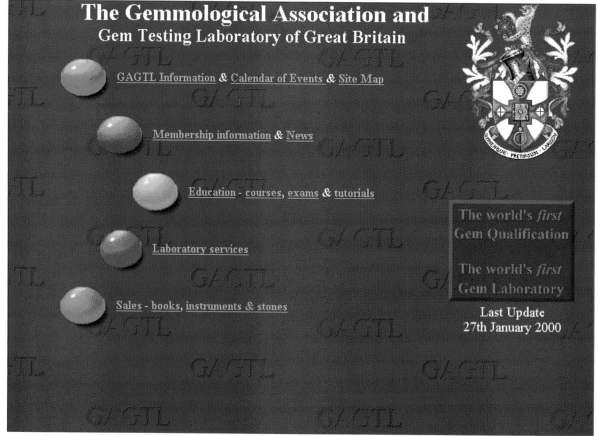

chat forums and directories for interests or hobbies outside the norm. You can contribute to those activities, or even email site owners with more accurate or up-to-date information. You could even build your own site.

One of the most fantastic attributes of the Net is the speed at which it can deliver information and the ease with which you can receive it. After all, few things in life are as easy as clicking on a hyper-link. The potential result of this ease and speed, is that long-dead interests - those that were pushed to the side by the time constraints of modern life - can be resurrected with a well placed bookmark.

So many people were once a bit of a stamp collector, or bird watcher, or any other type of enthusiast. Alas, they had to give up that interest because they never had the time. If this could be you - and I know it's me - you'll find memories flooding back as you browse through the list of hobbies and pastimes compiled for you here. Spoil yourself and spare a minute to have a quick look at that model aero-plane site, or the matchbox collector's homepage. You won't regret it, because those sites will have links to other sites that look interesting and, before you know it, you'll be surfing for information on that old hobby.

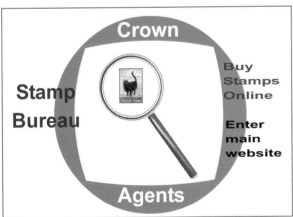

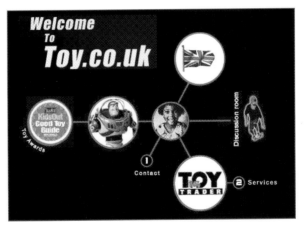

About.com

This is possibly one of the most amazing and impressive sites on the Internet. It will tell you about anything you care to name. Not only that, but the person telling you is always a recognised expert or enthusiast in his field. You can even ask the resident experts individual questions. Amazing.

www.about.com

Hobby World

Portal site that features hobbies of the month and talks with different aficionados from all over the world. **Hobby World** also features its own layout of the **Yahoo!** pastimes sections, as well as theme pages dedicated to more mainstream interests.

www.hobby-world.com

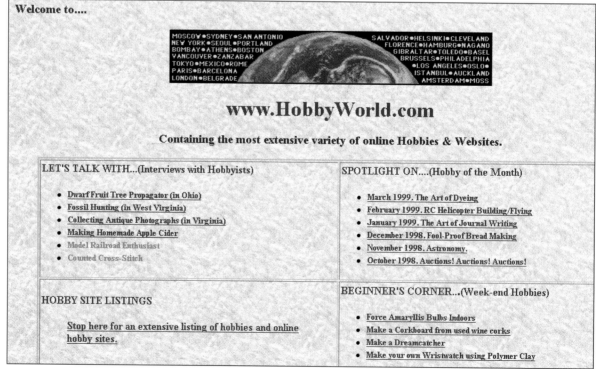

Yahoo! Hobbies

Nearly 50 categories to choose from mean that if you don't find your hobby or pastime here, you must be the only one doing it. The range is vast - from amateur Ham radio through collecting and genealogy to treasure hunting and urban exploration. There is even a section of the **Yahoo!** page that will let you start your own club.

http://dir.yahoo.com/Recreation/Hobbies

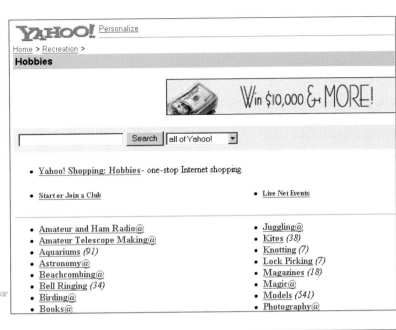

iCollector

The perfect online home for collectors of almost anything that can be classed as an antique. From jewelry and stamps to books and photographs. The site's mission is to refine the art of collecting, so you'll find information, auctions and price guides, as well as places you can find the objects of your desire in the physical world.

www.i-collector.co.uk

Ancestry.com
Search for ancestors by first and last names and by location, or you may wish to build your own family tree.

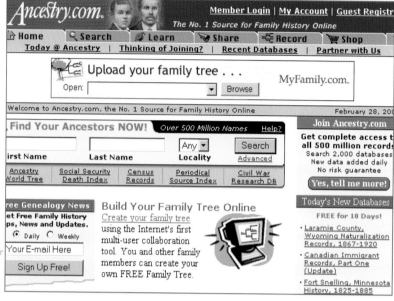

www.ancestry.com

Birds in a Cheshire Garden
Probably the most comprehensive bird watching site in the world, and a UK Yell Award winner in 1999.

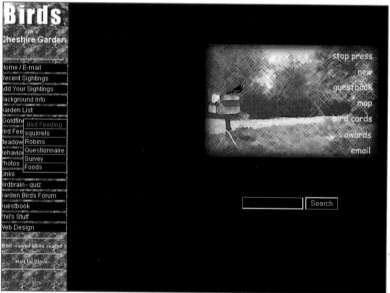

http://www.abcissa.force9.co.uk/birds/

Boats.co.uk
If sailing is what you do in your spare time, this is one site you'll want to check out for training courses, history and even weather checks.

www.boats.co.uk

British Gardening On-line

Everything for those who have their own wonderful gardens, or for those who just like to visit other people's.

www.oxalis.co.uk

Crown Agents Stamp Bureau

Extensive lists of stamps which can be searched by name or category. There are also some useful links.

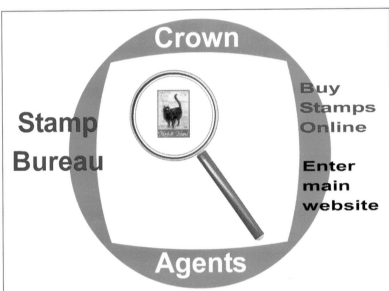

www.casb.com

GORP

Hiking, biking, fishing, canoeing, snow sports, and basically any other pastime that is spent outdoors, is catered for here. You can buy equipment, and book trips to wilderness resorts and dude ranches.

www.gorp.com

The Kite Flier's Site

If you like to go fly a kite up to the highest height, this site is a must for you. Over 500 kite-related sites, indexed and sorted, together with nearly 200MB of archive material.

www.kfs.org/kites

The National Association of Rocketry

Excellent resource for those into amateur rocketry. **NAR** is US-centric but has a wealth of information.

www.nar.org

Pet Healthcare Services

Sebastian the golden retriever and Pickle the Siamese cat guide you through various areas ranging from choosing and training your pet, to keeping them healthy. There is a sell at the end, but it's only £10 to ensure our furry friend.

www.pethealthcare.co.uk

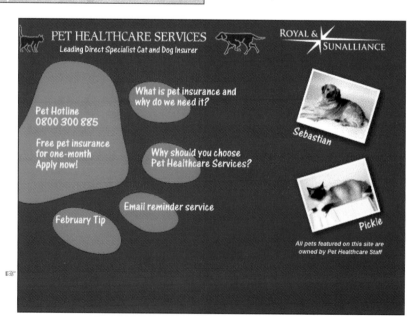

Teddy Bear.com

Shows, events, retailers, artists, auctions, magazines, museums. Just about everything you need to know about teddy bears is listed here.

www.teddybear.com

The Great Teddy Bear Hug Directory

Teddy Bear Talk

Teddy Bear Artists This section contains teddy bears created by teddy bear artists.

Teddy Bear Retailers Presently, this section contains a listing of teddy bear retailers by state and country.

Teddy Bear Manufactures Presently, this section contains a listing of teddy bear manufactures.

Teddy Bear Museums This section includes locations of teddy bear museums around the world.

Teddy Bear Magazines This section lists teddy bear magazines.

Teddy Bear Clubs and Associations Included in this section are teddy bear clubs and associations.

Teddy Bear Fun Just for fun!

Teddy Bear Shows and Events Included in this section is a monthly listing of teddy bear shows and events.

Teddy Bear Auctions Included in this section is a monthly listing of major teddy bear auctions. Al current auction reports.

Tower Hobbies

An excellent place to shop for anyone who enjoys planes, cars and boats of the remote controlled variety. They have a good online catalog and will deliver practically anywhere.

www.towerhobbies.com

Toy.co.uk

Independent UK site for those who must have everything in its box.

www.toy.co.uk

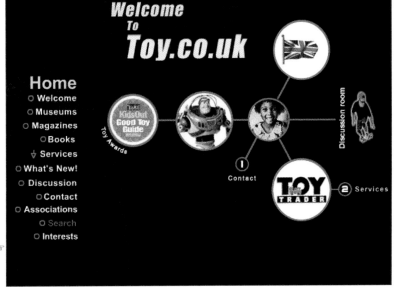

Ancient Coins/Edward J. Waddell Ltd

One of many auction sites that cater for the hobby of coin collecting.

www.coin.com

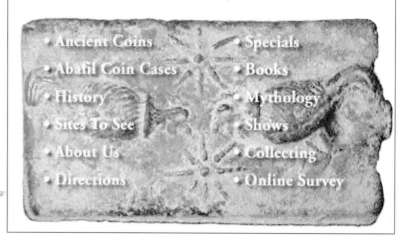

Big Little Railroad Shop

A small shop in New Jersey who claim to be able to provide you with any model train you desire. You can also shop online.

The Big Little Railroad Shop

Welcome to the Big Little Railroad Shop!

We're a small model railroad shop located in Somerville, N.J. Although we say that our shop is small, our service isn't! We've been doing business electronically since 1977 and have now moved onto the World Wide Web. If somebody makes it now, or made it then, we either have it in stock or can get it for you!

Read about this odd car and the other October Micro-Trains Releases

Stop by our catalog to look for that particular item. If you want to know what's new, be sure to read our new releases newsletter. It has all the latest information about the companies and products that you're interested in! If you can't find what you're looking for there

Archie's Place by Downtown Deco

www.biglittle.com

Birdwatching.com

For everyone who enjoys watching our feathered friends. You can read other peoples bird stories, and order videos and books.

www.birdwatching.com

Birdwatching

Your lifetime ticket to the theater of nature

Birdwatching Dot Com is about wild birds and the sport of birding. It's for everyone who is interested in birdwatching and enjoying nature. We hope you'll find some good ideas here to help you have fun watching birds.

Birdwatching includes all kinds of activities. You can explore the world with the focus of finding birds you've never seen before. Or simply enjoy the migrant birds who come through your yard in fall, like the White-throated Sparrow at right, attracted by your bird feeding station.

Bird Brain birding database for Mac

"Nature Ear" Binoculars For Your Ears

HOME
BIRDING GIFTS
BIRDING FAQ
BIRDING TIPS

Calligraphy Centre
Learn about calligraphy and all related lettering arts.

www.calligraphycentre.com

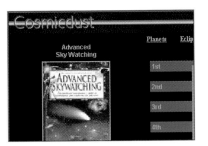

Cosmic Dust
A thorough calendar of astronomical events.

www.cosmicdust.co.uk

CraftShop.com
All you could need for the country craft hobbies, from ceramics to knitting needles.

www.craftshop.com

Doctor Who News
For the very latest news about the world's favorite Time Lord.

www.whonews.fsnet.co.uk

European Train Enthusiasts
Not only news and sightings of Europe's best trains, but also some choice layouts from the club's members.

www.ete.org

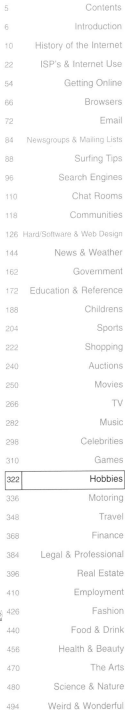

GardenGuides

Aimed at the experienced gardener, the site is divided into sections dealing with flowers, vegetables and herbs.

www.gardenguides.com

The Gemmological Association

Everything you ever wanted to know about gemstones but didn't know where to ask.

www.gagtl.ac.uk

Horology.com

Lists of time pieces for the dedicated collector.

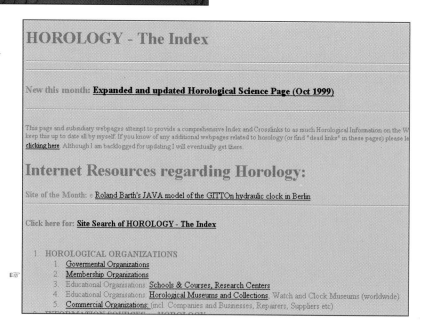

www.horology.com

mySeasons

Good resource for plant and flower care.

www.myseasons.com

PetCat

A cat cornucopia produced by cat food manufacturers, *Whiskas*.

www.petcat.co.uk

Pets' Corner

Although very cat and dog centric, this site does cater for other animals.

 www.petscorner.co.uk

Railtrack

Probably the most useful site in the UK for train spotters due to the full network timetable.

www.railtrack.co.uk

The Ringing World

If you like bell-ringing, you'll love **The Ringing World**. A journal of bell-ringing with a list of contacts covering every aspect of the hobby.

www.luna.co.uk/~ringingw

Welcome to *The Ringing World* Online. We are now undergoing a major re-development of our web site, and thus most of our information services are temporarily unavailable.

You can still use the online forms to send us your peals, quarter peals and notices; and the *Ringing World* indexes for 1993 - 1999 may also still be used.

If you would like to send us suggestions for the new site please email us at RW@ringingworld.co.uk

Remember - *The Ringing World* gives you a weekly fix of news, gossip and useful information about bell-ringing.

[mail us at RW@ringingworld.co.uk]

Hobbies

Roots Web

The oldest genealogical site on the Net. A great site for advice, guidance and a host of other links.

www.rootsweb.com

RootsWeb.com

- The Internet's Oldest and Largest FREE Genealogy Community. Keep Genealogy FREE. Co
- Hundreds of gigabytes (millions of pages) of FREE genealogy data, with more added every day on file in RootsWeb's WorldConnect Project.
- In a typical month, RootsWeb processes more than 180 million email messages on over 18,000 RootsWeb hosts more than 144,000 message boards and over 12,000 independently authored V
- Home of the RootsWeb Surname List (founded 1988), containing over 806,000 surname entries (founded 1987).
- Subscribe to the RootsWeb Review and Missing Links, the largest genealogy publications in th 397,000 readers.
- Proud sponsor of the largest volunteer genealogy projects on the Web, including: The USGenW WorldGenWeb, GenConnect, Immigrant Ships Transcribers Guild...and many others.

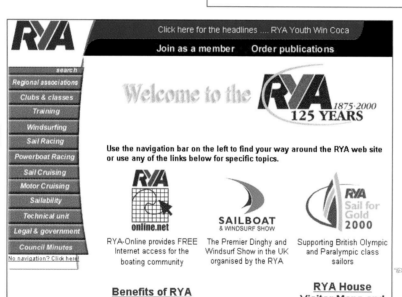

The Royal Yachting Association

The home for any dinghy or yacht sailor in the UK.

www.rya.org.uk

Stanley Gibbons

You can read a brief history on the man himself, and order stamps online.

www.stangib.com

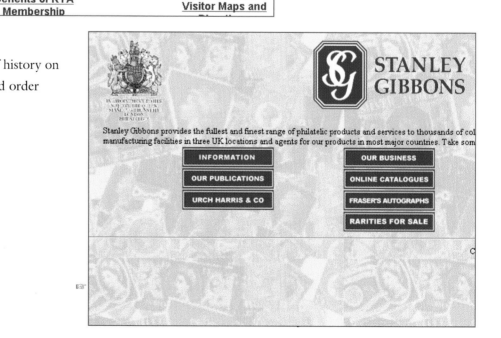

Star Trek.com

The amazing official site for the much-loved sci-fi show.

www.startrek.com

Training Your Dog

This excellent online video training facility takes you through every aspect of dog training.

www.trainingyourdog.com

TV Toys

Extensive selection of TV collectible toys for sale.

www.tvtoys.com

VetServe

A guide to veterinary information and animal ownership in the UK.

www.vetserve.demon.co.uk

Yachting & Boating World

The UK's largest marine portal, with a mass of useful links, including over 1,000 used boats for sale.

www.ybw.com

Motoring

ithin the past year or so, the Internet has been embraced by the motor industry to such a degree that you can now not only find out anything about automobiles and their peripheral sectors, but you can also buy a vehicle online. Everything from your pre-purchase research on new (or used) cars, to cutting out the salesman or dealership and buying your car, can be done on the web. There is a continuing migration of car manufacturers onto the Internet and, along with them, have come a plethora of auto web sites where you can get the specifications, read the latest road tests, and check prices.

In a study from JD Power & Associates, it was found that 40 percent of consumers in the US, who recently purchased a car or truck, used the Internet to shop for the vehicle. This compares to just 25 per cent of consumers in 1998. Over 25,000 buyers a month used the Net to research a new vehicle purchase. The overall figure for those buying new cars who used the Internet as a guide was only 2.6 per cent, but this is a 100 per cent rise on 1998 figures, and indicates that the growth in this sector will be huge.

According to Fletcher Research, the number of UK residents using the Internet in this way has been estimated to reach some 44,000 a month by 2003, representing 20 per cent of the national new

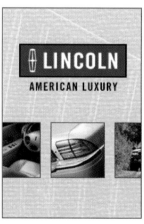

car market. At the moment, British consumers mainly use the Net to inform their purchasing decisions while, in most cases, the actual purchase is made offline. This has been attributed to two main factors. First, the number of sites on the web where you can actually purchase a car has been very low, and second, there is a perceived need for consumers to take a vehicle for a test drive before purchasing.

The second-hand market has also been growing, with the number of sites offering second-hand cars on the increase. Indeed, it has been suggested that the used car market is where the initial boom will come from, as online databases of second-hand cars are easier to use, and cover more of the market than a paper publication can. With classified ad publications you have to search through the pages looking for the right vehicle, price or area, whereas a simple search facility on web sites means a considerable reduction in the amount of time expended.

The Internet has not only facilitated the delivery of vehicle information and car sales, though. Car enthusiasts now have access to endless data about every make and model of car, news about new models and concept cars, as well as a huge gallery of pictures of the favorites. Likewise, any sector connected to the car industry has also moved online, making life easier for motorists. Breakdown clubs, other associations, as well as parts and spares companies, have joined the Net gold rush and some have even set up Internet-only divisions under separate names.

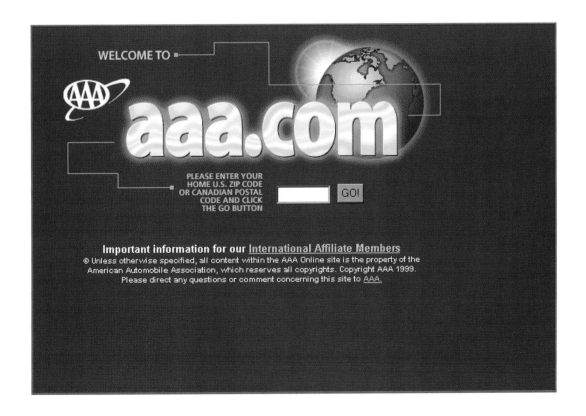

WELCOME TO

aaa.com

PLEASE ENTER YOUR
HOME U.S. ZIP CODE
OR CANADIAN POSTAL
CODE AND CLICK
THE GO BUTTON

GO!

Important information for our International Affiliate Members
® Unless otherwise specified, all content within the AAA Online site is the property of the American Automobile Association, which reserves all copyrights. Copyright AAA 1999. Please direct any questions or comment concerning this site to AAA.

4Car

A great new site from UK broadcaster, Channel 4. You can read from the massive database of road tests and check out the latest news, browse through the site's list of classified ads and check the price of new ones. There are great 'spy shots' of new designs and concepts, and you can even see what a selection of different cars would look like in different colours.

www.4car.co.uk

Autobytel.com

This site has excellent versions for both US and UK online car buyers, as well as a great range of other information. You can get details on makes and models as well as great special offers from manufacturers. **Autobytel** will find you a competitive deal on the car of your dreams, but you'll have to use the telephone to complete the deal.

www.autobytel.com

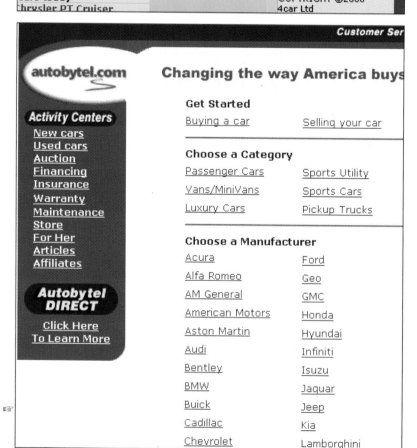

GM

One of the few motor manufacturers in the world that's offering its vehicles for sale on the Net with GM BuyPower. The GM brand covers Pontiac, Cadillac, Chevrolet, Saab Opal, Vauxhall and others. The UK Vauxhall site has special Internet models for sale, at reduced prices, online as part of the BuyPower brand.

www.gm.com

www.vauxhall.co.uk

What Car?

One of the UK's leading car magazine's online presence, this site has the latest information on models and prices. It's a great place to start your car research, as you can compare the specs of different cars, use a search facility to point you in the direction of your nearest new car dealer, and then order brochures and even make an appointment for a test drive.

www.whatcar.co.uk

Motoring

AutoSuggestion

Great independent site with features, news, road tests and the AutoExpert feature that lets you enter the specifications you want in a car, and will then give you a list of cars that conform to your needs.

www.autosuggestion.co.uk

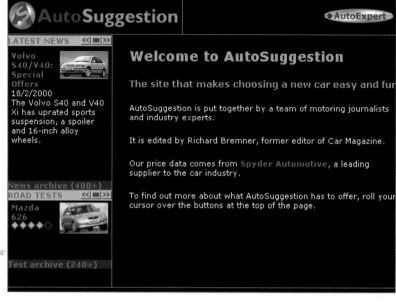

Castrol

This UK motoring portal claims to be a complete guide to motoring, and it does have a wealth of information, services and links.

www.castrol.co.uk

Edmunds.com

US site that will give you the low-down on what you should be paying for a used car.

www.edmunds.com

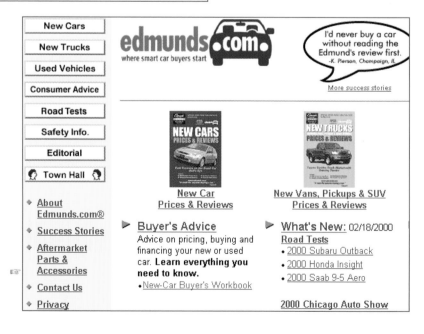

Parkers

The ultimate UK catalog of used car prices. Find out how much you should be paying for that 'old banger', or get a valuation on your own.

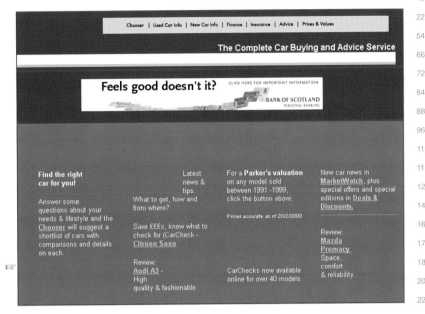

www.parkers.co.uk

Office of Defects Investigation
Recall Database

There are two ways to search the Recall Database. If you wish to use the "drill down" method, choose a year from the drop-down list in the box to the left below and click on the "Submit Year" button. You will then be provided with a list of Makes for the chosen year, and so on for Models. (Please note that for items where the manufacturer did not identify the model year, a date of 1900 was used. Also, when searching for trucks or vans, be sure to include truck with the make, i.e. Ford Truck.) This is a good way to search the Recalls Database if you are unsure of the exact spelling of certain information. However, if you are sure of the *exact* Make, Model and Year information, enter it in the appropriate areas in the box to the right and then click on the "Submit Query" button. Using the text boxes also gives you the flexibility to tailor your queries for specific information (i.e. all Recalls for a particular make and year).

Please note that if you do not find your car listed as you use the pulldown boxes it means we do not have a recall for your car in our database.

No Frames

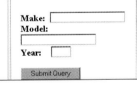

Recall Database

Scary US site that will tell you if the car you're driving has been recalled. One search of the Recall Database (that goes back to 1949) at the National Highway Traffic Safety Administration will tell you whether you're safe or not.

www.nhtsa.dot.gov/cars/problems/
recalls/recmmy1.cfm

Road Trip USA

If you've ever fancied taking a trip across the USA in a convertible, this site will give you an itinerary to work with, as well as point out things to see and do along the way. A true masterpiece.

www.moon.com/road_trip

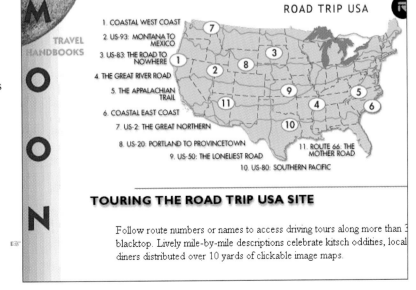

American Automobile Association

Information about AAA membership, benefits, and automotive services.

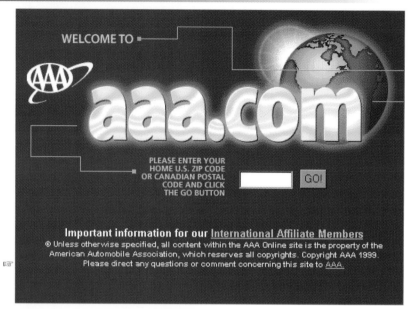

www.aaa.com

The Automobile Association

Not just a breakdown service, the UK's AA also sells insurance, rates hotels and restaurants, and provides a travel news service called Roadwatch.

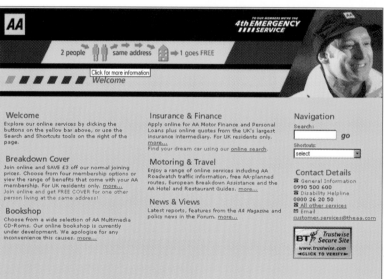

www.theaa.co.uk

Aston Martin

If you've ever drooled over James Bond's DB5, you'll love the company's understated site.

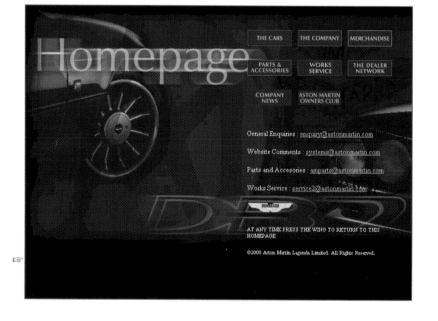

www.astonmartin.com

Autohit

A portal site with links to all manner of other sites covering news, statistics, buying, insurance, spares, private number plates, tax and accidents.

www.autohit.com

Automotive Industry Online

A US industry site where you'll find up-to-the-minute news, and a great section on the history of the car.

www.ai-online.com

AutroTrader

You'll find cars, agricultural vehicles, caravans, mobile homes, vans, HGVs, boats and bikes for sale on this site.

www.autotrader.co.uk

Autoexpress

UK classified ads site with news and previews, as well as a price guide.

www.autoexpress.co.uk

BSM

The UK's leading driving school has a great site including an online theory test. See if you can get 30 out of 35.

www.bsm.co.uk

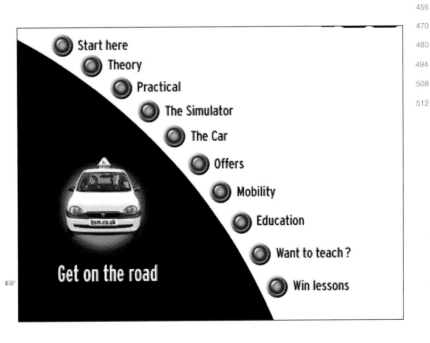

BMW

The German car makers have an excellent site, including a large section on their product placement in the James Bond films.

www.bmw.com
www.bmw.co.uk

Cars & Culture

A cool site for fashion conscious drivers with hip cars featuring resources, games and quizzes.

www.carsandculture.com

Car-Imports

For those in the UK who have to pay more for right-hand drive models, try an imported car from Mazda, Mitsubishi, Nissan, Subaru or Toyota.

www.carimports.com

Car Museums
Great portal site of links to most of the auto museums in the world.

www.team.net/www/museums

Car Safety
Advice about safe driving, what to do in the event of an accident, traveling with children,

www.carsafety.co.uk

Classicar
US site covering every aspect of classic cars, from articles, news and forums, to classifieds, insurance and more.

www.classicar.com

Fish4Cars
Concentrates on the second-hand market with nearly 200,000 vehicles for sale in the UK.

www.fish4cars.co.uk

International Association of Auto Theft Investigators (IAATI)
Get advice on vehicle security from this International organization of law enforcement, and insurance fraud investigators.

www.iaati.org

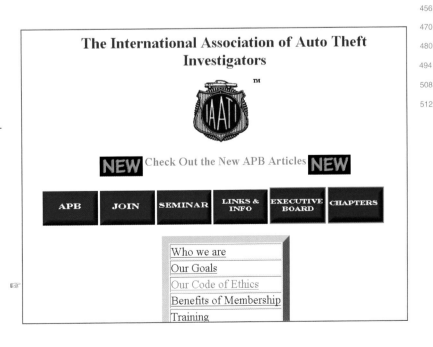

Lincoln

One of the archetypal American car manufacturers has a great site.

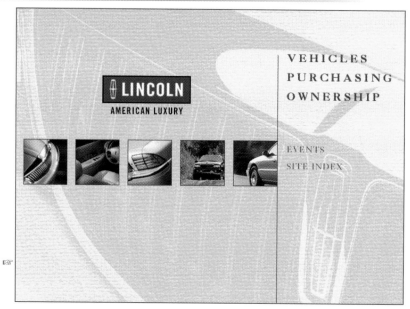

www.lincolnvehicles.com

New Car Net

An independent and unbiased guide to all the new cars in the UK.

www.new-car-net.co.uk

The RAC

Provides UK travel news, hotel guides, and has an excellent Route Planner that will tell you either the fastest, or the shortest, route between two postcodes.

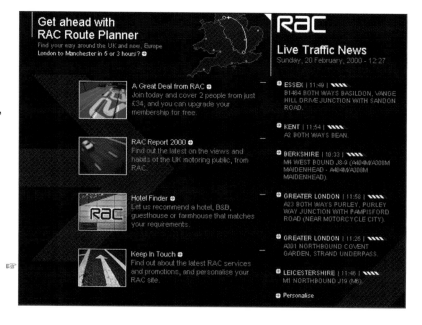

www.rac.co.uk

The WWW Speedtrap Registry

A useful site if you want to travel somewhere in the US in a hurry, as it points out places where speed cops lurk.

www.speedtrap.com

Top Gear

Perhaps the UK's favorite show about things roadworthy, its web site has vehicle tests, the latest news, and a forum.

www.topgear.beeb.co.uk

Volkswagen

Award-winning sites from the German manufacturer attracting attention because of the new Beetle.

www.volkswagen.com

www.volkswagen.co.uk

The Wheel Rack

See what your make, model and color of car would look like with different sets of wheels on it.

www.tirerack.com/wheels/wheel-rack

World Wide Wheels

Outstanding US site featuring a searchable database of cars, car merchandise, auto research tools and more.

www.wwwheels.com

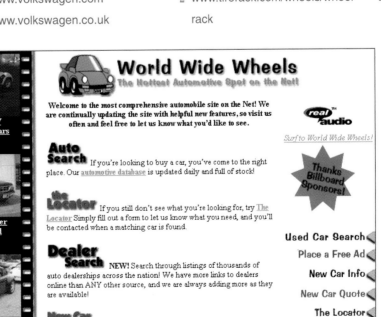

Travel

The travel market is one of the biggest on the Internet. By 2003, over 25 per cent of American households will be booking travel, flights, holidays, and the like via the Internet. This is because it has such a wide appeal. No matter whether you are a budget backpacker, a family of four or a booted and suited business traveller, the Internet has a spectrum of sites all aimed to help you get the best deal when travelling - be it abroad or in your own country.

You will find rough guides to various destinations for those on a budget, speciality sites for those who are into extreme sports, and the latest exchange rates for those globetrotter with currency to change. Business people will find the optimum time to catch their flight for a meeting on the other side of the globe and how to book it online; families will find great family deals as well as details of what jabs you need for what destinations.

One of the best aspects of the Internet is its immediacy. You can go online, find a deal, and book it in a matter of minutes. In the past it has been the job of travel agents to discount vacations and flights as tie runs out for the holiday companies to fill their order books. Now this is possibly the most popular aspect of booking online.

The Internet offers an easier, more sophisticated, and far more enticing deal for consumers. Why trawl down to the travel agents to

find that they don't have the brochure you're after, when doing it all electronically is a breeze? Whether you're booking a holiday, a flight, a hotel room or hiring a car, the Web is hassle-free, cheap and quick.

The Internet can be so cheap, you will scarcely believe it. Because these 'dot coms' have no physical presence and thus no expensive overheads that they have to pass on to the consumer, in Europe you will be able to find flights between major cities for as little as £7.50 (around $12).

Not only will the Internet supply you with the wherewithal to book a trip, it will also provide you with the opportunity to learn the language of the country you are visiting online, point out where you can buy books about your the destination, let you read others' experiences. It even has maps for you to look over.

A2btravel.com

Check the arrival and departure times or book any travel from over 400 airlines, at over 20 airports in the UK and Ireland. The site also has details of some 20 ferry operators, you can convert currencies (including the rate for gold and platinum) and the site provides links to many top holiday sites.

www.a2btravel.com

www.a2bairports.com

www.a2beurope.com

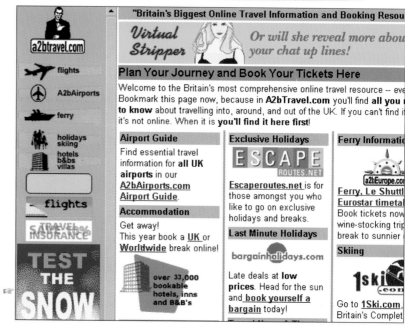

Expedia

If you need to find out about and/or book flights, hotels, cars, vacations, or cruises, **Expedia** covers it all. This is one of the best sites on the Web, and is available in versions that are tailored to the US and the UK markets.

www.expedia.co.uk

Travelocity

Another great site that covers both American and UK interests that lets you 'go virtually anywhere'. Book flights, organise your car hire, reserve a hotel, get weekend deals, and check out the comprehensive destination guide.

www.travelocity.com

www.travelocity.co.uk

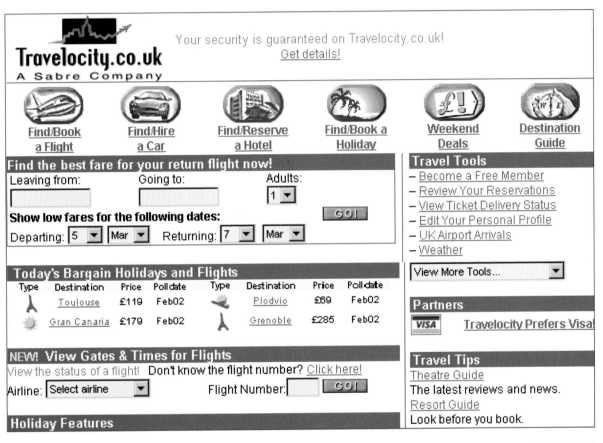

Travel Page.com

Excellent portal site with an astounding number of links and its own content in the form of guides covering every country, thousands of hotels, and resorts, comprehensive cruise line links and information on all major airlines and airports. There are reviews by the site's visitors and you can contribute, too.

www.travelpage.com

Bargainholidays.com

The well-established cut-price holiday site from **EMAP online**. You can get a brochure and book online and with links to its two winter holiday sites, **1Ski** and **Board-It**, the site really is comprehensive.

www.bargainholidays.com

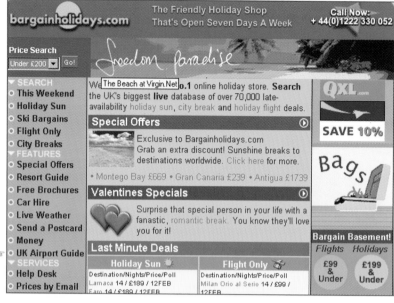

Tourism Offices Worldwide Directory

With an area dedicated tourist offices in the US and one for everywhere else, this site could prove invaluable if you need to find a country's official Web site, address, or phone number.

www.towd.com

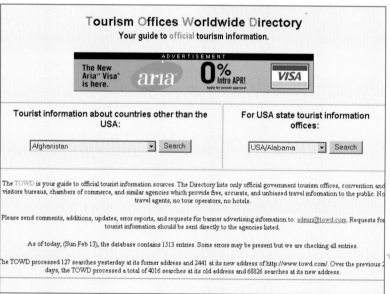

eBookers.com

Book car hire, flights, hotels, and insurance for travel around the globe. There is an auction facility and details on useful stuff like airport parking.

www.ebookers.com

Go Now Travel

The late deals and package holiday sales site from Page & Moy. Although in its early stages, the site will offer car hire, flights, cruises, hotel booking, brochure requests, and insurance. A real one-stop shop.

www.go-nowtravel.com

Lastminute.com

The amazingly successful site with tons of excellent last minute offers – from seats at the theatre and weekends away to seats on planes and full-blown holidays. Covers the UK, France, Germany, and Sweden.

www.lastminute.com

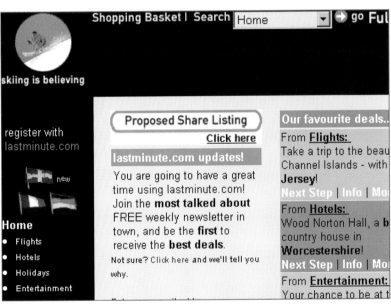

Oneworld

American Airlines, British Airways, Canadian Airlines, Cathay Pacific Airways, Qantas, Finnair and Iberia have banded together to bring better benefits, city guides, and flight details. Only on the Net!

www.oneworldalliance.com

Rentadeal.com

Online car hire reservations from many companies across the US, Canada, Mexico, and Europe. Just say where you need to rent your vehicle and the site will find you a deal.

www.rentadeal.com

Thetrainline.com

Great UK resource for traveling by train. You'll have to register, but you can then check the time tables and book your ticket online.

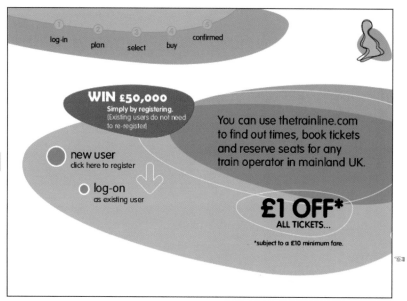

www.thetrainline.com

Travel.com

The indispensable travel search engine and listings site, with links to travel vendors, accommodation, flights, car hire, and packages to names a few.

www.travel.com

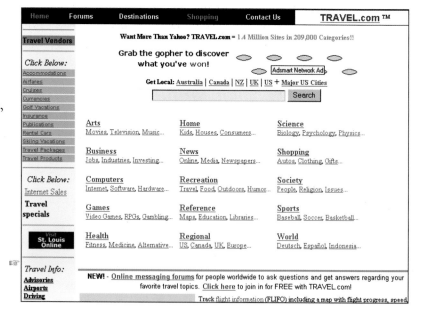

Trrravel.com

Despite the odd name, this UK site has a great deal of valuable content on offer. There are bargains, links, guides to resorts and airports, as well as bookable flights and city breaks.

www.trrravel.com

Vacation.com

Supposedly the US's biggest seller of package tour, adventure holiday or trips that just let you make your own way. There are hundreds to choose from.

www.vacation.com

World Vacations.com

A one-stop shop for all your holiday needs, from planning your vacation to finding out about a destination, to booking a holiday or making reservations at a hotel.

www.worldvacations.com

1Ski.com

The place to go in the UK for your skiing holidays, as this site has nothing but.

www.1ski.com

ABTA

The Association of British Travel Agents is the best known British holiday industry body.

www.abtanet.com

Access-Able

Great site for the disabled or older passenger, with information on companies that cater for them.

www.access-able.com

Aeroflot

Russia's national airline lags behind in the online booking stakes, but the site is useful for its destinations.

www.aeroflot.co.uk

Aer Lingus

The national airline of Ireland has some useful content, but not great technology.

www.aerlingus.ie

Air Canada

Schedules, reservations, package deals - all from **Air Canada**'s home on the Internet

www.aircanada.ca

Air France

The usual mix of flight and holiday information, frequent flyer offers, and online booking.

www.airfrance.com
www.airfrance.co.uk
www.airfrance.fr

Amtrak

The US national train operator has a great site that features times, bookings, offers, routes, and more.

www.amtrak.com

All-Hotels

Not quite as the name suggests, but some 10,000 of them world-wide with online reservation.

www.all-hotels.com

AmericanAirlines

Simple flight schedules and booking site augmented by offers and membership.

www.aa.com
www.americanairlines.com

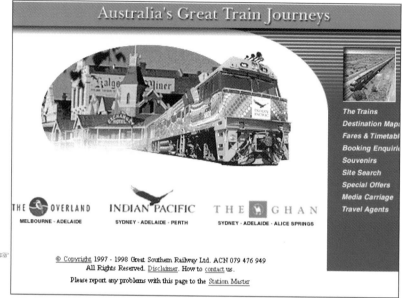

Australia's Great Train Journeys

Check out and book your luxury train journeys across Australia.

www.gsr.com.au

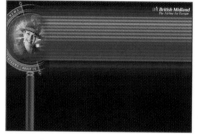

British Airways

Special offers, online booking, and a great customisable city guide.

www.british-airways.com

British Midland

Another airline that has cottoned on to the beauty of online booking and offers.

www.britishmidland.com

Budget Rent-a-Car

Confusing site, but one of the few to offer worldwide information on car hire and booking for most regions.

www.drivebudget.com

Canadian Pacific Railways

Useful site for information on the Canadian rail network.

www.cpr.ca

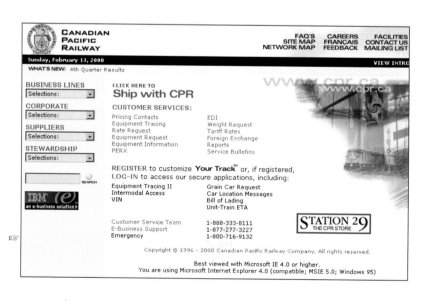

Cathay Pacifc

Good site for those traveling to the Far East, centering on Hong Kong.

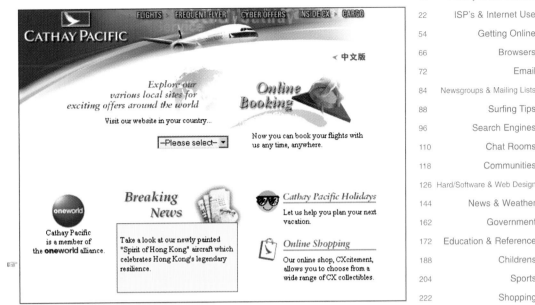

www.cathaypacific-air.com

Continental Airlines

Search for flights, or select the home page that best suits your region.

www.continental.com

Cunard

The site where you'll find the *QE2*, but much more than just a place to find out about one ship.

www.cunardline.com

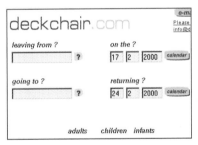

Deckchair.com

Offers simple, cheap flights. That's it, nothing else.

www.deckchair.com

DeltaAirLines

Organise your flight requirements, from reservations to upgrades as well as offers.

www.delta-air.com

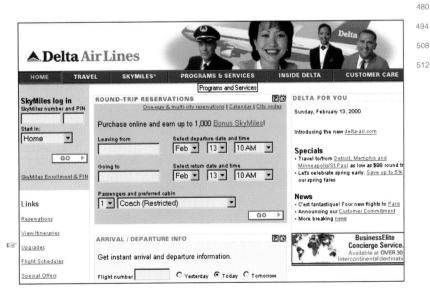

EasyRentacar

Amazingly cheap car hire from the man who brought you amazingly cheap airfares.

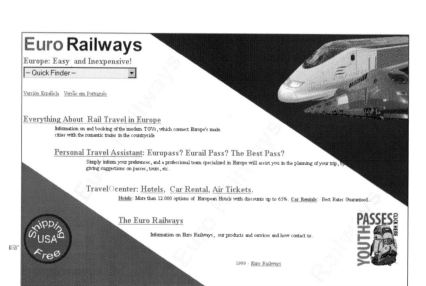

www.easyrentacar.com

EasyJet

Online ticket sales account for up to 25 per cent of easyJet's total ticket sales, which are very cheap.

www.easyjet.co.uk

Emirates

Find out about one of the most luxurious airlines, and soon you'll be able to book online too.

www.emiratesairline.com

Oginet European Camping Index

If you have a tent or caravan and want to camp in Europe, this'll be a good starting place.

www.oginet.com/camping

Euro Railways

Get the low-down on what European rail travel has to offer – particularly for the student.

www.eurorailways.com

eTravel.org

Independent travel news, information and advice. A very good web site.

www.etravel.org

Finnair

The site includes a very quick flight finder and booking.

www.finnair.com

Foreign Languages for Travelers

Incredible site offering online tuition in over 70 languages with categories covering basic words, numbers, shopping, directions, travel, places, and times/dates.

www.travlang.com/languages

Greyhound

The world-famous US bus company has a useful site with maps and online ticket purchasing.

www.greyhound.com

Go

The British Airways subsidiary claims one third of all its sales come from the Net.

www.go-fly.com

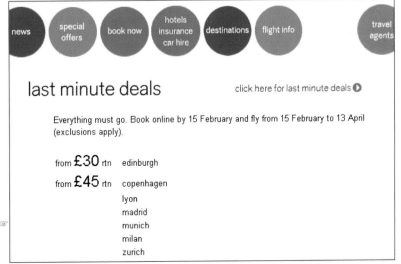

Help for World Travelers
Irrepressible US traveler, Steve Kropla gives advice and help to the globetrotter.

www.kropla.com

HotelGuide.com
A directory of over 60,000 hotels from all over the world.

www.hotleguide.com

Hotel *World*
Search this site's 9,000 hotels from all over the world. You can book most of them, too.

www.hotelworld.com/index.html

KLM Royal Dutch Airlines
Dutch airline with online flight booking and a call-back service.

www.klm.com

LateRooms
If you want to get a cheap hotel anywhere in the world, try this late booking facility.

www.laterooms.co.uk

Leisurehunt

Another hotel search and booking facility, but this one covers the globe.

www.leisurehunt.com

Lonely Planet

The famous travel books have an excellent web site.

Lufthansa

Useful flight information and an online booking facility.

Lunn Poly

One of the UK's most popular travel agents. You can check availability, but you can't book online.

www.lonelyplanet.com

www.lufthansa.com
www.lufthansa.co.uk

www.lunn-poly.co.uk

Luxury link

For some of the most extravagant holidays on the planet can be found here, if you have the money!

www.luxurylink.com

Mapquest

The most amazing maps, from country level, down to street level. Very useful.

www.mapquest.com

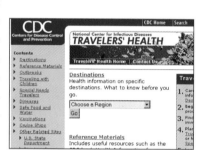

National Center for Infectious Diseases

Choose your destination and this US government web site will tell you what jabs you need.

www.cdc.gov/travel/index.htm

Orient Express

Not just the site of the famous train, you'll find cruises and hotels here as well.

www.orient-express.com

Qantas

Details of arrivals, departures, destinations, and online booking.

www.quantas.com

Railtrack

Useful rail timetable search as well as station news.

www.railtrack.co.uk

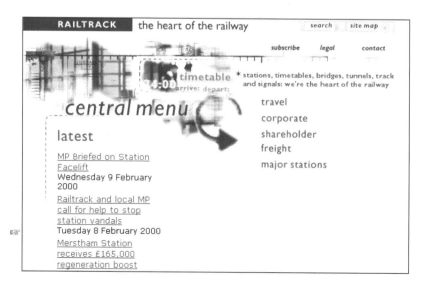

Rough Guides

The archetypal young backpackers travel guides to every destination on the planet.

www.roughguides.com

Ryanair.com

Fly to over 25 destination in Europe and UK for very low prices.

www.ryanair.ie

RV USA

A site especially for those Americans who own or want to own an Recreational Vehicle.

www.rvusa.com

Space Online

UK-based discount fares sites, with flights worldwide.

www.space-online.com

Teletext

UK-centric site offering flight and package deals, with travel advice, weather, and ideas.

www.teletext.co.uk/holidays

Travel

Thomas Cook

One of the UK's major travel agents also has a very good site.

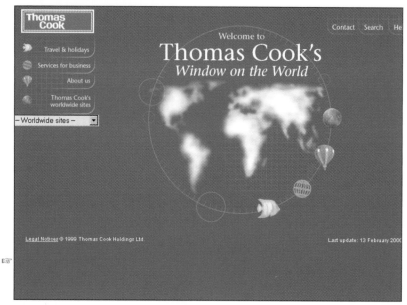

www.thomascook.com

www.thomascook.co.uk

Thomson Holidays

Another of the UK's high street travel shops, offering good services online.

www.thomson-holidays.com

Travel Advice Unit - Foreign & Commonwealth Office

The UK's FCO advises British and western travelers where they should and shouldn't really go on holiday.

www.fco.gov.uk/travel

Travel Health Online

Everything you could need to know about tropical diseases, stomach upsets, and other foreign ailments.

www.tripprep.com

TWA

Schedules, reservations, bookings, and package vacations.

www.twa.com

United

Great online presence from one of the world's best airlines.

www.unitedairlines.com

Virgin Atlantic

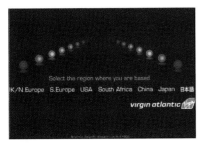

Covering, Europe, the US, South Africa, China, and Japan, Virgin offers competitions along side its online booking.

www.virgin-atlantic.com

The Subway Page

Useful links to many of the world's underground railway systems – from Amsterdam to Zurich.

www.reed.edu/~reyn/transport.html

World Travel Guides

Great guides to the world's countries, includes links to flights, car hire, cruises, and hotel bookings.

www.travel-guides.com

Hostels.com

For those traveling on a budget, this is an indispensable resource.

www.hostels.com

Finance

As it can with so much in life, the Internet can simplify the intricacies of handling your personal finance. We all know that personal finance can be an area of life that is often ignored, purely because it seems to be so difficult to find the right deals, and it ultimately becomes a hassle. Not so on the Internet. No matter what stage of expertise you are at - from novice to professional - the web offers countless sites dedicated to answering your questions.

You will find that no matter with whom you bank, or what company you use for insurance purposes, they will all have web sites, and some will offer financial products over the Internet that they don't on the High Street. You will also find companies that don't even have a presence in the physical world. These are the virtual companies that can offer you cheaper deals and better interest rates, as they don't have the massive overheads of other financial institutions.

Apart from bank accounts, other products such as insurance mortgages and investment trusts are now all available online. For the moment, most pensions have resisted the Internet, but it will only be a matter of time before they join the online revolution. Even so, most pension brokers supply full details and advice on their sites, and you can register your interest. All that's missing is the ability to sign up for them on the web. Instead they email, post, phone or fax you back to complete the transaction.

Imagine that you need a mortgage or a pension. Where would you start in the physical world? You might visit your bank or maybe you know someone who is a financial advisor. How do you know the advice they are giving you is the best? They may be tied to selling one company's products, and contractually obliged not to mention any other products, even though they may suit you better. You could always buy a magazine or a book on the topic. But why spend the money? The Internet can help you with these decisions in an impartial way that won't cost you more than the price of a phone call.

As well as banking and buying financial products, the web has become a hive of activity for those interested in share dealing. In the US, day trading has become a remarkable phenomenon and it is set to do the same in the UK. The development of share dealing on the web is seen by many as the final opening out of what has remained for years a closed preserve of the rich. Now you can invest however much you wish, in whatever stocks and shares you want.

All of this, from checking the balance of your bank account and finding a pension, to sorting out a mortgage or buying and selling shares, is done on your computer. Soon you will be able to do it on your TV or even on your mobile phone. Some have gone as far as to suggest that the Internet might mean the end of notes and coins. I think we've got quite a few years before that becomes true - if it does - but one thing is certain, the personal finance business will never be the same again.

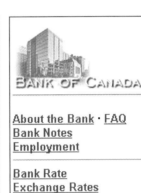

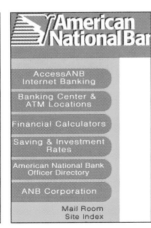

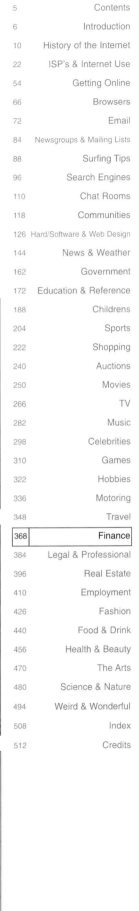

Finance

Bloomberg.com

This US site seems to have every base covered when it comes to monetary advice. Not only are there the usual market analyses, financial product reviews and the like, but Bloomberg also has advice on investing in art and wine. In addition, as Bloomberg has its own TV channel, there are downloadable programs about the companies and products behind the business news.

www.bloomberg.com

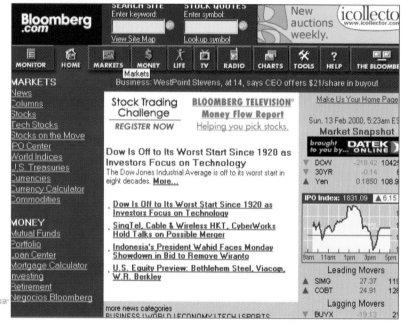

Interactive Investor International

Shrewd and supportive UK site that provides excellent content on a broad range of topics from financial products to its real forte - shares. You can view a share's price as well as a graph of its most recent behavior. There are online polls on topical financial issues, petitions to the Chancellor, and a company brochure request service.

www.iii.co.uk

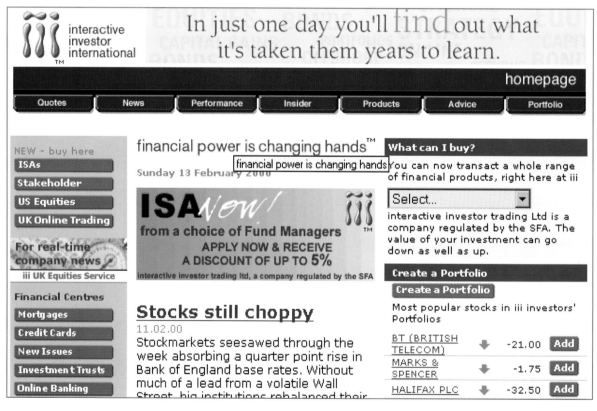

The Motley Fool

Credited with starting the online personal finance and share dealing revolution, **The Motley Fool** now operates in the US and the UK. Its no-nonsense, slightly irreverent approach, coupled with the wide spread of subject matter (although it does concentrate on the investment side), has won 'The Fool' many fans on both sides of the pond.

www.fool.com
www.fool.co.uk

This is Money

Launched in 1999, **This Is Money** is one of the UK's best finance sites. Its great content covers almost everything, from making and saving money to deciding what to spend it on. With an archive of *Daily Mail/Evening Standard* articles, its own ISA advisory center, and a chance to have your own money and legal questions answered online, this site is hard to beat.

www.thisismoney.co.uk

Finance

BankSITE

International directory of banks that also includes consumer guides, interactive calculation tools, and forums.

www.banksite.com

Charles Schwab & Co

A pioneer of online share dealing, **Schwab** offers share dealing in Europe and the US. It may have been one of the first, but it's also still one of the best.

www.schwab-worldwide.com/europe

E*TRADE

If Schwab was the pioneer of online share trading, **E*TRADE** is the next generation snapping at its heels. This site, too, has bases in the UK and the US.

www.etrade.com
www.etrade.co.uk

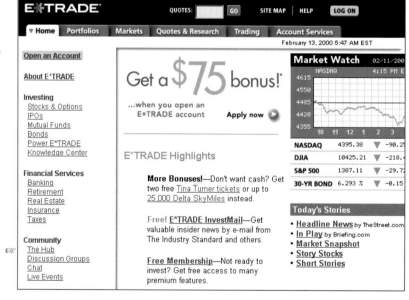

first-e

The original Internet bank has 'branches' in the UK and Germany. It offers a range of accounts and investments, including the new IPO services, to catch those Internet stocks at the first floor.

www.first-e.com

FT Your Money

Recently launched personal finance site from *The Financial Times*. Its great content, and good organisation, makes it the ideal first stop for anyone organising their finances.

www.ftyourmoney.com

Money Advisor

An excellent all-round US site. It has a whole lot of interactivity in the form of financial calculators, and links to a vast array of sites and products.

www.moneyadvisor.com

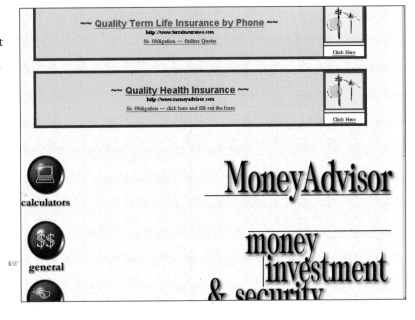

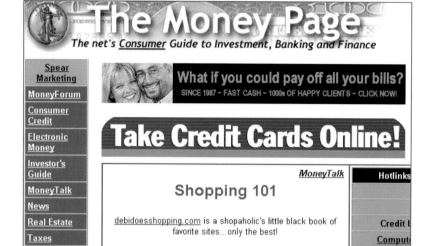

The Money Page

Consumer guide for Net users who need to know about US finance and banking.

www.moneypage.com

mrs cohen.com

With its no-nonsense style, and clear content backed by real financial experts, Mrs Cohen is aimed primarily at the grey market.

www.mrscohen.com

MyStockSite.Com

If the list of sites here doesn't deliver what you're after, try this gem of a site that offers great links from a series of drop-down menus.

www.mystocksite.com

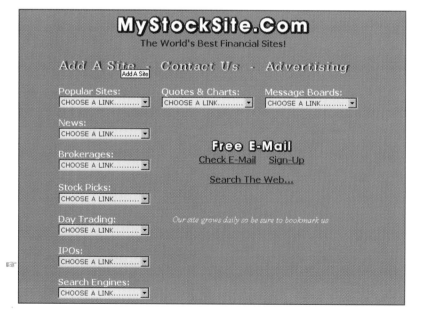

Ostman's IPO Alert

If you need the inside track on initial public offerings (IPOs) - that's company flotations on the stock markets to you and me - this is the place for you.

www.ostman.com/alert-ipo

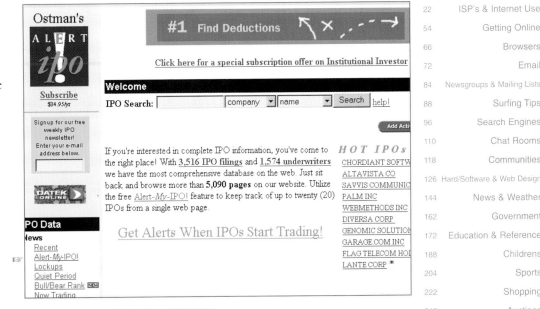

worldlyinvestor.com

Everything the US investor could want to know about the markets, divided up by sector, as well as excellent advice from respected columnists.

www.worldlyinvestor.com

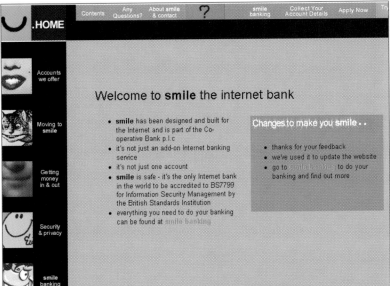

smile

Probably the best dedicated online bank in the UK. Operated by the Co-operative Bank, you can apply, view, and manage your account all online.

www.smile.co.uk

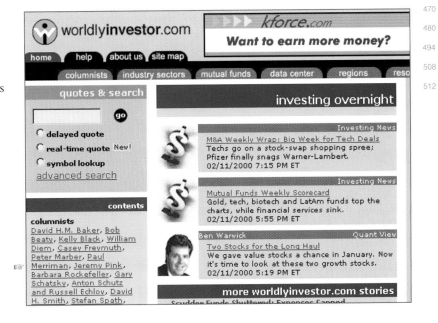

American National Bank

One of the principal US banks with an online banking facility.

www.accessanb.com

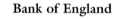

Bank of America

The merger of BankAmerica and NationsBank has produced a nationwide, online financial institution.

www.bankamerica.com

Bank of England

Even more important than it used to be as it sets and alters interest rate levels.

www.bankofengland.co.uk

Bank of Canada

Bank rates, exchange rates, and general statistics for the Canadian financial sector.

www.bank-banque-canada.ca

Barclays Bank

One of the UK's big four banks is also an ISP.

www.barclays.co.uk

Barclays Stockbrokers

Real-time, online dealing from
8.00am to 4.30pm GMT
Monday-Friday.

www.barclays-stockbrokers.co.uk

Egg

Another very good UK Internet
bank account.

www.egg.co.uk

E-Loan

Online mortgages for both the
US and UK markets.

www.eloan/com
www.eloan.com/uk

Federal Reserve Financial Services

Details all the services it provides to US financial institutions.

www.frbservices.org

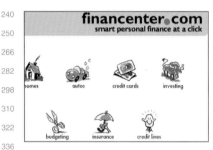

financenter.com

Amazing site with great lists of financial calculators for home and car loans, pensions, return on investments, and a whole lot more.

www.financenter.com

Financial Scandals

Small portal site all about money laundering, scams, and frauds. With hundreds of useful links.

www.ex.ac.uk/~RDavies/arian/scandals

find

Alphabetised lists and descriptions of a huge range of financial products and companies.

www.find.co.uk

Financial Scandals

A Guide with Links to Information Sources

Derivatives, non-existent gold reserves and co[...] have been the stuff of frauds on an almost inc[...] scale. The activities of Nick Leeson, Toshihid[...] Hamanaka and other super star traders have m[...] robbing activities of Jesse James and the outla[...] Wild West seem like pathetic, kindergarten stu[...] comparison. This is a guide with lots of links t[...] these and other lesser-known financial scandal[...] the cases in these pages involve real or suspec[...]

Welcome to

find
financial information net directory

The leading Internet directory for UK financial services.

LAST UPDATED 12/02/2000

Instant on-line share (CFD) trading...

investments — Fund Management Companies

insurance — Insurance Companies

Freequotes.co.uk

The first source of real-time share prices on the Net.

www.freequotes.co.uk

Barclays Stockbrokers
Real-time dealing from £11.99

Enter Stock Code:

—Select—

Stock Code Search
View Hotlist
Edit Hotlist
Charting
Profile
Messageboard
Alerts
News Services
Personal Finance
Financial Directory
Support

	FTSE 100 6193.3 + 0		FTSE All Sha 2944.96 + 0			
Click on an index or stock to view a FREE REAL-TIME QUOTE						
Your Hotlist [Edit] [Refresh] [Stock Code Search]						
Stock	**Mid**	**Change (%)**	**Bid**	**Ask**	**Curr**	**Link**
FRE	769.25 (11FEB)	+ 44.75 (6.18)	Closed	Closed	GBX	
SCO	303 (11FEB)	+ 37 (13.91)	Closed	Closed	GBX	
DUC	3357.5 (11FEB)	+ 370 (12.38)	Closed	Closed	GBX	
IMS	860 (11FEB)	+ 5 (0.58)	Closed	Closed	GBX	
BT.A	1001 (11FEB)	- 21 (2.05)	Closed	Closed	GBX	

Inland Revenue

If you need an explanation of English tax, this is the place to start. It offers PAYE and NIC tables, as well as downloadable self-assessment forms.

www.inlandrevenue.gov.uk

Sunday,

Inland Revenue

Good morning! Welcome to the **Inland Revenue** web site - featuring news and information national insurance matters in the United Kingdom.

The **Inland Revenue** is responsible, under the overall direction of Treasury Ministers, for th administration of income tax, corporation tax, capital gains tax, petroleum revenue tax, inhe national insurance contributions and stamp duties. The Department's job is to provide an tax service to the country and Government.

The Inland Revenue
- What's New
- Press Releases
- Offices
- Helplines & Orderlines
- About Us

Featured Areas
- Self Assessment
- Corporation Tax Self Assessm
- Construction Industry Scheme
- National Insurance Contributio
- Gift Aid 2000
- Electronic Business

IRS

The place to go to find out about US taxation.

www.irs.ustreas.gov

Lloyds TSB

Another of the big four UK banks, recently merged.

www.lloydstsb.co.uk

London Stock Exchange

The best place for UK share ownership and trading details, including NASDAQ, TechMARK and AIM.

www.londonstockexchange.com

MasterCard

A great site, but the best thing is the ATM locator. Just choose a country and it'll find you a cash machine.

www.mastercard.com

Market Harborough Building Society
The first UK broker to offer an Internet-only mortgage, with online application forms.

www.mhbs.co.uk

Merchant Investors

Join the Internet share bonanza by investing in a fund dedicated to Net businesses, such as **Yahoo!** and **eBay**.

www.merchant-investors.co.uk

MoneyWeb
UK personal finance advice and information, and an independent financial advisor finder.

www.moneyweb.co.uk

MoneyWorld UK
Portal site with many links to other finance-related sites and products. Also has an easy-to-use glossary.

www.moneyworld.co.uk

Mortgages-Online
Guides you through the processes involved in getting a mortgage in the UK, and gives comparisons of accounts.

www.mortgages-online.co.uk

NASDAQ

In 1999, it was the stock market for the next millennium. So now it's here, why not check it out?

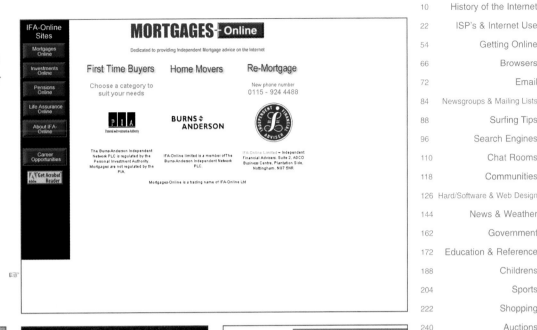

www.nasdaq.com

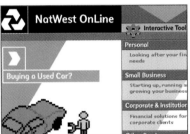

NatWest Online

Recently purchased by the Royal Bank of Scotland, it used to be one of the UK's big four.

www.natwest.co.uk

netISA

Barclays-managed site offering online ISAs investing in Britain's top 100 companies.

www.netisa.co.uk

OANDA – The Currency $ite

Everything you need to know about currencies, including a handy converter.

www.oanda.com

The Royal Bank of Scotland

With a large area dedicated to Internet services, it's not hard to see why this is one of the UK's fastest-growing banks.

www.royalbankscot.co.uk

Save & Prosper

Provides downloadable application forms, reports on its funds, monthly market summaries, and even an audio feed of financial information.

www.prosper.co.uk

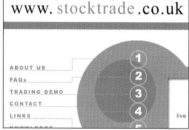

Screen Trade

Online insurance site supplying household, travel, and motor cover.

www.screentrade.co.uk

Stocktrade

UK's first online broker that was launched in 1996.

www.stocktrade.co.uk

Thomson Real Time Quotes

While most sites feature delayed share information, Thomson delivers it all in real time.

http://rtq.thomsoninvest.net/index.sht

UK Online Investing

Portal with UK stockbroker commission tables, 2,000 UK company reports, and stock forecasts.

www.ukonlineinvesting.com

Virgin direct

The online bank account and financial products from Sir Richard Branson's company.

www.virgin-direct.co.uk

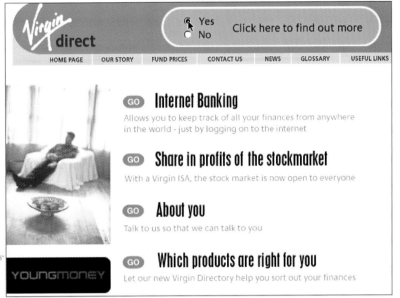

VISA

Much like MasterCard, Visa has a good site with a great ATM locator.

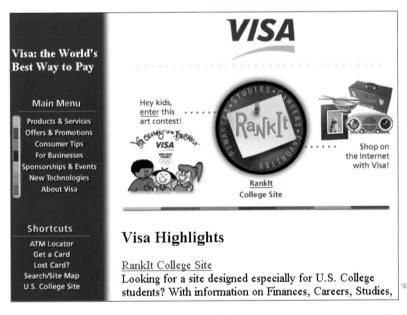

www.visa.com

www.wisemoney.com

Excellent UK site for beginners covering loans, mortgages and insurance. Also has a financial services' search engine.

www.wisemoney.com

Legal & Professional

In the world of business you can only stay ahead if you stay informed. Fortunately, there's no other media that is more immediate than the Internet. If a rival's, or your own, stock prices rise all of a sudden, or if news comes in that a law has been passed that might endanger a product or market, you can act on it immediately.

Many directors use a scrolling banner of headlines called 'news tickers', so they never miss a thing. And considering the names on the Net - the **FT**, **Bloomberg**, *Business Week* and *The Economist* to name a few - you know that the information will be reliable.

It is always amazing that this quality of news is not only so immediate but also entirely free. This unique quality of the Net does not just hold true for news either. You can find the best in company information and marketing research - all for free. Some sites do ask a fee for these services, but if you are unprepared to pay, another site that offers the same - or similar - information for free, is just a mouse click or two away.

Some of the information carried by business sites amounts to nothing less than online tutorials in better management, marketing, finance, human resource, and customer relationship management. Because the success of a site is dependent on how many people visit, and how long they stay, information providers are keen to ensure that their content is as good, and as thorough, as possible. Management magazines are a particularly good case in point.

This amazing offer of great information for free does not just extend to business specific material. Possibly the most expensive kind of advice a business has to pay for is legal advice, but again the Internet can ride to the rescue - if you know where to look. Just as there are business sites that want to attract you as a visitor, so there are legal sites seeking the same goal. To keep you on the site, they are willing to give up a certain level of information for free. You will also find any number of legal-to-legal portals and search facilities that offer services that otherwise might have cost you money - such as legal procedures.

The widespread nature of the Net means you can check all this information, not only in your own country, but also anywhere in the world. And the information doesn't end at business news, legal advice, and company information. You will also find that governments are very keen on buoyant economies, and part of keeping them buoyant is to keep their constituent industries informed as to the latest law and practice requirements.

In effect the Internet can be a very valuable business advisor to you, with a wealth of experience and knowledge far beyond the capability of one company - let alone an individual. Handled correctly the business information you'll find on the sites listed here may well keep you one step ahead of the competition.

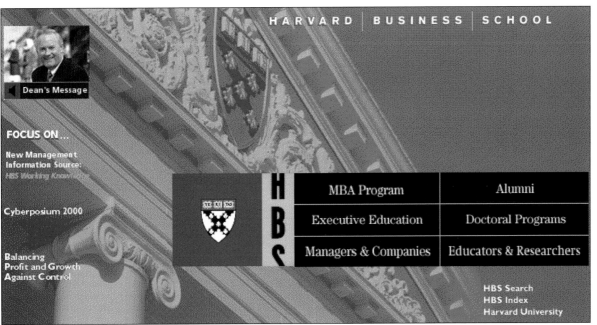

Legal & Professional

American Bar Association

Claims to be the world's largest voluntary professional membership association. Features include law student resources, legal and professional resources, and a section on international law. It also contains a business lawyer section that includes case law, book reviews, and listings of recent literature.

www.abanet.org

Business Link

A very useful site for anyone involved in any type of business. By being linked to a network of advice centers, and business services, it is able to offer good support, and help you with a fair amount of business needs. Some its many services include business abroad, developing your business, financial management, starting a business, and selling and marketing tips.

www.businesslink.co.uk

Welcome to the Business Link National Site

 go go go

Business Link National Web Site

It's our business to help your business

Business Link Services   Find your local Business Link   What does BLNC do?

CyberSpace Law Center

Excellent resource of legal precedents for those interested in the business side of the law - particularly involving the Net. You'll also find legal news, a search engine, and even an interactive course on how to find legal content on the web.

www.cybersquirrel.com

Smartbiz.com

Thousands of free how-to resources geared specifically to business from America's top writers, books, and publications. Just type in the keyword and away you go. There are sections covering jobs, trade shows, hot tips, and you can even subscribe to a free email newsletter keeping you abreast of what's new.

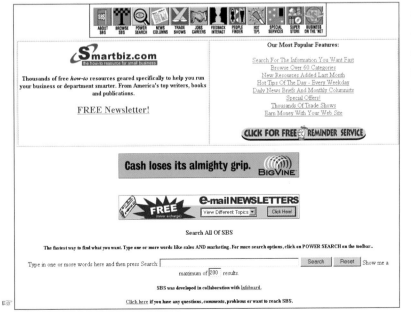

www.smartbiz.com

Legal & Professional

Bizreference.com

Aimed at small business owners, consultants and business free-lancers, this site acts as a 'virtual back office' - assisting with the day-to-day running and improvement of your firm.

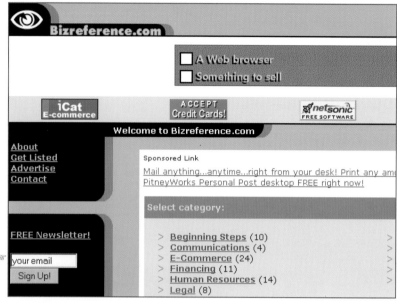

www.bizreference.com

Bloomberg.com

For the latest and best in US-centric business news, **Bloomberg** has to be a first port of call. It offers a broad range of market-related headlines and in-depth coverage.

www.bloomberg.com

Business Owner's Toolkit

Outstanding small home office site that has a wealth of content - running the gamut from starting out with a small business, to selling, or just plain 'getting out'.

www.toolkit.cch.com

The Economist

Content from the latest issue of this revered magazine, mixed with archive material including special reports covering subjects such as the Internet.

www.economist.com

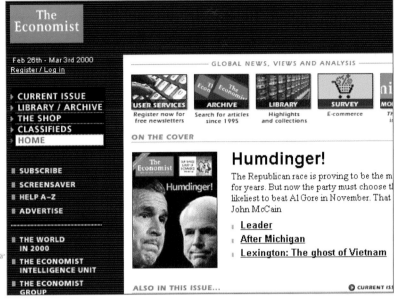

Entrepreneurial Edge

If you're an entrepreneur in need of support, this site will act as your bible and agony aunt rolled into one.

www.edgeonline.org

UK business Net

Many hundreds of links to business events, courses, news, resources, trade links, individual company information, and more, from all over the Net.

www.ukbusinessnet.com

Legal & Professional

Allbiz.com

UK local and national company listings, with descriptions and links to the web sites of those included.

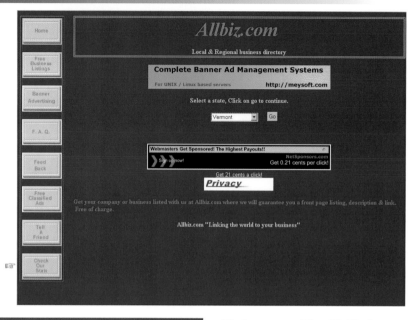

www.allbiz.com

@brint.com - The BizTech Network

Outstanding portal site that offers free membership, a wide range of resources, and a personalisation option.

www.brint.com

Business Resource Center

US-based resource for general help and business planning, including some very useful document templates.

www.morebusiness.com

BusinessWeek online

All the latest business news with a US bent.

www.businessweek.com

CBI

Great resource for UK businesses from the self-proclaimed 'voice of employers', the Confederation of British Industries.

www.cbi.org.uk

City 2000 Legal Index

A handy listings site for London's city lawyers that covers bailiffs, forensic scientists, legal back-up services, and more.

www.city2000.com/legal/index.html

DTI

With a good range of information for small businesses, employees and consumers in the UK, the Department of Trade

www.dti.gov.uk

Ernst & Young Business Innovation

Useful articles, and even a forum, from Ernst & Young's consulting services.

www.businessinnovation.ey.com

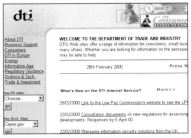

Legal & Professional

Fast Company

Wide-ranging magazine site with lots of content from the paper version, as well as a community area and a careers' section.

www.fastcompany.com

Federation of Small Businesses

Articles and news stories with a focus on the smaller firm in the UK.

www.fsb.org.uk

FindLaw

Comprehensive US legal search facility and listings site that covers everything from the constitution downward.

www.findlaw.com

Fish4It

Very clear and thorough listings service of UK businesses. No matter what service you need, you'll find someone to help you here.

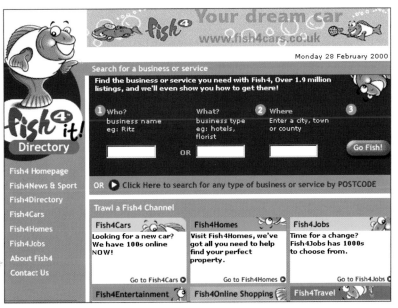

www.fish4it.co.uk

FT.com

Recently redesigned, the new FT site has a wide range of useful resources for business people, and those with an interest in business or personal finance.

www.ft.com

Harvard Business School

Find out what it takes to get into one of the best business schools in the world.

www.hbs.edu

Inc.com

US entrepreneurial magazine that's widely recognised as the leader in serving the needs of American small businesses.

www.inc.com

Interactive Investor International

As much financial information and advice as a business could need - all in one place.

www.iii.co.uk

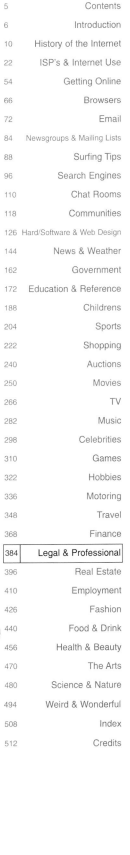

Legal & Professional

Internet Legal Resource Guide

As the name suggests, a thorough listing of resources on the web. It contains research from all over the world including the UK, Canada, and Australia.

www.ilrg.com

MAIN INDEX
Text Only

NEW!
Forms Archive

Academia:
Law Journals
Law Outlines
Law Schools
Law Students
Pre-Law
Study Abroad

Professional:
Associations
CLE
Experts
Forms Archive
Forms Index
Lawyers/Firms
Practice Areas

USA Research:
Fed. Executive
Fed. Judicial
State Index

Global Research:
World Index
Australia
Canada
United Kingdom

Other:
Legal Indices
Legal Usenet
News Sources

ILRG:
About ILRG
Awards/Honors
Founders
Guest Book

Internet Legal Resource Guide

Welcome to the **Internet Legal Resource Guide**™. A categorized index of more than 4000 select web sites in 236 nations, islands, and territories, as well as more than 850 locally stored web pages and downloadable files, this site was established to serve as a comprehensive resource of the information available on the Internet concerning law and the legal profession, with an emphasis on the United States of America. Designed for everyone, lay persons and legal scholars alike, it is quality controlled to include only the most substantive legal resources online. The selection criteria are predicated on two principles: the extent to which the resource is unique, as well as the relative value of the information it provides.

[   ] [All Areas of Site ▾] [Search] Enhanced Search

4,500 New Definitions   Click Here to Buy!

Annotated Index of Features:

Legal Profession:

I   ILRG Legal Forms Archive
   A locally maintained archive of more than eighty legal forms. Keyword searchable.
II America's Largest 250 Law Firms
   Visit the web sites of the largest 250 law firms in the United States. Compiled by the New York Law Publishing Company, this listing of law firms is known as the *National Law Journal 250*.
III ILRG Web Index: Off-site web resources indexed.
   1. Continuing Legal Education—Index to the CLE resources on the web. See also the Index to CLE State Requirements (USA).
   2. Lawyers & Law Firms—Features ILRG's index of lawyers & law firms, law firms rankings, essential lawyer locate databases including the West Legal Directory and the Martindale-Hubbell Lawyer Locator, legal employment databases, and a listing of other major web indices of law firm web sites.
   3. Legal Associations—Non-profit associations and organizations on the web, including professional associations at the local, state, national, and international levels. Also featured is an intelligent agent-based .ORG search.
   4. Legal Experts—Index to sources on the web to locate a legal expert and other consultants.
   5. Legal Forms Sources—In case you do not find the legal form you need within the ILRG database, check here for a listing of all known sources for law-related forms on the web.
   6. U.S. Corporate & Business Forms, Filing Instructions—Check here to find a comprehensive index to legal forms that have been promulgated by U.S. state governments, as well as links to the applicable corporations act and other information helpful to the registry

The IoD aims to be the prime organisation helping directors to fulfil their leadership responsibilities in creating wealth for the benefit of business and society as a whole. The IoD has 50,000 members in the UK, with members on the boards of three-quarters of the Times Top 100 companies, while 65 per cent are directors of small and medium-sized companies.

Website

Member Login
Membership
Products & Services
Professional Development
Policy
Job opportunities
Shopping
New to the Internet?
Contact Us
Search
Feedback
Location map

INNOVATE OR DIE

Annual Convention to champion innovation
An impressive gathering of business speakers will address the Annual Convention which will examine the premise that UK companies must "Innovate or Die".

A key speaker will be one of the 1990's greatest innovators and huge start-up success, Stelios Haji-loannou. Having grown discount airline easyJet from two aircraft at Luton airport in 1996 to one of Europe's most successful budget airlines, Haji-loannou launched the world's largest internet café last summer in Victoria, London.

Stelios Haji-Ioannou

Press R

IoD say:
needed fo
National
Banks
improve q
IoD
Credit c
back e-co
survey
UK reta
the Intern
understan
products s

New on

Airport
UK city
Memb

IoD

The Institute of Directors' home page offers membership, support, and news for company directors world-wide.

www.iod.co.uk

'Lectric Law Library

Thorough online library of legal features, concentrating on the business sector.

www.lectlaw.com

The 'Lectric Law Library™

Welcome To The
'LECTRIC LAW LIBRARY

Quite simply the best legal resource that we have come across on the Web. - CNN Wonders of the Web

Hi Visitor! I'm Ralf Rinkle, the Library's beloved Head Librarian, respected Legal Scholar in Residence & admired Chief Counsel.

If this is your first visit you'll want one of our beautiful Library Cards. Hey, Don't Worry! It's FREE & there's NO REGISTRATION or forms to fill out! Just come with me on a short tour that'll explain the basics so you don't get lost or in trouble when you're on your own. And since I revise & update it at least constantly I urge you "regulars" to come along for a refresher.
* *"Ralf's Tour was absolutely the greatest experience of my life by far!"* -- Usual Visitor Reaction *

OK, just follow me for my 'LECTRIC LAW LIBRARY TOUR. . . . Oh yeah! If you run into some scrofulous, shady looking characters inside, don't freak-out or call the net-police. They're probably just lawyers or judges, and are usually quite harmless . . . at least outside a courtroom.

And you folks who've taken the new Tour can just wipe your feet and go right into
The ROTUNDA.

Si a jure discedas vagus eris, et erunt omnia omnibus incerta.
If you depart from the law, you'll wander without a guide, and everything will be uncertain to everyone.

Informative and entertaining. Who could ask for anything more from a Web site?...a first-rate Web site that should be in the

New Business Kit

Very clean and concise web site from chartered accountants, Sanders & Shaw, aimed at those just getting their businesses up and running.

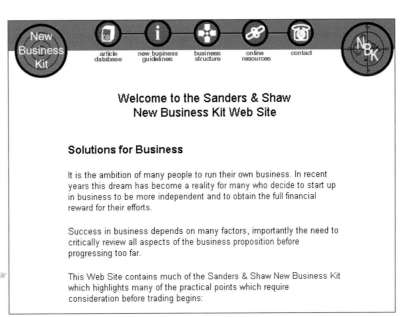

Welcome to the Sanders & Shaw New Business Kit Web Site

Solutions for Business

It is the ambition of many people to run their own business. In recent years this dream has become a reality for many who decide to start up in business to be more independent and to obtain the full financial reward for their efforts.

Success in business depends on many factors, importantly the need to critically review all aspects of the business proposition before progressing too far.

This Web Site contains much of the Sanders & Shaw New Business Kit which highlights many of the practical points which require consideration before trading begins:

www.new-business.co.uk

Real Business online

Similar to **Inc.com** for the UK market, the site features a huge array of very useful content culled from the paper version of the magazine.

www.realbusiness.co.uk

SBA

The US government Small Business Administration has a plethora of information covering every base of business management.

www.sba.gov

Smallbizsearch.com

Aimed at SMBs in the UK finding other small businesses, but includes other resources.

www.smallbizsearch.com

Where2go

Where to go if you need to find a specific business or service online.

www.where2go.com

Buying and selling property has always been a complicated, costly and time-consuming business, but the advent of the web and what it can do has - to a certain degree - changed all that. In the mid-Nineties, estate agents or realtors, were slow to identify the potential of the medium, and even feared that it would put them out of business as pundits predicted death for any company with 'agent' in its business description.

That has not held true for estate agents, and most companies have recognised the huge benefits they can derive from Internet technologies. Instead of destroying the real estate brokers businesses, e-commerce has simply changed it. Those who do not know what the web can do - and that's almost everyone - are still happy to view basic details of a property. So most online estate agencies still only display prices, location and description, accompanied by a single photograph.

The potential has hardly been tapped and you can expect to see big changes in the very near future. So what is possible? The basic answer is a whole lot more than most sites have up there at the moment. Most only extend the interactivity of their sites to a searchable database of properties. Some of these only allow you to enter a single item of search data, such as the number of bedrooms or the level of price, rather than a range of criteria, which would speed up and narrow your search.

Away from searching, what can you do once you have found your property? Again, most sites do what their high street counterparts do, but you can have 360-degree picture technology, with areas such as doors that you can click on to move to the next room. Some might prefer a video tour with a voice over by an estate agent or, even better, a surveyor. And why just have the address of a property when you could have a map, a satellite image, and a list of local details like crime figures, tax rates, school league tables, etc?

These things can be, and in some cases are, done right now, but there are many other things you will be able to do in the not too distant future. You will be able to find the property you want, arrange a mortgage, employ legal services and hire a moving company. If you really don't want to, you will not even have to physically visit the property you are buying. With sites such as **Really Moving** (www.really-moving.com) in the UK, we are almost at that stage now.

Property Search

Neighborhood Information

Mortgage Information

CENTURY 21® Connections

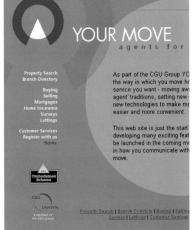

THE HOMEDIRECTORY

75,000 properties online, more than any other site in the UK!

:H for your new home online!

G? Everything you need to help you move home.

\L TOURS

HomeAdvisor

ome Page | Getting Started | N

Download 1999 tax forms

MoneyCentral

op for Rates* 2/5
- 30-yr fixed 7.875%
- 15-yr fixed 7.500%

Hom
Find an
homes 1
and apɛ

Century 21

Possibly the biggest online property search facility in the US, backed up by some great functions such as a neighbor-hood information resource, and a mortgage quotation finder. **Century 21** also gives you tips on moving home, buying prop-erty for investment, and a glossary of real estate terms.

www.century21.com

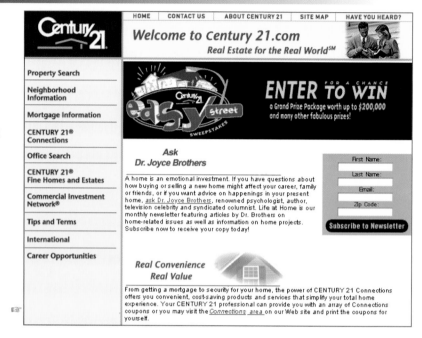

Coldwell Banker

One of the very best US real estate sites. It has a nationwide proper-ty search facility, a mortgage checker, and an exclusive service designed to help you manage the details of buying and selling your home before, during, and after your move.

www.coldwellbanker.com

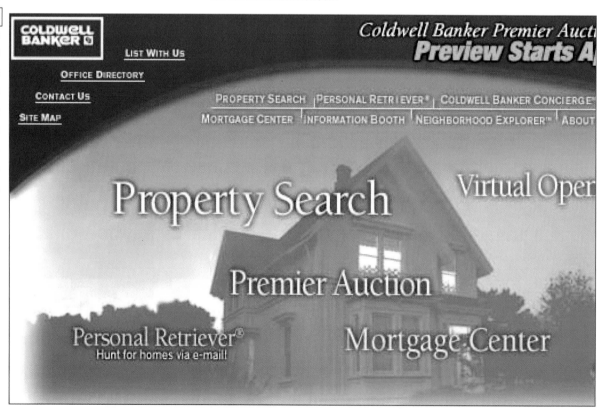

Reallymoving.com

Offers a unique service in the UK covering all elements associated with moving home - from finding a property, to instant quotes from solicitors, removal companies, surveyors, insurance, cleaning companies, etc. It's free, and you can get online quotes for each of these services at any time of day or night.

www.reallymoving.com

Winkworth

One top UK estate agent really showing the world how it could and should be done. Using the 360-degree technology of Ipix, you can take a virtual tour of the company's top properties on offer. Once past this though, the site does stray back into the 'one picture and a description' format.

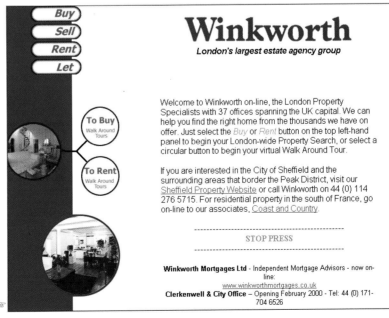

www.winkworth.co.uk

Fish4Homes

Search through what is claimed to be the biggest resource of properties in the UK (more than 90,000). Good search facility, poor delivery.

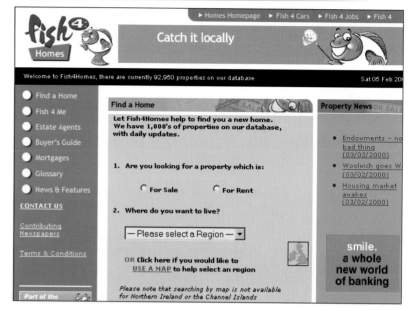

www.fish4homes.co.uk

Hamptons International

This well-known UK site also deals in property from Spain, France, Italy, Portugal, Cyprus, the Caribbean, Singapore and Hong Kong.

www.hamptons.co.uk

HM Land Registry

Although you cannot find out who owns what land online, you can download and print off forms to find out by post.

www.langreg.gov.uk

The Home Directory

Over 75,000 UK properties to search through and good advice on moving and mortgages. You can also take a virtual tour of some areas.

www.homedirectory.com

THE HOMEDIRECTORY

HomeDirectory

Home
Login
Search
3D Images
Moving
Join
Help

75,000 properties online, more than any other site in the UK!

- **SEARCH** for your new home online!
- **MOVING?** Everything you need to help you move home.
- **VIRTUAL TOURS**
  Explore Colchester in 360 degrees. NEW!
- **JOIN** for updates of new homes matching YOUR

This Week on IRED:

Is Standing Falling? Lieberman
April Cybertips Peckham
Perspective: Poland Mitropolitski
Prospecting Databases Zeller
Competitive Cutting-Edge Mr. Internet
Pocket Listing 101 Blackstone
Tax Season Alice Held

ired.com
INTERNATIONAL REAL ESTATE DIGEST
The World's Foremost On-Line Real Estate Magazine

The Directories
US Real Estate
World Real Estate
Consumer Services
Agents' Services
Submit a Site
Enhance it!

Features
Builders
Buyers Agents
Discount Brokerage
Finance
For Sale by Owner
Software

Prime Locations the best!
Attitude!
Web-Biz
Site Map
  Search IRED
  About IRED

Send comments and new or broken link reports to becky@ired.com
For advertising info e-mail sales@ired.com
@ 1995-2000 IRED.Com, Inc.
817-481-4877 Fax-817-488-3693

International Real Estate Digest

If you are after a real estate agent online, this should be one of your first stops. Over 30,000 links.

www.ired.com

Irish Property News

One of the best property sites dealing in Irish homes, for sale or rent. Lots of content and an excellent search facility are the outstanding features.

www.irishpropertynews.com

Knight Frank

Good central hub with property links to Africa, Asia, Australia, Europe, North America, and the UK. Also covers commercial sales and rentals.

www.knightfrank.co.uk

RealEstate.com

An amazingly broad site covering 15 countries in Europe and North America. Excellent content, help and tips, as well as mortgages and property experts' advice.

www.realestate.com

The Real Estate Library

Contains essential resources for buyers, sellers, homeowners, real estate professionals, and anyone seeking to connect with the world of real estate.

www.relibrary.com

Realtor.com
Covers every aspect of buying, selling, moving and owning your home that you could want to know about.

www.realtor.com

Up My Street
Almost anything you could wish to know about the area you live in, or one you might be moving to, in the UK.

www.upmystreet.com

Virtual Res.com
America's virtual **Real Estate Store** has the biggest list of US links, and some great advice for buying and selling a home.

www.americas-real-estate.com

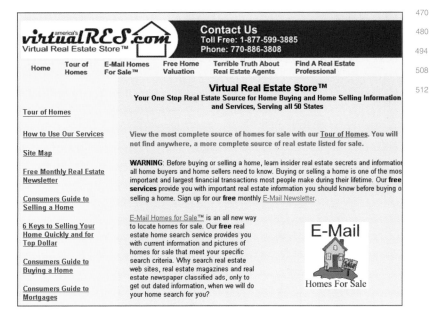

Eurocom

Specialises in apartments in London or continental Europe, and student accommodation.

SERVICED APARTMENTS IN LONDON

STUDENT ACCOMMODATION IN LONDON

SERVICED APARTMENTS IN EUROPE

Euracom has many years of experience of booking Serviced Apartments in London and now also arranges apartments in major European cities together with Student Residences in London at budget prices.

Apartments in London - Student Residences in London - Apartments in Europe

EXCLUSIVE INTERNET OFFER ON LONDON APARTMENTS 5% DISCOUNT ON OUR STANDARD RATES WHEN YOU BOOK ONLINE!

www.euracom.co.uk

Find a Property

Over 8,000 properties advertised by agents in the UK, Spain, Portugal, and France.

www.findaproperty.com

Haart

Useful site, despite lack of images, but (like a good real estate agent) will offer you houses outside your price range.

www.haart.co.uk

HouseWeb

Good UK portal with some excellent information. Its property listings, however, are limited.

www.houseweb.co.uk

Home Hunter

One of the first online-only UK estate agencies and still going strong.

www.homehunter.co.uk

Welcome to Home Hunter, the UK estate agent that is online for you, 24 hours a day, seven days a week. Buying and selling your property may be among the most costly procedures you'll ever undertake - so let us cut the costs for you. With Home Hunter, it costs you nothing to search for the property that you want, in the place and price range of your choice. Or, if you have property for sale, you can place an entry in our housing list at a minimal fee (for a little more, you can expand your entry to include images and other information).

Home Hunter is easy to use. If you are

Homes.com

US site that covers the entire country, with some excellent content too.

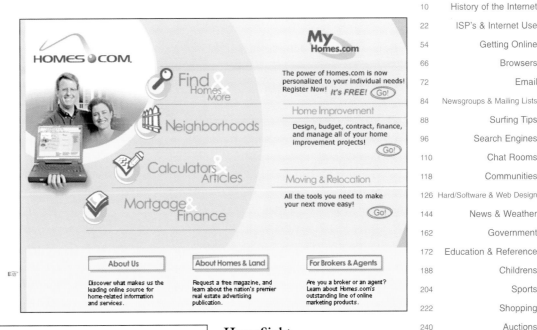

www.homes.com

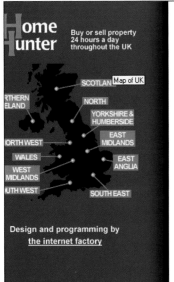

Home Hunter

Buy or sell property 24 hours a day throughout the UK

SCOTLAND
NORTHERN IRELAND
NORTH
YORKSHIRE & HUMBERSIDE
EAST MIDLANDS
NORTH WEST
WALES
WEST MIDLANDS
EAST ANGLIA
SOUTH WEST
SOUTH EAST

Map of UK

Add a property   Contact us

Design and programming by the internet factory

Welcome to Home Hunter, the UK estate agent that is online for you, 24 hours a day, seven days a week. Buying and selling your property may be among the most costly procedures you'll ever undertake - so let us cut the costs for you. With Home Hunter, it costs you nothing to search for the property that you want, in the place and price range of your choice. Or, if you have property for sale, you can place an entry in our housing list at a minimal fee (for a little more, you can expand your entry to include images and other information).

Home Hunter is easy to use. If you are looking for property to buy, click on the labels on the map of the UK on the left to select the area of the UK where you wish to buy (or, if you prefer, use the text links). This will take you to a screen where you

HomeSight

Similar to **Up My Street**, but offers slightly different information about an area.

www.homesight.co.uk

ITL HomeSearch

One of the largest and most comprehensive property sites in the UK.

www.itlhomesearch.com

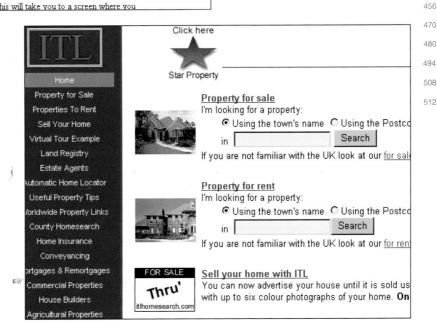

ITL

Home
Property for Sale
Properties To Rent
Sell Your Home
Virtual Tour Example
Land Registry
Estate Agents
Automatic Home Locator
Useful Property Tips
Worldwide Property Links
County Homesearch
Home Insurance
Conveyancing
Mortgages & Remortgages
Commercial Properties
House Builders
Agricultural Properties

Click here

Star Property

Property for sale
I'm looking for a property:
◉ Using the town's name ◯ Using the Postcode
in [   ] Search
If you are not familiar with the UK look at our for sale

Property for rent
I'm looking for a property:
◉ Using the town's name ◯ Using the Postcode
in [   ] Search
If you are not familiar with the UK look at our for rent

FOR SALE
Thru'
itlhomesearch.com

Sell your home with ITL
You can now advertise your house until it is sold using with up to six colour photographs of your home. **On**

Listing Link

Well-established US site, with over 10,000 agents, and a nationwide reach.

http://listinglink.com

Luxury Property.com

With affiliates in Europe, the US and the Pacific, this site is worth a look, if only to dream of the properties on offer.

www.luxuryproperty.com

Microsoft Home Advisor

Useful site from the software company - especially the glossary of real estate terms.

http://homeadvisor.msn.com

Moving.com

US site that aims to help you move as easily and speedily as possible.

www.moving.com

The National Association of Estate Agents

Deals with everything about being, or dealing with, an estate agent in the UK.

www.naea.co.uk

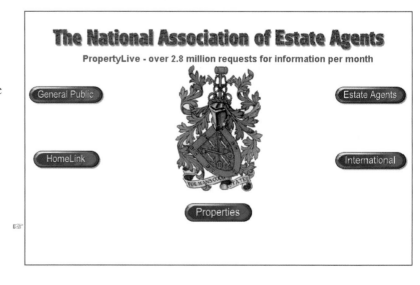

Nerex

You need to register, but this email service operates in both the US and the UK.

www.nerex.com

nerex

Buying or S...
Find out why 75,000 p...

Properties and Finance on...

Click Here To Find Out About Nerex

Members Login
MEMBER ID [   ]
PASSWORD [   ]
[ENTER]

Forgotten Your Login?
Enter Your Email Address
[   ] [ENTER]

SELLING A PROPERTY?...
Use Nerex to contact 1000's of bu...
Click here to start using Nerex.

LOOKING TO BUY?....
Pre-qualify online for a mortgage a...
commercial property for sale in yo...
using Nerex.

GOT A WEBSITE?....
Give us a link or display our banne...
Click here to start earning from...

New Home Network.com

New nationwide US site that deals exclusively in newly constructed homes.

NewHomeNetwork.com™

ch Listings
rch Options
Search Results

formation

/s
nce
& Advice
Directory

Mv

• Live
• Coming Soon

Featured Builder

Search Listings: Search Options

www.newhomenetwork.com

Number 1 Expert.com

Track down a real estate expert almost anywhere in the US or Canada.

www.number1expert.com

Did we mention our rates are lower?
click here

#1 NUMBER1EXPERT.com™
Find Your NUMBER1EXPERT™

Find | Ask | Tips | Library | Who | Resources | L

Looking for homes? info? a...
A top real estate expert in your area i...
you right now ...

Alabama	Illinois	Montana
Alaska	Indiana	Nebraska
Arizona	Iowa	Nevada
Arkansas	Kansas	New Hampshire
California	Kentucky	New Jersey

Properties Direct

UK site that covers some 70 estate agents, and over 1,000 properties.

www.properties-direct.com

Property City

One of London's best online estate agencies. Features a mortgage calculator.

www.propertycity.co.uk

Property Live

Good starting point for UK properties, as it's sanctioned by the National Association of Estate Agents.

www.propertylive.co.uk

Property Sight

One of the best sites for British property with offerings from 250 estate agents.

www.property-sight.co.uk

Real Estate Australia

An outstanding Australian site with a great search engine and top content.

www.realestate.com.au

See It First.com

Limited to certain areas in the US, this site has film and 3D pictures of houses for sales.

www.homesonvideo.com

www.seeitfirst.com/site/main_hov.html

SeeItFirst.com

Go: You Are Here: Home | Real Estate

Go: Real Estate

Real Estate

START WIRELESS INTERNET TRADING, WITH 5 COMMISSION-FREE TRADES CLICK HERE!

Ameritrade℠

Go on a Video Home Tour

About Real Est

At the SeeItFirst.com Re Channel, you can g Interactive Video Home over the U.S. - 24 hours days a week

Interactive Video Tours Available

Videographers Available

Videographers Available

Check This O

Place A Video

Got Que Click

Real Estate Search

WotProperty

Welcome to WotProperty UK

Welcome Page
Quick Searches
Company Search
Specific Search
Send Comments
Company Entry
Legal Notes
Property Links

Service provided by **Wotnot Web Works Ltd.** who are a Web Site design Company based in London, UK. To develop or refurbish your site please contact us

Wot is WotProperty UK ?

WotProperty UK is a free and independent service to help find sites for UK based commercial and residential property agents. There are currently 267 web sites listed.

We will list any appropriate property related site including magazine and agency group sites, property associations and other Internet facilities. It is FREE to be listed on this site.

How to make a search

1. **Quick Searches**
   A varied selection of links to search either alphabetically, by regions or business types. For a more specific search use one of the options below.

2. **Company Search**
   Simply enter a letter or part of a company name for a list of possible matches. You can select whether the search checks the first letter only or the whole agent name.

3. **Specific Search**
   This search allows you to select the area in the UK and the type of business you are looking for. You can also limit your

WotProperty

Find sites for UK-based commercial and residential property agents.

www.wotproperty.co.uk/main.mv

Your Move

Details all the properties this big UK estate agent has on its books.

www.your-move.co.uk

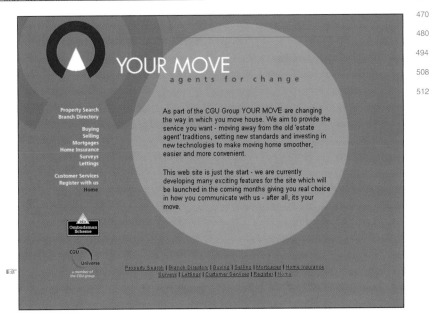

YOUR MOVE
agents for change

Property Search
Branch Directory

Buying
Selling
Mortgages
Home Insurance
Surveys
Lettings

Customer Services
Register with us
Home

As part of the CGU Group YOUR MOVE are changing the way in which you move house. We aim to provide the service you want - moving away from the old 'estate agent' traditions, setting new standards and investing in new technologies to make moving home smoother, easier and more convenient.

This web site is just the start - we are currently developing many more exciting features for the site which will be launched in the coming months giving you real choice in how you communicate with us - after all, its your move.

Ombudsman Scheme

CGU Universe
a member of the CGU group

Property Search | Branch Directory | Buying | Selling | Mortgages | Home Insurance
Surveys | Lettings | Customer Services | Register | Home

Employment

Whether you are looking for a job for yourself, or looking to fill a vacancy, the Internet can be your best friend. There are many hundreds of job sites specifically tailored to help you get the job you always wanted, be it in IT or zoo keeping. It is just a matter of knowing where to look.

Using the Net can also give you the edge on finding and applying for the best opportunities before the competition, given the speed and immediacy of the medium. Many sites have useful areas that give advice on how to improve your career prospects, or how to break into specific careers. And don't forget to check the sites of the companies you would like to work for, as they often post situations vacant there first.

As you can imagine, there are many different kinds of job sites offering different services. Some are a straightforward classified ad service, similar to what you'd find in the newspapers, while others offer a fully interactive job-finding service.

The basic rules to using a job site are simple. As you would with any other kind of medium, avoid sites that only list the job title and include no great detail. Some sites appear to offer only this service, but actually have links through to proper job descriptions, salary, location details, and so forth. You might find the job of your dreams on a site like this, but it is unlikely.

The best sites will guide you through the job-hunting process. So, instead of having to guess the title that site has given a job and type it into an empty field, good sites will offer pull-down menus for you to choose the most relevant job title. This is not to say that sites that don't offer this service don't have the job for you, it's just it may take a little more time to find it.

If you really want to get involved in your search for employment, some sites let you upload or type in your CV. They then send that CV to vacancies that match your criteria. This is very useful, but it does mean a certain lack of control as to which companies get your details. Once you have a job, remember to delete your CV from the sites.

As an employer placing a job ad, remember that the cheapest and easiest option is to place the ad on your web site. If you are going to do this, ensure that your site has enough information about your company to make the job attractive.

If you run the job vacancy in a newspaper, include your company's URL. Applicants will find more information on your site and you can include an online application form.

When you decide to place an ad with an employment site, remember to check the number of visitors to the site. It's no good placing an ad online if no one is going to see it. Don't be fobbed off with the number of hits the site gets, ask for unique visitor numbers or, at the very least, the number of page impressions. And don't forget to shop around. As you will see from the following list of sites, there are many excellent ones out there and you can get some good deals.

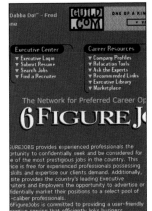

Monsterboard/Monster.com

Monsterboard is one of the best-known job sites and includes links to other useful US-based services. You'll also find career information and tips on creating the perfect CV. UK job-seekers can go to the UK site, while those after employment in Europe can go via **Lycos** to **Monster**'s European content.

www.monster.co.uk
www.monsterboard.com
www.lycos.co.uk/webguides/career

Gonyea Guide to Online Career & Employment Site

This site is great for career and employment information as it is aimed at everyone - from job hunters and recruiters, to human resources managers and headhunters. Although it has a US bias, others can check out the Working Abroad section or take a 'strengths and weaknesses' test.

www.onlinecareerguide.com

Jobs Unlimited

Covering areas such as retail, manufacturing, agriculture, and construction, rather than the usual online industries, this site links to vacancies in the US, Canada, Australia, and Europe, as well as to the UK. Jobs Unlimited isn't always as comprehensive as some other sites, but it's selective about the career information and links its offers, making it easy to use and a top flight resource.

www.jobsunlimited.com

FREE Web Sites
FREE Forms
FREE Guestbooks

http://maxpages.com

LinkExchange

(800) 388-7478
piracy@spa.org
Report Software Piracy

Top Jobs on the Net

One of the best UK-based sites that also has vacancies in six other countries. You specify your search criteria and **Top Jobs** finds the situations that suit you best. The site is updated daily and will email you to alert you when suitable new jobs are posted.

www.topjobs.net

Career Mosaic UK

Career Mosaic is one of the original databases of jobs online. It has survived because of its simplicity.

www.careermosaic-uk.co.uk

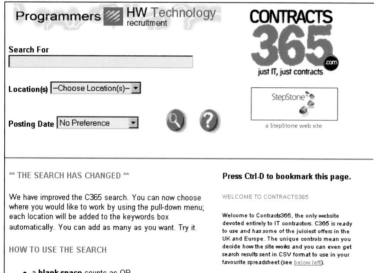

Contracts 365

A good search-based site that concentrates on IT jobs in the UK and Europe.

www.contracts365.com

Cooljobs.com

Want to be a video games tester, circus act, MTV presenter, or a stunt pilot? This is the place for you.

www.cooljobs.com

Dot Jobs

This site gathers classified listings from an array of UK publications, and puts them in one place for you to search.

www.dotjobs.co.uk

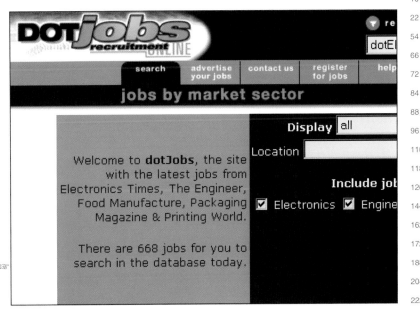

Fish4Jobs

A UK site that harvests its job ads from the nation's local press. **Fish4Jobs** is excellent for those Brits looking for something outside London.

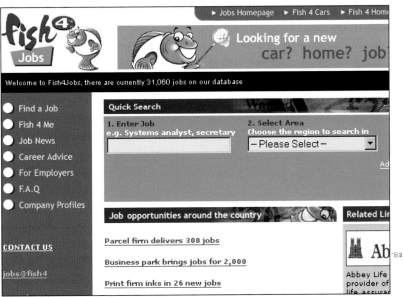

www.fish4jobs.co.uk

Gis-a-Job!

Covers both US and UK IT markets, with thousands of jobs, from hundreds of agencies. You even get a joke of the day.

www.gisajob.com

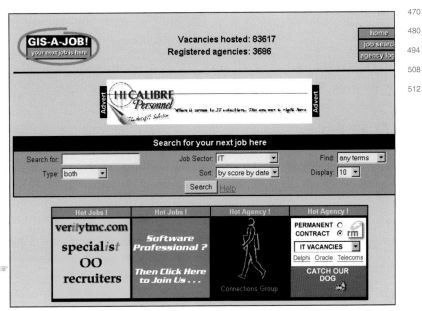

i-resign.com

When you find that perfect new job, you have to resign from the last one. So check out the best and funniest resignation letters here. Also has a salary rise calculator.

www.i-resign.com

jobbox.net

Pan-European employment site that also offers interview, and application form, hints, and tips. You'll have to register, though.

www.jobbox.net

jobsUnlimited (*Guardian - UK*)

Search *The Guardian*'s jobs and courses ads. The site also has a personalised career manager - a search engine that chooses and saves ads tailored to your specifications.

www.jobsunlimited.co.uk

StepStone

One of Europe's best employment sites, covering a wide
variety of industries and sectors.

www.stepstone.co.uk

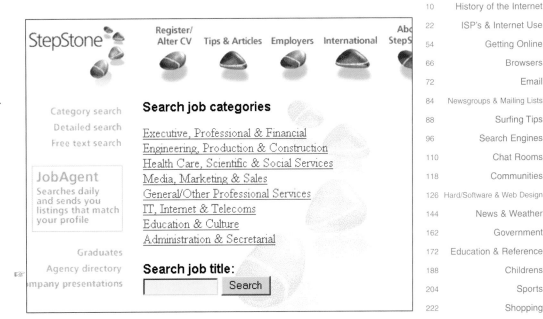

Taps.com

Deals in both UK and international markets with the pick of
the jobs, keyword or role search
facilities.

http://taps.com

Yahoo! Employment

Employers can place unlimited
job ads for only £700, while UK
job-seekers will find almost every
industry covered.

http://uk.classifieds.yahoo.com/uk
/emp

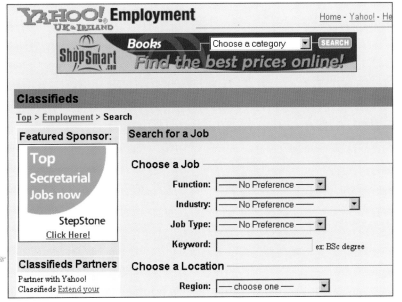

1st Resume Store International

Gives advice on resumes, CVs, and application letters. Also has great links to other sites.

www.1stresumestore.com/joblinks.htm

6 Figure Jobs.com

The site where the management cream go to be offered jobs.

www.6figurejobs.com

America's Job Bank

A joint venture between the US Department of Labour and the Employment Service.

www.ajb.dni.us

Appointments Plus

The online version of the UK's *Daily Telegraph* appointments section.

www.appointments-plus.co.uk

Ask Jobs

US jobs search engine with useful links to other sites.

http://askjobs.com

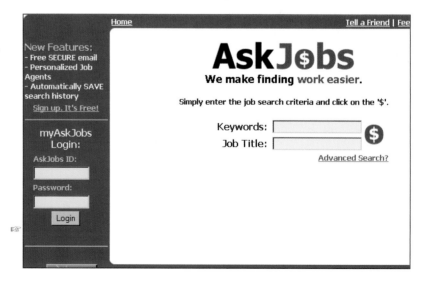

Career Path.com

US site powered by the country's leading newspapers.

www.careerpath.com

CareerShop.com

Features automated services for those who want to advance their careers.

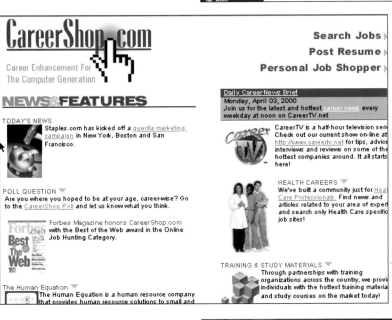

www.careershop.com

Career Web

Features jobs from 14 countries including Brazil, China, and Saudi Arabia.

www.cweb.com

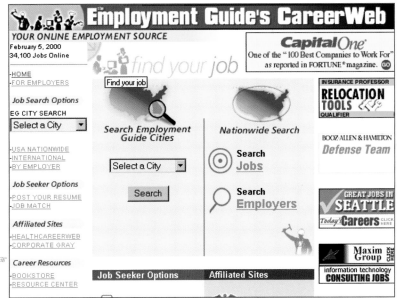

Christian Jobs

Jobs in US business and churches where religion is important.

www.christianet.com/christianjobs

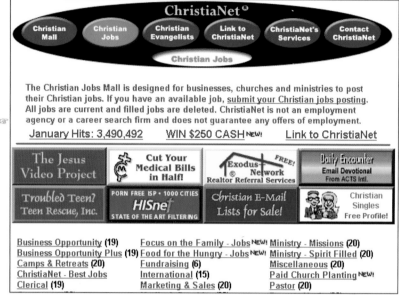

CV Store

This is an online jobs service for IT, Internet, and New Media people in the UK.

www.cvstore.net

Department of Social Security

UK government site dealing with National Insurance, the job-seeker's allowance, etc.

www.dss.gov.uk

Dice.com

A key site for computer professionals in Canada and the US.

www.dice.com

Disability Net

UK site for jobs specifically targeted at disabled people.

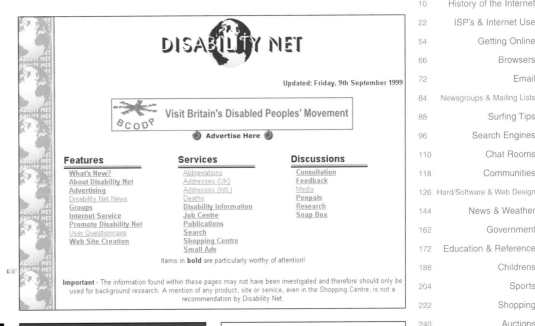

www.disabilitynet.co.uk

Ejobs

US based site for those in the technology industry.

www.ejobs.com

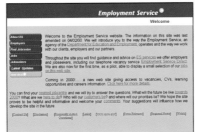

Employment Service

Lists details of UK Employment Centres, and Government initiatives.

www.employmentservice.gov.uk

Estate Agency Personnel

UK site for those looking for a permanent position in the property or financial services sectors.

www.estateagency.co.uk

GAAPweb

Specialist site for financial sector and accountancy positions.

www.gaapweb.com

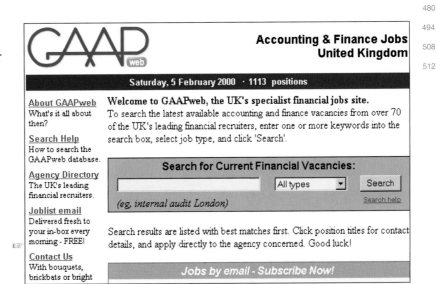

GO Jobs

US site for banking, clerical, engineering, healthcare, and sales - among others.

www.gojobs.com

The Help-Wanted Page

Classified ads, job fair details, and some useful links to other job sites.

www.helpwantedpage.com

The Irish Jobs Page

Ireland's leading recruitment site covering almost every sector.

www.exp.ie

Jobs Jobs Jobs

Draws on local **Usenet** postings as well as submitted listings.

www.jobsjobsjobs.com

Job Options

Hunt for jobs and compare your salary to the industry standard.

www.joboptions.com

Job Search

Search the collection of ads from agencies or submit your CV.

www.jobsearch.co.uk

Jobsite

One of Europe's leading multi-sector sites with emailed updates and alerts.

www.jobsite.co.uk

JobVillage.com

A comprehensive job site and resource for job hunters.

www.jobvillage.com

Jobz

The premier independent data-base of employment opportunities in Australia.

www.jobz.ozware.com

London Careers

A good place to start for those after a job in London.

www.londoncareers.net

netJobs

A site specialising in permanent and contract IT work in software.

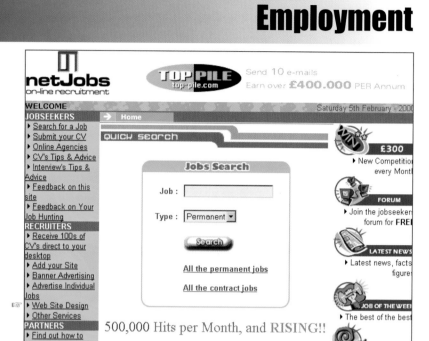

www.netjobs.co.uk

Net-Temps

One of the best temporary and contract job sites around.

www.net-temps.com

People Bank

A good joint effort between Carlton and *The Daily Mail* in UK.

www.peoplebank.com

PharmiWeb

PharmiWeb deals specifically with the pharmaceutical, medical, and life sciences industries.

www.pharmiweb.com

Price Jamieson Online

One of your first stops for the best new media jobs.

www.pricejam.com

Recruit Media

Deals with jobs in the IT, financial, commercial and business information markets.

www.recruitmedia.co.uk

Reed Online

One of the largest jobs sites, with a broad range of categories.

www.reed.co.uk

Fashion

Fashion is a real mixture of the very high tech and a complete lack of understanding of the medium. There are very few major online fashion retailers, and even fewer high street names, that sell on their web sites. It has been suggested that clothing is precisely the wrong product to try and sell on the Internet, due to the lack of physical shopping experience.

So many purchasing decisions in clothes shopping are done because the item feels or looks nice once it is tried on, and it is thought that only a strong brand name will overcome this potential resistance. Whereas with other items, such as books and CDs, price is a prime consideration in the buying process. Recent research has raised the link between these two factors, and it is still not clear which is the bigger influence on the purchasing decision.

Some research cites branding and consumer loyalty as being more important than price and delivery, with most – 70 per cent – prepared to pay a little more so they can buy their fashion items online. Research also shows that those buying clothing and sporting gear are least likely to be concerned about price. This explains why boo.com - the recent high tech fashion retail site - concentrates on brand names.

Away from the retail world, fashion designers have not been quick to use the Internet. Quite a number do not even have a web presence, while those that do only have rudimentary and, ironically, rather badly designed sites. Yves Saint Laurent is one of the exceptions to this rule, but even here we see static photographs of the designer's collection, when we could have so much more - films of the catwalk, a voice-over explaining influences and reasons for the design, and the like.

There are a number of fashion portals already online, and most of them are reasonable sites with a good mixture of links, listings, and content, but some can be a bit spartan due to the lack of other fashion sites. Clothing has some good business-2-business representatives in this field, and there are more in the pipeline, but Fashion Guide and Fashion Net stand out as excellent consumer portals.

For some reason the many fashion-led magazines on the market have not transferred well to the Internet. They either have very skimpy content, or completely ignore the industry that supports them, in favor of just duplicating content from their paper version on the web. Again, there is one very fine exception to this rule and that is - as you might expect - *Vogue*.

If this were a school report for the fashion industry on the Internet, my verdict would have to be 'could do better'. It is apparent that the fashion industry has been very slow to realise what the Internet could do for it, and I expect that we'll see more boo.coms and fashion portals in the next 12 months. If we don't, I cannot see how that figure I mentioned at the beginning of this Intro will be possible.

WELCOME

Welcome to Janet Reger's new collections. We hope you enjoy browsing through our lingerie, and if you would like stockist information or wish to be included on our mailing list, please contact Janet Reger on +44 (0) 207-584 9360 or visit 10 Beauchamp Place, London, SW3 1NQ.

A.P.C. is a french men and women's fashion brand, distributed around the world through its own distribution network and its international mail order catalog.

Bluefly.com

It claims to be "the outlet store in your home" and it really is. There are thousands of styles of designer fashions, gifts, house and home items from top name brand designers — all at 25% to 75% off retail prices. You can shop by product category, by designer or by price range and there are great "Trend Watcher" and "Designer Spotlight" sections.

www.bluefly.com

Fashion Guide

Trends, shows, and the latest designs from Paris, Milan, Tokyo, New York and London. There are also sections on fashion news, beauty and textiles. If you want to study fashion you can find a list of colleges and schools that provide courses as well.

www.fashionguide.com

Fashion *Net*

A very extensive array of fashion items available. Women can choose from labels such as Paul Smith, Club Monacco, and Victoria's Secret. Men can also browse through Paul Smith and Club Monacco ranges, as well as APL and Guess? If you're looking for casual wear, Gap and Esprit are two of the names available to you. There is also a vast array of accessories including footwear, watches, and jewelry.

www.fashion.net

Vogue.com

Top catwalk coverage including slide shows, behind-the-scenes, and backstage 'buzz'. *Vogue* also takes a look at last season's fashions and decides what your favorites were. You may even want to send a still of your favorite garment this season to a friend. All this, and abridged content from the paper version of the magazine.

www.vogue.com

Designers Direct.com

Men and women's designer clothes and fashion accessories at bargain prices. Delivery is from the US and will reach you almost anywhere in the world within 4–7 days.

www.designersdirect.com

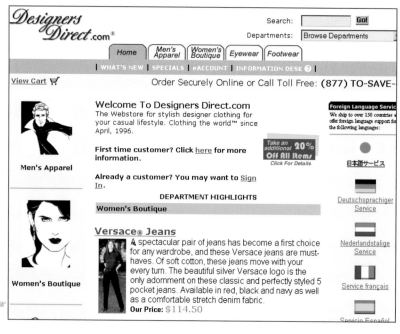

fashionangel.com

Concise fashion resource covering a wide variety of topics, from designers and fashion 'zines, to online shopping and 'the look'.

www.fashionangel.com

Fashion Planet

Features on fashion and models (past and present) and a look at international fashion trends. It touches on lifestyle by following Prince Michael of Italy around the world.

www.fashionplanet.com

Fashion Showroom

Useful resource of photographs from this season's catwalk fashion shows, collections, and accessories.

www.fashionshowroom.com

Fashion

First View

Collections from top designers about six weeks after they are seen at the runway shows (a password is needed to view the runway shows before this). Clothes, books, and videos are available to buy online.

www.firstview.com

Gap

Everything you can buy in store - chinos, leather jackets and cotton T-shirts.

www.gap.com

NEW! PHOTOS NEW!

Milan Womens Fall 2000 Collection

MISSONI

To see photos....click here

inshop.com

Gives you the low-down on the latest from the shops in the US and other major fashion cities, and lets you personalise the data so you can keep abreast of new developments from your favorite designer.

www.inshop.com

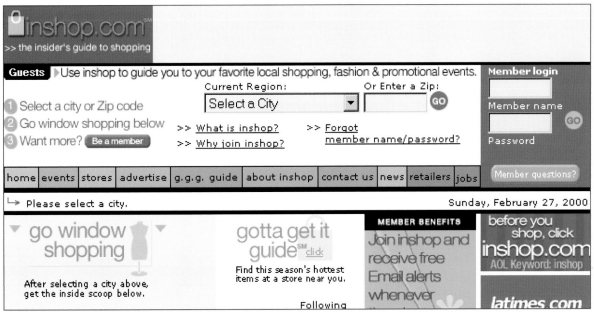

Lands' End

Inwear, outwear, and swimwear, available to be delivered all over the world. You can also see how clothes are going to look on the virtual model made up to your size, shape, and hair color.

www.landsend.com

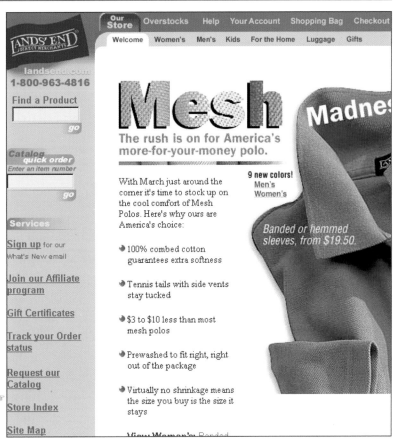

levi.com

Although the main US site is under construction, you can still get to the very cool sites of Levi Europe, where you'll find diverting games and animations, as well as the products for you to look at in detail.

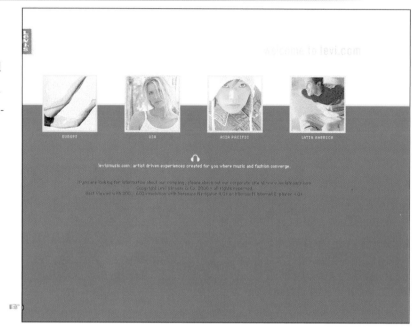

www.levi.com
www.eu.levi.com

Ready2Shop

Excellent shopping resource that lets you in on the best bargains, and tells you what's hot, and what isn't, in the UK fashion market.

www.ready2shop.com

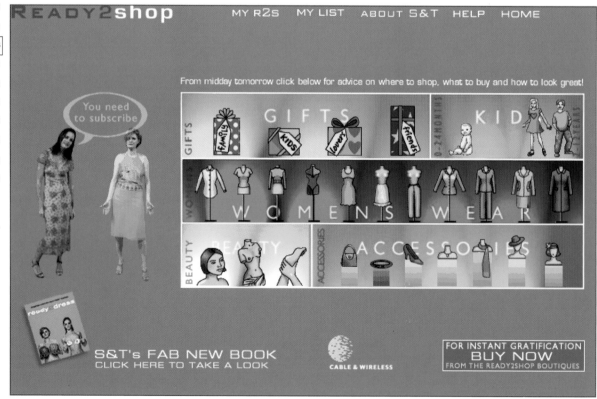

United Colours of Benetton

The jumper company continues its controversial ad campaign online, but you can get past that and use their online catalog to shop.

www.benetton.com

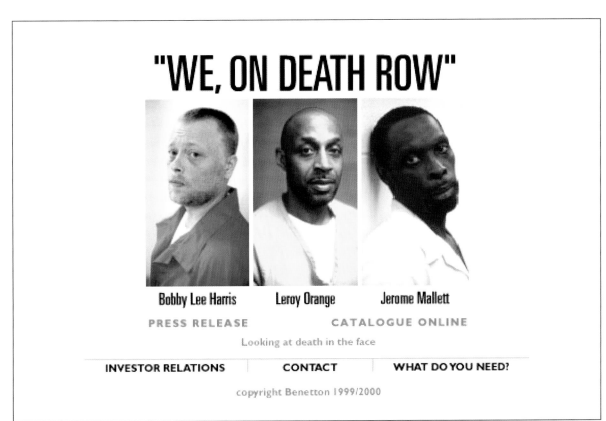

Costumes

An extensive site examining fashion and costumes from all places and times. If you are looking for a little inspiration for your own designs, or need to check something, try here.

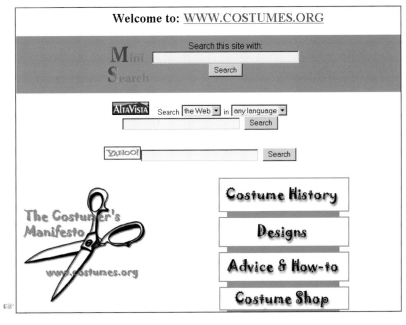

www.costumes.org

APC

A French brand offering men and women's clothes which can be distributed around the world.

www.apc.fr

A.P.C. is a french men and women's fashion brand, distributed around the world through its own distribution network and its international mail order catalog.

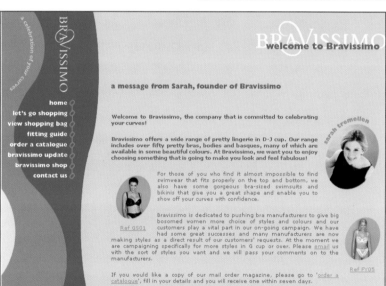

Bravissimo

Lingerie and swimwear for women with more curvy figures.

www.bravissimo.com

Fashion/Food/Fun

Fashion and costumes through the ages, includes armor and uniforms.

http://members.aol.com/tchrfro-moz/fashion.html

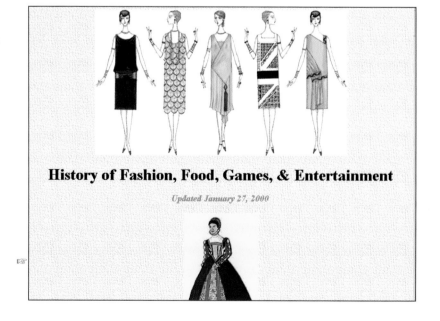

Fashionlive.com

Visit catwalks around the world and get a glimpse of styles from top designers.

www.fashionlive.com

FashionMall.com

Here you can purchase clothes, some beauty products, and have make-up questions answered online.

www.fashionmall.com

iafrica.com

Fashion news, model talk, and interviews with designers.

www.iafrica.com

Fashion

Janet Reger

Very good catalog site from the exclusive lingerie guru. No online sales alas.

www.janetreger.co.uk

Pregnancy Today

Fashion tips for pregnant women, sizes and flattering styles.

http://pregnancytoday.com

The Regency Fashion Page

Fashion from 1790 to 1829 with influences from Princess Charlotte's wedding and Jane Austen.

http://locutus.ucr.edu/~cathy/reg3.html

Women's Wear Daily

A great portal site that links through to fashion industry sites not just limited to women's fashion.

www.wwd.com

Auf Wiedersehen?

MILAN -- Moments of excitement and aesthetic pleasure are commonly associated with fashion -- but genuinely emotional ones are more rare. It was, however, a very moving occasion when Jil Sander showed her collection on Thursday, which was her first for the Prada Group and may be her last. It was a strong yet graceful fall collection, featuring sleek and refined looks worn with, believe it or not, high heels. There were clean-cut suits, turtlenecks with full skirts and a very distinctive, graphic print, featuring randomly located, big black circles on white. Here, her blouse in that pattern and long, narrow skirt. For more on Sander, including the possibilities for her future, see pages 6 and 7. For more on the season, see pages 8 to 11 of Friday's WWD.

PHOTO BY GIOVANNI GIANNONI

Yves Saint Laurent

A useful site for slide shows of YSL's collections, but no online buying.

www.ysl.com

Zoom

UK shopping portal with names like Racing Green, Principals for men and women, and Dorothy Perkins.

www.zoom.co.uk

Food & Drink

You might not immediately associate something as totally inorganic, and definitely inedible, as the Internet with food and drink. After all, what can the Net do with food? Well, the answer is, quite a lot. Given the multi-national nature of the Internet, you will find that every culture is represented online. And where every culture is represented, its cuisine cannot be far behind. Sure enough, there are an enormous amount of web sites dedicated to people's national cuisine, or the cooking skills and recipes of their ancestors.

No matter what you need the perfect recipe for - from Hungarian goulash to Japanese sushi - you will be able to find it on the Internet. And you won't just find one recipe for that dish, you'll find many variations. You'll also find recipes that have been handed down from generation to generation, that have never been tasted outside a certain family circle, as well as the most obscure countries' delicacies. You can just browse through some of the mouth-watering pictures of well-prepared food that populate these recipe web sites.

Once you've decided on the meals you're going to prepare, you'll need to buy the right ingredients. Many food and drink sites include areas where you can buy produce, usually from local stores, but quite often you can go further afield for your foodstuff. And it's not just the supermarkets and hypermarkets that take orders online. You will find that many companies, from the manufacturers to exclusive and specialist food stores, will be happy to take your order and deliver to your door. So, no matter whether you fancy a hamper from Fortnum & Mason, a fresh salmon trout from Scotland, or pâté de foie gras from Strasbourg, the Net will deliver.

Alternatively, you may just want to check the healthiness of particular foodstuffs. While recipe sites make up the majority of food related web sites, there are also some outstanding sites dedicated to individual foods. Some are more general and only deal with meat or fish or fruit, while others zero in on their topics to dedicate pages of information (and recipes!) to the salmon, blueberries or the potato.

Perhaps, though, the idea of preparing food after all this Internet activity is too much. Don't worry, the Internet has the answer to that problem as well and can point you in the direction of the professionals to provide your sustenance. If you fancy hiring a chef, a butler, or a wine expert you'll find agencies on the web that can help you.

Less extravagantly, you could always treat yourself to a night out. You'll find a wealth of information on eating out, be it round the corner or across the globe. Indeed, there are as many restaurant guides on the Internet as there are restaurants in the physical world. You can read reviews, find out opening times, check the chef's biography and even see the menus. Some restaurants have online booking facilities as well. If you don't want to stray from your home, but still fancy a treat, there are many services - mostly based in the US and UK - that will deliver take away food straight to your door.

The Internet is an equally good source of information when it comes to drink. Everything from water to home brewed moonshine is included on the Internet. You can find out how to mix the best cocktails; discover the best bars or pubs; have beer, wine, and spirits delivered, or learn from which springs different bottled waters come.

Food & Drink

Epicurious Food

A wide-ranging and thorough web site dealing with every aspect of food. The many sections include recipes from global cuisines, cook book reviews, top destinations for eating world-wide, and advice on healthy cooking. There's even a cooking dictionary, a metric conversion table, and a guide to the etiquette of holding a dinner party. Don't miss the amazing online video guides to preparing food.

www.epicurious.com

FoodLines

Run by a US husband and wife team, **FoodLines** is a veritable feast of content. You can swap recipes, find out about nutrition, check the Q & A section for food basics, and get the low-down on the latest food festivals happening around the world. In addition there are sections dealing with food consultants, books, magazines and almost every other aspect of food.

www.foodlines.com

I Drink

Idrink is a quick and easy reference tool for mixing drinks for you and your guests. From traditional favorites to the latest trendy concoctions, you can look like an expert in no time. The information on 5,865 drinks has been compiled from recipes submitted by professional and amateur bartenders everywhere.

www.idrink.com

Simply Food

A multi-award winning site from UK company, Carlton, Simply Food is quite simply one of the best food sites on the Internet. You name it, it's here. There are features from well-known chefs and critics, a great 'marketplace' of food shop links, and a daily newsletter you can subscribe to. Find a food-related job, discover how to go organic, or just browse the eclectic mix of recipes.

www.simplyfood.co.uk

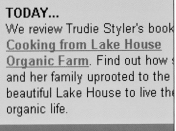

Beer Travelers

The Beer Travelers are on a quest to find the best bars in the US. Establishments covered include taverns, British and Irish theme pubs, and German beer halls in the US.

www.beertravelers.com

The Beverage Network

Reviews of over 500 different beverages including fizzy drinks/sodas, tea, coffee, water, iced teas and other soft drinks, as well as industry news and classifieds.

www.bevnet.com

The Cook's Thesaurus

If you're reading a recipe and come across a food or term you're not familiar with, this site will be indispensable.

www.switcheroo.com

Domino's Pizza

Great multi-national site. Find your nearest restaurant anywhere in the world and in some countries, including the UK, you can see the menu, decide on your meal and order your pizza via email.

www.dominos.co.uk

www.dominos.com

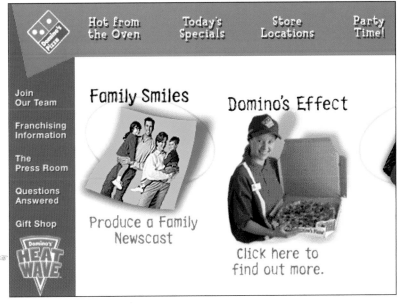

The Internet Food Channel

Great site for those interested in trend spotting. You'll find food research and statistics, consumer behavior, dining out, shopping for groceries, and new products.

www.foodchannel.com

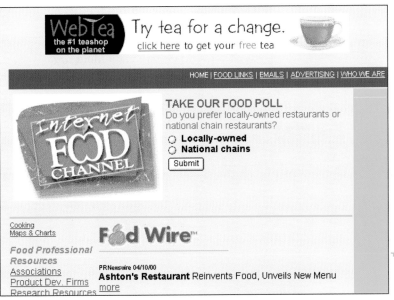

The National Food Safety Database

Great US site concerned with food safety covering concerns of the public, teachers, and those in the food industry.

www.foodsafety.org

Mimi's Cyber Kitchen

This site claims to have been the first food portal on the internet, having been established in 1995. Whether this is true or not, Mimi's Cyber Kitchen is one of the greatest food-related sites on the Net. It's a nice-looking site with an amazing array of links and content. There are also hundreds of recipes.

www.cyber-kitchen.com

Restaurantrow.com

Amazing site that lists over 100,000 restaurants in 47 countries. Can be a bit limited outside the US, but still a very worthwhile site.

www.restaurantrow.com

Restaurants.co.uk

An amazingly detailed search facility that lets you find a restaurant anywhere in the UK, get its details and even write a review of it.

www.restaurants.co.uk

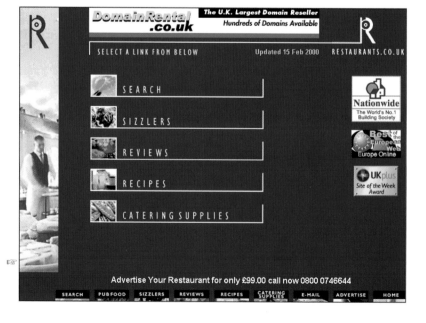

Tastings.com

Plenty of information for those interested in buying and enjoying good wines, beers, and spirits. With links to journals, and books that the company publishes, as well as industry news.

www.tastings.com

Top Secret Recipes

If you've ever wondered how you can make your own Big Macs, Coca-Cola, Hershey bar, or Kellogg's breakfast cereals, you will find recipes for them here. Happy hunting!

www.topsecretrecipes.com

Vegetarian Central

A great resource for vegetarians from all over the world. Includes a search engine as well as features and links to sites covering nutrition, cooking, animal rights, shopping, and more.

www.vegetariancentral.org

Allrecipes.com

As the name suggests, this site has a hoard of recipes for you to try.

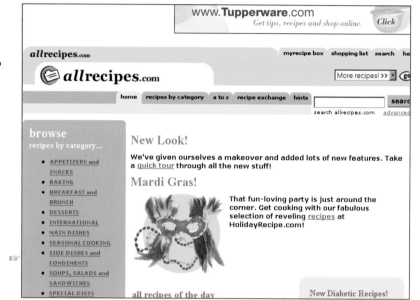

www.allrecipes.com

Books-For-Cooks

The place to go if you need a cook book online. Also has free content.

www.books-for-cooks.com

Ask a Chef.com

Recipes from the professionals. Having difficulty getting your soufflé to rise? Try here.

www.aksachef.com

BarMeister

Covers every type of game you might find in a bar or pub, along with specific drinking games.

www.barmeister.com

Betty Crocker

Plan the week ahead in recipes, buy Betty's books, or order some of Betty's food!

www.bettycrocker.com

Beers Direct/Lastorders.com

Order bitter and lager in the UK and have them delivered.

www.beersdirect.com

Bottled Water Web

Detailed mineral and trace element analysis of waters from the major bottling companies.

www.bottledwaterweb.com

Campaign for Real Ale

A site for those dedicated to traditional beers, ciders, and perries.

www.camra.org.uk

Food & Drink

Coca-Cola

As one of the fizzy drink's ads once said, if you haven't heard of coke, welcome to planet earth...

www.coke.com

Cocktail.com

The online bible of mixing the perfect cocktail. Find the best recipes and methods, or suggest your own 'lethal' concoctions.

Culinary Café

Microsoft's very own food site is a very good portal.

www.cocktail.com

www.yumyum.com

Culinary.com

A great portal site with more links than there are grains of rice in a risotto.

www.culinary.com

Cyberchef

The Net home of celebrity chef, Daniel Boulud, with a slant on pasta and rice.

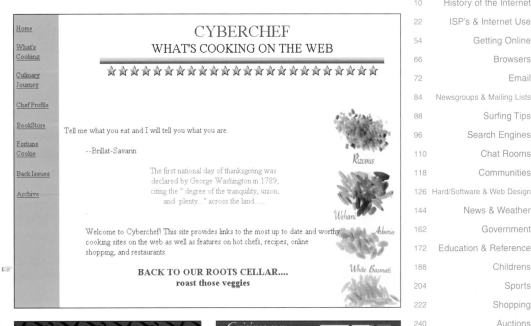

www.cyberchefs.net

Daawat.com/Drinks

If you want juice or milkshakes, you'll find this site a useful starting place.

http://uk.daawat.com/drinks.htm

Drinks Direct

Order wine and spirits for yourself, or as a gift for someone else, in the UK.

www.drinks-direct.co.uk

e-Cuisines.com

Great recipe and nutrition site.

www.e-cuisines.com

Foie Gras from Strasbourg

Find out all about the king of pâtés, or order some from the factory.

www.bruck-foiegras.com

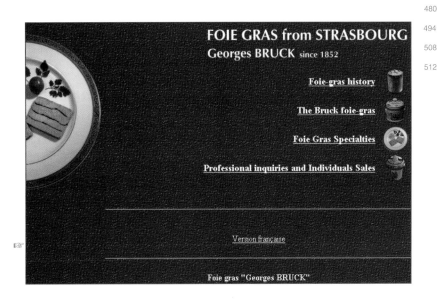

Food.com

Find out about getting take away food in the US.

www.food.com

The Food Museum

Focuses on how food influences, and even makes, history.

www.foodmuseum.com

FoodnDrink

A great London restaurant guide with reviews and information.

www.foodndrink.com

Food Resource

Very simple, but hugely useful site that has hundreds, if not thousands, of links to other food sites.

www.orst.edu/food-resource/food.html

Fortnum & Mason

Order hampers with champagne and caviar from the world's most exclusive store.

www.fortnumandmason.co.uk

Good Pub Guide

UK guide to the best public houses in the country.

www.goodguides.com

Heinz

Get details of the company's products, and buy them online for home delivery.

www.heinz-direct.co.uk

KosherInfo

Important dietary information for Jewish people - or those having them to dinner!

www.kosherinfo.com

Meat Direct

UK residents can order any meat - from steak to pheasants - online and get it delivered.

www.meatdirect.co.uk

Menu-OnLine

Great idea of looking for a restaurant by price or item on the menu - mainly US.

www.onlinemenus.com

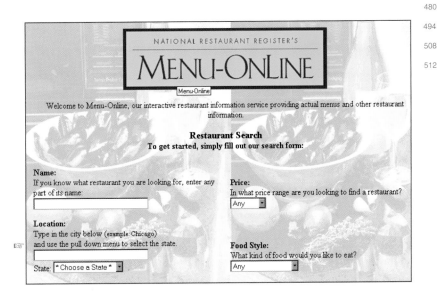

Meals.com

Used to be CompuCook, but still dedicated to daily and weekly food and menus.

www.my-meals.com

Organics Direct

UK site dedicated to selling the best organic produce at the cheapest prices.

www.organicsdirect.com

Salami.com

Not just salami, but lots of top quality Italian food for sale online.

www.salami.com

Smirnoff

International web site of probably the world's most famous vodka.

www.smirnoff.com

Supermarket Guru

Gives hints and tips on how to shop smart at supermarkets.

www.supermarketguru.com

Tesco online

One of the few UK supermarkets to offer nationwide delivery from online ordering.

www.tesco.co.uk

VegDining.com

Guide to vegetarian restaurants around the world.

www.vegdining.com

Water.com

Useful information on water, as well as delivery in the US.

www.water.com

▼

455   Next ▶

Health & Beauty

The concept of healthcare and medicine on the Internet has made the headlines every now and then because of impotency drug Viagra or even a long-distance online diagnoses that saves a man's life. However, the rate of medical-related Web sites being launched has suddenly snowballed and it is estimated that by the year 2004, the online health market in the states will have risen from $200 million in 1999 to $10 billion in 2004.

This growth is expected to be mirrored in Europe is attributed to the increasing acceptance of purchasing things online – especially women. Possibly the first to really realise the potential of this market was Amazon, which launched drugstore.com in early 1999. The site covers all aspects of this market from pharmacy drugs to health products and 'wellness'.

As it is you can find an enormous amount of medical information online. As well as the sites listed overleaf remember that you can go to the newsgroups for help and advice for dealing with particular illnesses or diseases. However, bear in mind that you cannot know what qualifications people you speak to on the newsgroups might have, whereas the archive of the *British Medical Journal* is well respected.

The point of sites that give medical advice from doctors is –

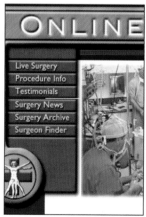

ultimately – to get people out of situations where they are making an unnecessary trip to the doctor, just for him or her to tell them that they just have colds. Some 89 per cent of Internet users believe that Internet consulting services will reduce the number of real time visits to the surgery and 71 per cent even believed that the Internet would force improvements in health care industry.

Access to medical information online will also result in a better-educated patient as well as one who does not have to pay needlessly for consultations. The ability to communicate directly with patients via email or IRC will help increase efficiency and result in a less home visits.

Away from actual health products, personal care items are expected to be worth $2.3 billion. It will come as a major surprise that most cosmetics companies do not even have an online presence, let alone an operational e-commerce site selling their products. Instead we have seen Internet companies that have filled this gap, but not many.

As with books, CDs and videos, competition in this market will be particularly fierce and those companies that establish an early presence could be in with a better chance of survival. Already around 45 per cent of Internet users go online to find health information but 49 per cent would not buy. So names that people trust or learn to trust

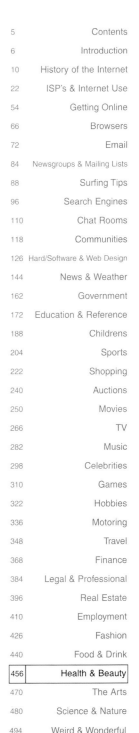

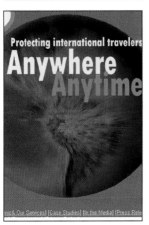

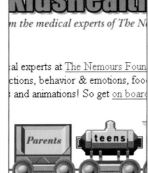

Beauty.com

Offers one of the best ranges of skincare products, make-up, hair products, perfume, after-shave, and accessories, for both men and women on the Web. You can search the site for the products you want or look at the makeovers that show you just how to use them to best effect.

www.beauty.com

NHS Direct

Launched by the UK government as a online help facility, NHS direct aims to help you with symptoms and general health questions, rather than act as a diagnosis or dispensary on the Web. It also offers a guide to healthy living, health news and an A-Z guide to the National Health Service.

www.nhsdirect.nhs.uk

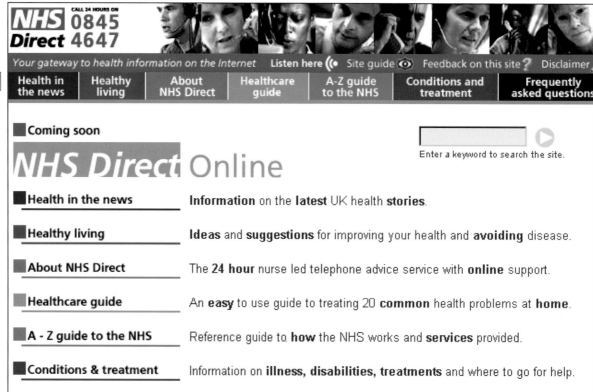

Think Natural.com

Innovative new Web site that combines health products, aroma-therapy and natural beauty materials in one place. The great thing about this site is its content. There is a wealth of information on vitamins and herbal extracts that help you to select the product that might be of benefit to you.

www.thinknatural.com

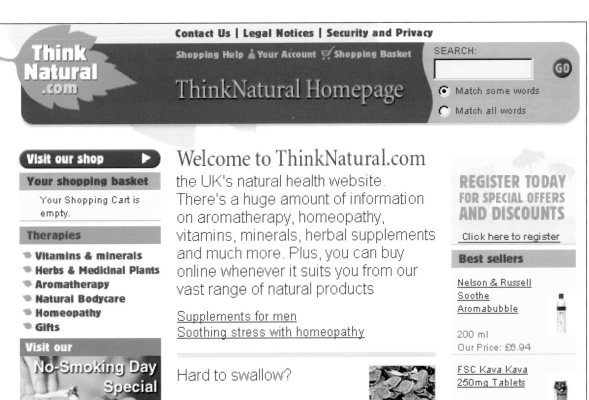

WebMD

Includes sports and fitness, a 'find a physician' facility and information on health issues. You'll find the latest research and medical opinions and special sections dealing with both men and women's health. There is also a calculator to predict your child's height and a 'desert wiz-ard' which tells you what you should do and for how long depending on what you have eaten!

www.mebmd.com

ClickMango.com

This brightly colored site claims to provide health information, practical beauty tips, celebrity health secrets and regular therapy reviews from Joanna Lumley.

www.clickmango.com

DoctorNet.com

A site where you can find a plastic surgeon to perform just about any operation from eyelid surgery to breast augmentation. Laser vision correction specialists are also available

www.doctornet.com

Drugstore.com

This site has an extensive list of medicines and hair and beauty products available to buy. US customers can even get their prescriptions delivered to them.

www.drugstore.com

Fragrance Counter

A good range of his and hers smells. Other products can be bought and it offers nutritional and weight loss advice as well.

www.fragrancecounter.com

Healthology

Advice on health issues from childhood to old age, including allergies, sleeping disorders, alternative medicine and weight management. You can also find out about prevention and treatment of certain illnesses and conditions.

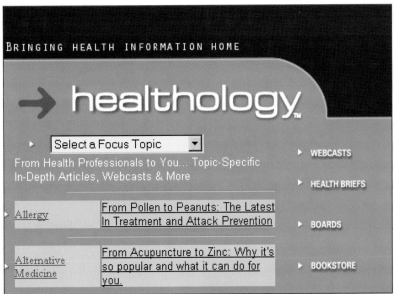

www.healthology.com

World Clinic

Famous for emailing a solo Russian yachtsman advice on how to drain an abscess on his arm, this site offers instant access to a real, live doctor online.

www.worldclinic.com

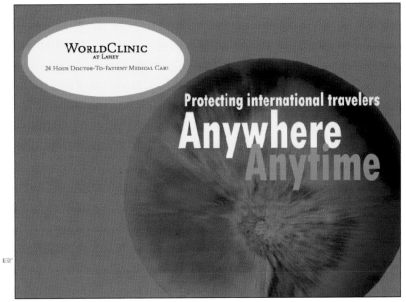

24 Hour Fitness.com

Sites that aims to make you bigger, better and stronger with dietary and exercise information.

www.24hourfitness.com

Alternative Medicine

An insight into other ways to treat illnesses. What products to buy and where to find specialised clinics.

www.alternativemedicine.com

New Approaches to Cancer

Looks at promoting the benefits of complementary therapy and a healthy diet in the battle against cancer.

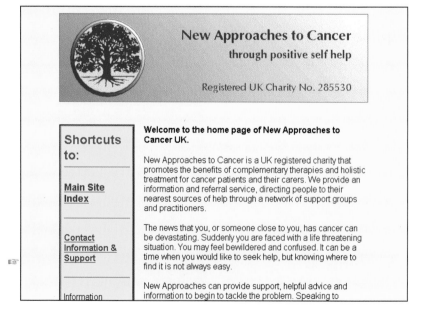

www.anac.org.uk

Avon

Ding dong - a site offering beauty tips and an online advisor. Avon products are also available to buy.

www.avon.com

BeautyCare.com

Portal site for beauty information, shopping, community, advice, trends, and more.

www.beautycare.com

The Body Shop

Advice on general wellbeing and natural remedies and beauty products.

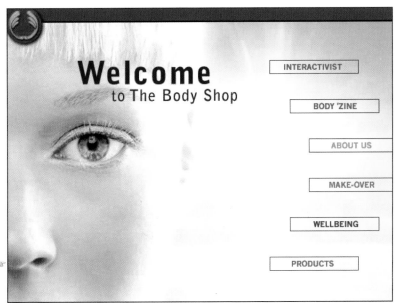

www.bodyshop.com

British Medical Journal

Great archive and resource of medical articles dating back to 1994.

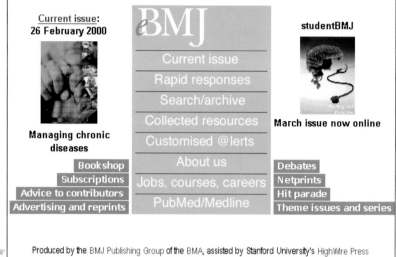

www.bmj.com

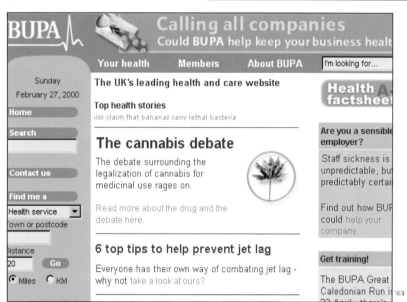

BUPA

If you really want to go for private medical care in the UK, try the BUPA Site.

www.bupa.co.uk.

Champneys

An exclusive health resort in England and Brussels

www.champneys.com

Department of Health and Human Services
Good US government hub for health-related sites and topics.

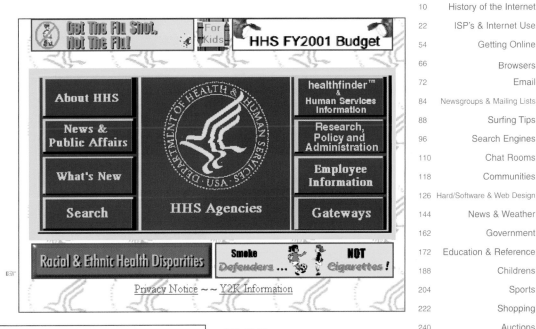

www.hhs.gov

eve.com
US only beauty product retailer.

www.eve.com

fitnessonline
Nutrition and fitness tips are here and how to be adventurous with exercise

www.fitnessonline.com

GP-UK site

List of and for General Practitioners in the UK.

www.schin.ncl.ac.uk/gpuk/gpuk_home.htm

HealthFinder

Great topic-by-topic health resource that let you learn more about disease.

www.healthfinder.com

HealthGate

A place to find advice on men and women's health. This includes teen and elderly health tips as well.

www.healthgate.com

Health in Focus

Here you can get questions answered, medical words explained and you can even talk to an online doctor.

www.healthinfocus.com

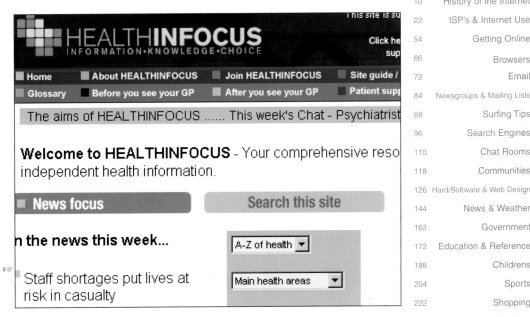

KidsHealth.org

A guide for parents on children's health and behavioral issues, form birth to adolescence.

www.kidshealth.org

Lush Times inline

You can buy fresh orange foam bath and massage bars made from Belgium chocolate here.

www.lush.co.uk

more.com

Foot care, skincare, and oral care products can be bought here. Items to stop you smoking and remedies for restless nights are available as well.

www.more.com

mynutrition

Nutritional information on healthy eating and good quality supplements. Also a guide to nutrition and health problems.

www.mynutrition.co.uk

Online Surgery

Here you can watch operations being performed. Anything from cosmetic procedures to brain surgery.

www.onlinesurgery.com

Virtual Makeover

A place to buy software that will allow you to change your hair style and color to see what suits you best.

www.virtualmakeover.com

Weightwatchers.com

The weight loss masters have bases in an amazing number of countries where you can find out about general information and meetings near you.

www.weightwatchers.com

Vitamins Network

Everything you could want to find out about vitamins as well as a vitamin shop.

www.vitamins.net

The Arts

The arts have always been seen as the preserve of the highbrow and not one that should mix well with scientific things of any kind. Any yet the Internet has brought the arts to life. After all, art galleries and theaters are often seen as places to be hallowed, to be whispered in. When you visit an art gallery in the physical world, for example, you might have to queue for hours, or arrive only to find the picture, artist, or exhibition you particularly wanted to see no longer on display.

These frustrations are banished by the web, where there are no constraints on space, so every painting, sculpture, lithograph, etching, sketch, and photograph can be displayed. Unfortunately, the museums and galleries have been slow to realise this, but some offer excellent sites complete with email feedback forms and other kinds of interactivity.

Most of the major galleries in the world now have representation on the Internet. This means that you can be in New York yet visit the Louvre in Paris, or in Istanbul while looking at Rodin's Thinker in Brussels. Some of the better sites provide special online exhibits and access to materials otherwise kept in storage.

If you cannot find what you're after at the gallery sites, you will have to turn to the amateur enthusiast. Just as there are tribute sites to Tom Cruise and Denise Richards, so there are to Salvador Dali and John Constable.

The web is also a very good master under which to study due to its nature of inter-related links. Help is never far away if you want to know more about an artist or learn the nuances of appreciating his or her work. With art, as with most things online, you can actually study to become a very good amateur enthusiast yourself.

Away from the art of galleries and gardens, the literary arts are equally well represented. The fact that you can find transcripts of all Shakespeare's plays online should tell you that the net is a great place to find all manner of resources for literature and the theater.

About this site | English | Nederlands

VAN GOGH MUSEUM AMSTERDAM

News

Exhibitions

General Information

Education & Events

As a prelude to the Light exhibition (fall 2000) you can visit an entirely new part of this internet site: the 'Light-site' (only in English).

AGE 1750-1900

The Collection

Artcyclopedia

Launched in 1999, **Arcyclopedia** is similar to WWAR, and has an A-Z list of over 6,000 artists, which provides direct links to those works on galleries web sites, no matter where they are on display. Recently added pages provide links to gallery sites worldwide, arranged alphabetically.

www.artcyclopedia.com

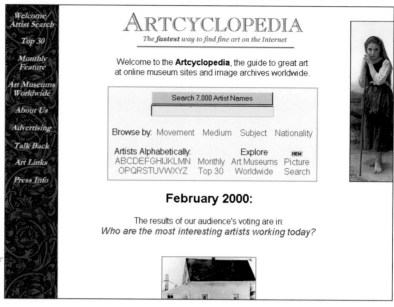

World Wide Arts Resources

Known as WWAR for short and dubbed the Yahoo! of the art world, this site provides thousands of links for artists, museums, the performing arts, art for sale, and even artists materials. If you are an artist of any kind, you're encouraged to submit your own site for inclusion.

www.wwar.com/

What's on Stage

If you enjoy performing arts you must visit this site. You can get the latest news as well as reviews of all the shows around the UK. This is also the place to stock up on your theater paraphernalia - a Starlight Express fridge magnet for example.

www.whatson.com

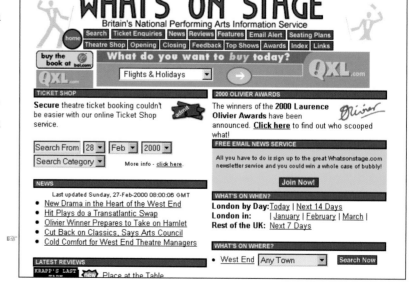

Art Museum Image Consortium/AMICO

Which currently has 50,00 thumbnail artwork images on-line and growing. Having said that, visiting the actual sites is always the best first stop so turn over for our own gallery of the very best that the web has to offer.

www.amico.org

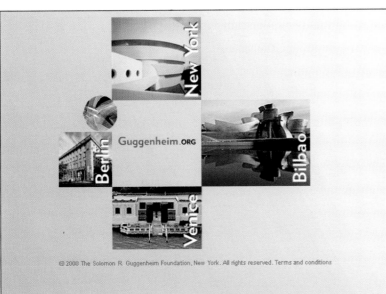

Guggenheim.org

Six sites for the price of one - links are provided to each of the Guggenheim museums (those in New York plus Bilbao, Venice, and Berlin). Scroll through the simple click-on menu of the many exhibitions, past and present for varied displays and discussions.

www.guggenheim.org

Louvre

Quick-loading thumbnail images make visiting the Paris musée du Louvre's site a pleasure, click on each work for enlargements and detailed histories. The Mona Lisa and the Venus de Milo are present and correct, plus many other major works from each department.

www.louvre.fr

The Arts

Museum of Modern Art, New York

Only solo exhibitions are currently available on-line but these are well chosen and displayed, including Pollock, Picasso, and Cindy Sherman. Also available is Dadabase, MOMA's on-line library of art resources and Art Safari, a queasy yet well-meaning exploration of modern art of all the family.

www.moma.org

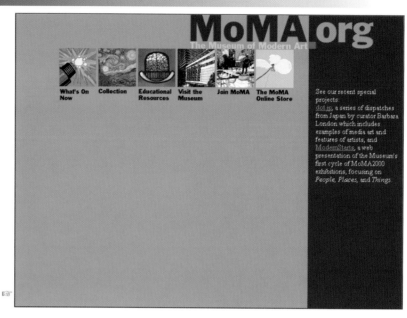

National Museum of Modern Art, Georges Pompidou Centre

A slightly awkward packing-case motif hides links to exhibition of Kandinsky, Picasso, and Realtime/Quicktime files of video works as well as its on-going Musees Nationaux Recuperation project to recover artworks lost during the Second World War

www.cnac-gp.fr

The National Gallery

Displaying artists from its huge collection of Western European art from 1260 to 1900, the site divides into the Gallery's respective wings, each housing a particular period. Thumbnail and enlarged versions are available along with intelligent discussions of each work.

www.nationalgallery.org

State Galleries of Berlin

This impressive site provides pages on all of Berlin's major art museums as well as special on-line exhibits. The English-language versions are still being worked on.

www.smb.spk-berlin.de

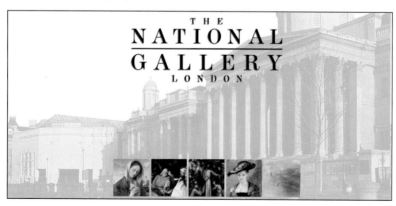

The State Hermitage Museum, St Petersburg

From prehistoric to Western European art, oriental sculpture to a tour of the Winter Palace, the State Hermitage site covers almost all bases. Its Digital Collection is truly impressive, allowing you to browse through a virtual gallery of much of its vast collection.

www.hermitagemuseum.org

Tate Gallery

Providing links to the Tates in London, Liverpool, and St Ives, and details of the future expansion plans to Bankside. The Tate's project to make its entire collection available on-line continues and currently stands at 8,000 works accessible through an A-Z index of artists.

www.tate.org.uk

The Whitney, New York

Showcases a different artist each month, complete with slide-show. Also displays recent acquisitions and its most famous collections.

www.echoyc.com/-whitney/

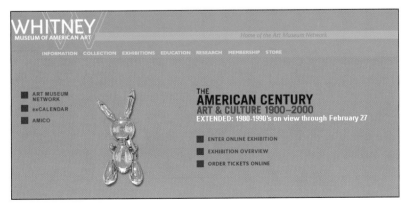

San Francisco Museum of Modern Art

Illustrates its own architecture and collections past, present, and future, the site also includes a link to the Bay Area Artfinder which features many local non-profit and artist-run galleries.

www.sfmoma.org

Actors Craft

Great resource for the thespians among us, with books, magazine articles, teachers, classes, words of inspiration, notes from the field, and much more.

www.actroscraft.com

The Andy Warhol Museum

The Warhol Museum in Pittsburgh has over 3,000 of his works.

Inspired by Warhol's artistic vision, The Andy Warhol Museum strives to be a dynamic art center and resource for anyone who wishes to gain insights

www.clpgh.org/warhol

The Center for Puppetry Arts

Learn the skills of puppetry, view the museum, or discover the history of puppet shows.

www.puppet.org

Center for Puppetry Arts!

The Center for Puppetry Arts is the largest organization in the United States devoted to the art of puppetry.

Visitors may attend Performances Monday through Saturday year-round in one of our three theaters.

The Center's Museum, PUPPETS: THE POWER OF WONDER, provides an interactive puppetry experience and includes figures as famous and diverse as Punch and Judy, Jim Henson's Muppets, Madame of "Wayland and Madame," and hundreds of other puppets from around the world and throughout history.

Our Education Programs offer daily workshops, outreach programs and adult education.

Learn more about the history of the Center.

Click here to Sign our guestbook!

Click here to View our guestbook!

Click here to check out the Center for Puppetry Arts video!

A British Punch puppet

Edvard Munch

This page from the Norwegian National Gallery's web site deal exclusively with Munch's work.

Nettutstillingen er et samarbeidsprosjekt mellom Nasjonalgalleriet og Museumsnett Norge

Edvard Munch i Nasjonalgalleriet
Munch og symbolismen

Innledning | Bilder | Biografi | Bibliografi

Munchs verker i Nasjonalgalleriet representerer ikke alene hovedverk i Munchs kunst. De betegner også høydepunkter i Nasjonalgalleriets samlinger. Nasjonalgalleriet kjøpte sitt første maleri av Munch i 1891. Og, takket være generøse donasjoner og regelmessige innkjøp parallelt med kunstnerens utvikling, teller Nasjonalgalleriets samling idag 58 malerier, 12 tegninger og 159 grafiske blad. Nasjonalgalleriets første utstilling på Internett, ønsker vi derfor å vie *Edvard Munch og symbolismen*.

In English

www.museumnett.no/nasjonal galleriet/munch

Gateway to Art History
Very good site that covers the subject of art history in book form.

www.harbrace.com/art/gardner

The Internet Theatre Database
Find details of where and when almost any play ever written was last performed.

www.theatredb.com

Museum Boijmans Van Beuningen
Covers the Middle Ages to the present day and features works by Rubens, Rembrandt, and Magritte.

www.boijmans.rotterdam,nl

National Galleries of Scotland
Four major galleries in Edinburgh linked together with histories of their exhibitions.

www.natgalscot.ac.uk

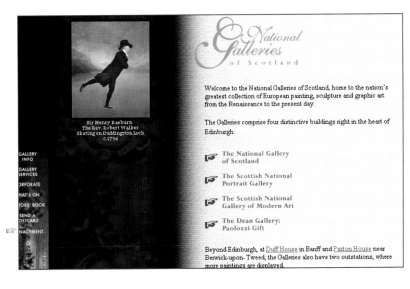

The Arts

Open.gov.uk
An A-Z of hundreds of UK public sector art galleries and museums links.

www.open.gov.uk/index/t-museums.htm

The Playwrights' Workshop Montreal
Great resource for those penning or putting on a production.

www.playwrightsworkshop.org

Playwrights' Workshop Montreal is a professional theatre centre dedicated to developing contemporary work and new writers for the Canadian stage. From dramaturgical

Playwrights' Workshop Montreal celebrates its 35th Anniversary

News
Updates and news releases from our offices.

Resource Library
Visit our resource library where you can view playwright portfolios and browse the **Carol Libman On-line Script Collection.**

Vincent Van Gogh
Interesting, mainly text-based site dealing with the enigmatic artist.

www.vangoghmuseum.nl

Shakespeare's Globe
A great listings site with details about the re-creation of the Globe and links to the Bard online.

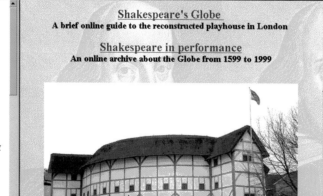

www.rdg.ac.uk/globe

The World of Mime Theatre

Comprehensive listings site covering all aspects of mime.

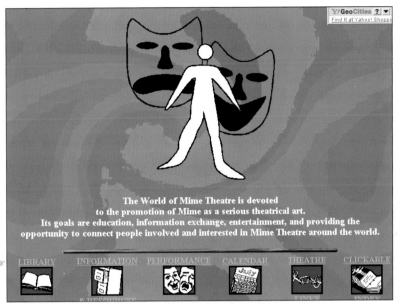

www.geocities.com/Broadway/5222

Arts & Letters Daily

A cultured collection of writing, art and literature with useful links.

www.cybereditions,com/aldaily

Broadway.com

View the latest Broadway openings, schedules, and showtimes, and theatre news and gossip.

www.broadway.com

479

Science & Nature

As you might expect from a scientific marvel like the Internet, the scientific content you can find on it is as amazingly diverse as it is enormous fun. For those who like to watch wildlife documentaries, the net can offer so much more in the way of interactivity, while if you like pure sciences such as physics or astronomy, the Internet can also quench your thirst for knowledge, too.

You will find annotated, abridged, and in some cases complete reference works, on every aspect of science and nature. You will find renowned authorities on subjects rubbing shoulders with people studying the minutiae of a topic in the back yards. Some sites have brought these tomes to life using animations, movies, and 3D images, while others offer interactivity.

The most recent example of the net being used in a giant experiment has been the SETI@Home screensaver. Thousands of people have downloaded the software that searches through recorded radio telescope data, looking for peak or recurrences that might mean a signal from ET. The net has also been used in the search for the largest prime number as well as online.

You will also find every nature organisation online and ready to accept your help, point you in the direction of useful information or tell you the latest news of its efforts. Many zoos are on the web, too, and actively pursuing a conservation stance. You will be able to find out opening times, feeding times, and in most cases, join in their work by sponsoring an animal online.

One of the most powerful tools at the Internet's disposal is its multi-media nature. You will find an amazing array of images and films on the web including satellite images of the earth and other planets, live web cams of various creatures from tigers and gorillas, to ants and even underwater scenes. And all this visually stunning information is available to you as you sit at a computer in your home or office. That in itself is always an amazing fact not to lose sight of.

This chapter complements the one on Education and Reference and serves as an extension to it. All of the information contained in the sites listed overleaf would be of enormous benefit to both children and students alike - no matter the age of either. As with all things nature related, many of these sites are easy on the eye and can simply be used to browse through and marvel at.

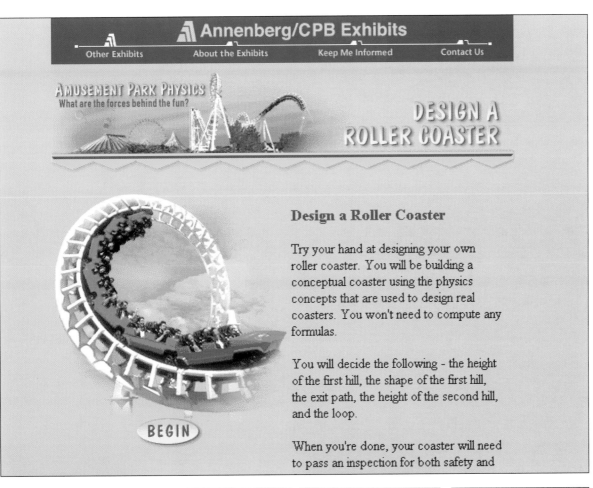

Annenberg/CPB Exhibits

Other Exhibits | About the Exhibits | Keep Me Informed | Contact Us

AMUSEMENT PARK PHYSICS
What are the forces behind the fun?

DESIGN A ROLLER COASTER

Design a Roller Coaster

Try your hand at designing your own roller coaster. You will be building a conceptual coaster using the physics concepts that are used to design real coasters. You won't need to compute any formulas.

You will decide the following - the height of the first hill, the shape of the first hill, the exit path, the height of the second hill, and the loop.

When you're done, your coaster will need to pass an inspection for both safety and

BEGIN

A Salute to Carruthers on Black History Month

Among the many people who contributed to the success of the Apollo missions to the moon was George R. Carruthers, PhD, a nuclear.

Rose Center

Site for the Frederick Phineas and Sandra Priest Rose Center for Earth and Space that opened at the American Museum of Natural History in New York City on February 19, 2000. Definitely worth browsing, the star sprinkling cursor is neat. The Natural History Museum site is also worth visiting at www.amnh.org/.

www.amnh.org/rose/rose.html

Science Museum, London

Great site featuring a vast array of exhibits that only account for half the site, so be prepared to spend some time here. Whether you use it to check out vacation ideas for children, news about current and future exhibitions, or corporate and commercial information, you'll find the site's as well designed as the museum itself.

www.nmsi.ac.uk

SCIENCE MUSEUM

HOME PAGE

ONLINE FEATURES

VISITOR INFORMATION

EXHIBITIONS

EDUCATION

COLLECTIONS

RESEARCH

CORPORATE AND COMMERCIAL INFORMATION

LINKS TO OTHER SITES

Search

Contacts

Feedback

About this site

Copyright

The Science Museum

What's New? - latest update 21/05/00

QUICK SEARCH ⬍ Go

Some of the highlights of our Website.

THE WELLCOME WING AT THE SCIENCE MUSEUM

Hands on Science!

FUSION

Making the Modern World

Leonardo and Renaissance engineers

Yell UK Web Awards 2000
NOMINEE just yell U

HOME | ONLINE FEATURES | VISITOR INFO | EXHIBITION

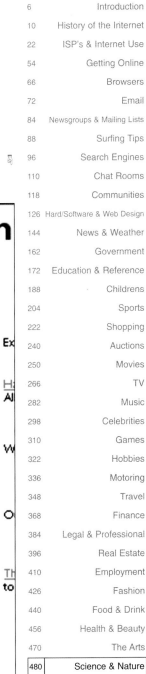

Explorezone.com

The amazing **explorezone.com** has it all, under sections dealing with the earth, space, weather, asteroids, comets, and meteors, to drought and fire, earthquakes, the environment, global warming, hurricanes, and the Hubble space telescope. You can search alphabetically if you can't see what you're looking for by section.

www.explorezone.com

Eric's Treasure Troves of Science

A very extensive resource of scientific data where you'll find the on-line encyclopedias of math and science compiled by Eric W. Weisstein. The subjects covered include astronomy, physics, chemistry, music, and rocketry. The whole site is full of images, animations and cross-references, really making the site the treasure trove it claims to be.

www.treasure-troves.com

Eric's Treasure Troves of Science

[**Browse the Treasure Troves** | **Sign the Guestbook** | **View Awards**]

Welcome to *www.treasure-troves.com*. Here, you will find the extensive on-line encyclopedias of math and science compiled by web encyclopedist Eric W. Weisstein. Here is some background on the Treasure Troves Project, and here is summary of the current extent of the treasure troves. You can also view a list of awards this site has earned.

The math encyclopedia is currently being distributed by CRC Press under the title the *CRC Concise Encyclopedia of Mathematics*. A CD-ROM version is sold separately, or as a combined book/CD-ROM bundle.

If you wish to be notified upon publication of the *physics* encyclopedia, please fill out the web form.

Please send comments, suggestions, and corrections to comments@treasure-troves.com, or sign the guestbook. For a description on how to link to my pages, please click here. You may either search my pages by topic alphabetically or search the archive (either in toto or by subject).

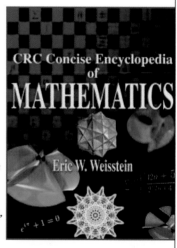

National Geographic

Much like its printed version, the *National Geographic* site is an outstanding resource for everything natural. Here you can source maps, view photography, and find out about exhibitions and live events. There is a useful children's section with plenty of activities and interesting nature trivia.

www.nationalgeographic.com

PBS

Animals, insects and underwater creatures. A fantastic section on the life of birds by Sir David Attenborough where you can read an article on crows who plant nuts on the road at traffic lights, wait for cars to drive over them before picking them up when the lights change again. A great resource for science, PBS has recruited Stephen Hawkins to help with unsolved mysteries and generally strange stuff.

www.pbs.com

Science & Nature

Amusement Park Physics

Investigate the physics of amusement parks. Learn how bumper cars work and the laws of motion involved in carousels. Design your own rollercoaster and enjoy the ride.

www.learner.org/exhibits/park-physics

Design a Roller Coaster

Try your hand at designing your own roller coaster. You will be building a conceptual coaster using the physics concepts that are used to design real coasters. You won't need to compute any formulas.

You will decide the following - the height of the first hill, the shape of the first hill, the exit path, the height of the second hill, and the loop.

Cool Science for Curious Kids

Science projects taken from museums made fun. Practical and realistic with a view to aiding children in the appreciation of science

The Howard Hughes Medical Institute invites curious kids to explore biology... on screen, off screen, and in between.

Dive into a miniature world —without a microscope

Cool Science for Curious Kids

Eat roots? Eat stems? NO WAY!!! Leap into our plant-parts salad.

Meet the dust— and other strange stuff —in your air. Do we really breathe this?

Why are snakes like lizards, and monkeys like moose?

Butterflies don't look like caterpillars. What's the connection?

www.htmi.org/coolscience

Exploratorium

On-line since 1993, this excellent science site from San Francisco continues to grow and develop. Current attractions include a live webcast of the 1999 eclipse and a whole section on earthquakes. Beautifully designed, its archive material alone should keep you browsing for hours.

www.exploratorium.edu

About Us — Online Store — Programs — Visit the Museum

www.exploratorium.edu
the museum of science, art, and human perception

Featured Resource

Have a science fair project coming up? Are you a teacher with a classroom full of students about to do science fair projects? Check out our Science Fair Resource.

Featured Exhibit

If you stare at the Fading Dot for a few moments, it disappears! More exhibits can be found in online exhibits.

Monday, February 28th, 2000

Join us live for our wacky science demo competition and webcast this Sat, Feb 26 at noon PST.

The year 2000 marks the peak of the current solar cycle. Find out all about it in this new resource.

Live dispatches from the AAAS meeting in Washington D. C.

New "Structures" activities, Ten Cool Sites for the month, Science Snacks you can build.

The Tiger Information Center

Very informative site on tiger conservation with a great section of interactive simulation games including surviving as a tiger and bringing poachers to justice.

www.5tigers.org

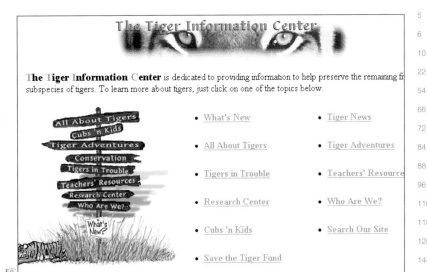

Glacier

All about Antarctica and the part it plays in our global system. You can join a group of explorers and learn about life and work at the South Pole.

www.glacier.rice.edu

PlanetDiary

Presents geological, astronomical meteorological, biological, and environmental news from around the globe. Records events and phenomena that affect the earth.

www.planetdiary.com

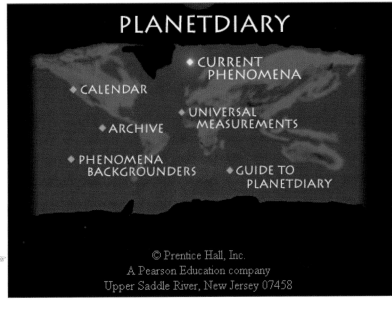

@griculture Online

Practical site for those interested or employed in the agricultural sector with links and content.

www.agriculture.com

Bad Astronomy

Corrects misinformation on astronomy.

www.badastronomy

Bizarre Stuff

Semi-scientific cookbook of tricks using - for the most part - things found around the house and especially in the kitchen.

Http://freeweb.pdq.net/headstrong

Cats! Wild to Mild

How did cats go from being wild animals to domestic pets? Cats facts big and small revealed here.

www.lam.mus.ca.us./cats/

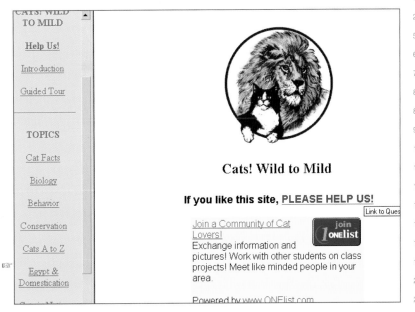

Conceiving a Clone

Learn about cloning techniques, join the moral debate or perform your own cloning experiment online.

http://library.avanced.org/2224355

Discovery.com

The home of several great TV stations on the web also has some great content.

www.discovery.com

Friends of the Earth

The central hub for all the Friends activities and web sites.

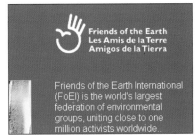

www.foei.org

A Global View from Space

Satellite imagery of weather and ocean patterns from space - complete global coverage of the earth.

http://sdcd.gsd.na.gov/isto/dro.global

Science & Nature

Greenpeace

Actively fight for the survival of the planet - or just see what those who are doing just that are up to.

www.greenpeace.org

Howletts Zoo

Amazing collection of animals on web cams, including tigers, gorillas, and elephants.

www.howletts.net

In Search of Giant Squid

Explores the complexities of the world's largest invertebrate and the myths and legends that have surrounded it for over 2,000 years.

http://seawifs.gsfc.nasa.gov/squid.html

NASA

The greatest collection of space-related content anywhere on the web.

www.nasa.gov

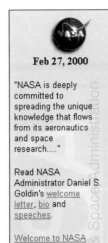
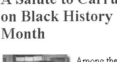

Feb 27, 2000

"NASA is deeply committed to spreading the unique knowledge that flows from its aeronautics and space research...."

Read NASA Administrator Daniel S. Goldin's welcome letter, bio and speeches.

Welcome to NASA Web

Do you dream of exploring space or working for NASA? If

A Salute to Carruthers on Black History Month

Among the many people who contributed to the success of the Apollo missions to the moon was George R. Carruthers, PhD, a nuclear, aeronautical, and astronautical engineer. He developed the first moon-based space observatory, an ultraviolet camera that was carried to the moon by the Apollo 16 astronauts in 1972. Dr.

today@nasa.gov

Interested in the latest information NASA has to offer? Then take a look at today@nasa.gov. This on-line newsletter, updated daily, contains the latest news about NASA science and technology.

- A Salute to Carruthers o Black History Month
- X-38 Drop Test Rescheduled
- NASA to Run Next Tes on X-38, Space Station Crew Return Vehicle

New Scientist

The very latest theories and news from the scientific community.

www.newscientist.com

NewScientist

jobs
editorial
news
features
opinion
letters
feedback
last word
search
contents

Subscribe to **NewScientist**

100's of **Science** Jobs

THEY'RE EVERYWHERE
Some black holes are small enough to swallow

FORMIDABLE FROTH
The GM beer that can keep its head while you lose yours

CRISP AND DRY
Can chemical engineers give us healthier French fries?

HANDY HINTS
Can a person's fingers reveal their sexual orientation?

BUGS BEHIND THE WHEEL
Movie-watching locusts could revolutionise road safety

THE XX FILES
A choice of chromosomes may help women live longer than men

Royal Botanical Gardens at Kew

The world-famous botanical gardens offer a variety of useful online resources.

www.rbgkew.org.uk

SETI Institute Online

A great site where you can download the SETI at home - a screensaver to help in the search for extraterrestrial signals from space.

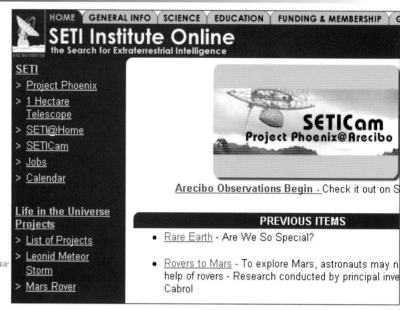

www.seti.org

Solar System Simulator

Color images of any planet or its satellite.

http://space.ipl.nasa.gov

Timeless Roses

A very comprehensive guide to all types of roses - old and new.

www.timelessroses.com

Volcano world

Listings of volcanoes around the world and all the latest eruptions.

http://volcano.und.nodak.edu

Wild Wings

Information on migrating snow geese. You can follow your favorite goose and guess its next stop over point and arrival date.

http://north.audubon.org

WWF

The world's largest conservation organisation, it has a global network active in some 100 countries.

www.wwf.org

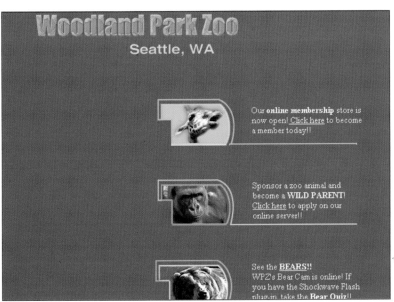

Woodland Park Zoo

A great site from the Woodland Park Zoo in Seattle, with sponsorship of animals, video of wolves, and whole lot more.

www.zoo.org

Yuckiest Site on the Internet

Questions answered on bodily matters, yucky games to play, and plenty of information on worms.

www.yucky.com

Science a Go Go

Science news and an assortment of links available here.

www.scienceagogo.com

Weird & Wonderful

The one thing you won't find a shortage of on the Internet is weird and wonderful sites. The net is an online community of over 250 million people, so all life is embodied in it. As such, you will find a staggering cornucopia of people's beliefs, theories, unique senses of humor, and pet subjects. This mixed bag can make for disturbing viewing, but some of the sites stand out, and it is those that I have attempted to bring together here.

The first thing you'll notice on your trip through the weird and wonderful, is that there's a great deal of information about the unexplained on the net. Every base is covered, from serious attempts to establish scientific truths, to the personal (and one might say deluded) experiences that individuals claim to have had with any number of paranormal events. No matter what area of the paranormal interests you, you will find a whole host of sites dedicated to it. There are UFO conspiracy theorists rubbing shoulders with the flat earth society, and those who think the Apollo Moon landings were faked, a few clicks away from a web cam set up for sightings of the Loch Ness Monster.

Although there is a lot of it on the net, the paranormal is by no means the be all and end all of the weird and wonderful sites you'll find. There are some real labors of love on the web that have been put together painstakingly, and almost professionally. These deserve just as much of the spotlight as all the UFOs and ghosts.

Humor on the Internet is a weird thing in itself. There are thousands of sites dedicated to what their owners find funny. This may be one specific incident, a TV show, or something more general like slapstick (or gore!). Sometimes these humor sites capture the essences of the country this sense of humor is peculiar to. Other times the sense of humor is just plain peculiar. Humor is very individual - what one person finds hilarious, another may find shocking, or even sick.

So there are sites that cover the weird ways in which people manage to kill themselves - specifically the Darwin Awards - as well as repositories of jokes from the knock-knock to the more adult variety. In one corner you have the innocuous site that lists misheard song lyrics or advertisements that never made it, while in another are off-the-wall humor sites such as Handbag! and Stick Figure Death Theatre.

You'll find an amazing array of creativity, with popular icons the main inspiration. For example, Pulp Phantom is an animated series about characters from the *Star Wars* movies in a *Pulp Fiction* gangster environment. Elsewhere you'll find how to build your own stormtrooper's outfit, or disgusting things to make in your kitchen.

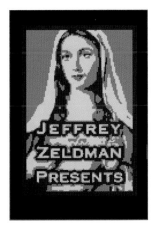

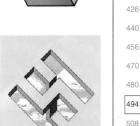

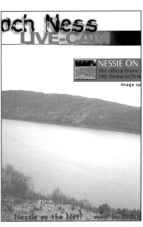

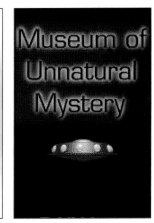

Weird & Wonderful

Darwin Awards.com

These mad awards are given to those who - in the spirit of Charles Darwin's natural selection - celebrate evolution in action by commemorating the remains of individuals, who contributed to the improvement of our gene pool, by killing themselves in really stupid ways. The really sad thing is, they are checked to ensure they are true.

www.darwinawards.com

www.darwinAwards.com
The Official Darwin Awards

February 15, 2000

Evo

What Are They?

In the spirit of Charles Darwin, the Darwin Awards commemorate the remains of individuals who contribute to the improvement of our gene pool by removing themselves from it in really stupid ways.

Photogenic Pilots in Peril

Source: Anonymous

February Spo

▶ **Millennium D**
Shocking Fall
Polar Bear Swin

▶ **Darwin Awa**
Resistance is F
Walking on Wat
Wild Animal Les
That Sinking Fe

▶ **Stupidity Aw**
Chimney Safety
Doggone Foot
Scoutmaster Sn

▶ **Personal Ac**
Packing the Wa
Coke -- the Rea
Newton's Laws

▶ **Urban Lege**
Unfortunate Hus

New Story Me

Museum of Unnatural Mystery

A wonderful online museum with exhibits of all the classic unexplained and weird phenomena the world has to offer. From flying saucers and ghosts, to dinosaurs and strange archaeological anomalies, all matters are considered from a scientific point of view. There are plenty of links to other sites, a section telling you how to do some amazing science in your own kitchen, virtual tours of the places long since destroyed or changed (such as the Seven Wonders of the World), and much more.

www.unmuseum.org

Archive of Misheard Lyrics

A fantastically funny site that lists the song lyrics that people have been singing incorrectly for years. Alas, the site is not taking submissions anymore, but what's there is enough to make this site a gem.

www.kissthisguy.com

Crank Dot Net

Excellent resource of web sites belonging to cranks and anti-cranks. The sites are sorted into sections such as extraterrestrials, science, religion, and the like. The sites are all reviewed and given a crankishness rating.

www.crank.net

Funny.com

Claims to be the Internet's biggest resource of jokes online, with over 19 million to choose from.

www.funny.com

Handbag!

Forget the UK-based women's portal, this is a very off beat 'magazine' about life in the fictional Lancashire village of Caton.

http://homepages.themail.co.uk/bakerjp

Handbag!

our url is http://www.handbag.homepage.org.uk

Welcome to Handbag! (hair and nails, diet, beauty and gossip) - the hottest "zine" on the web for elderly women of all ages and genders, coming to you from the quaint village of Caton, Lancashire.

Issue 1 - Virtual tour of Lancaster, I married myself!, transform your home, Is your son a homosexual?

Issue 2 - With music! addictive, escapist romance, arthritic romances and lives tragically shattered in Benidorm. And Dr Pam helps an obsessed Eric Cantona fan.

Issue 3 - Meet the Team, Cursed by the Spirits, Pensioner love-interest, scratch-card addiction! And all the usual from Pam, Cresta and Millie.

Issue 4 - Are you a Pensioner?, Secretarial Social Inadequacy, Petshop Detective, Pam's psychic advice, Millie's Postbag, & Cresta's Fashions!

Issue 5 NEW! Are YOU common? Take our fun quiz and find out. Plan your dream wedding with Dr Pam Rudge, read about Sandra and Kelly-Marie's lottery war. Take an online tour of Caton village, the home of Handbag! Plus the usual features.

TONS OF COOL STUFF AHEAD!!!HOURS AND

Welcome to the most comprehensive collection of optical and sensory on the world-wide web. This award-winning collection consists of innume interactive demonstrations, up-to-date and reliable scientific explanations, projects, illusion artwork, interactive puzzles, 3D graphics, suggested read bibliographies, perception links, and much more. There is literally hours an of fun and cool material here! Most of the effects, demonstrations, and artv appear here for the first time. We hope that you will agree that this site is w web was best suited for!

To benefit the many diverse visitors (over 4000+ separate users a day average!) we have decided to make two sites (containing more or less the material, although the level of explanations will be different.

Introductory Level. This level contains all the material, but with explanat are easily understood. This level contains an added section on recommend school science projects.

Impossible Window I@1997 IllusionWorks

Loch Ness

Official home of the world's most famous monster. There are clips and photos of sightings, as well as a web cam.

www.lochness.co.uk

Illusionworks

The site not only has a great collection of optical illusions, it also explains what's happening in your brain when you view them!

www.illusionworks.com

News of the Weird

Great news stories from around the world that are just plain weird - from dumb criminals to bizarre weather.

www.newsoftheweird.com

orientation.com

Great site that acts as a hub to many sites outside the English speaking world. The site wants to develop and connect Internet communities beyond North America and Western Europe.

www.orientation.com

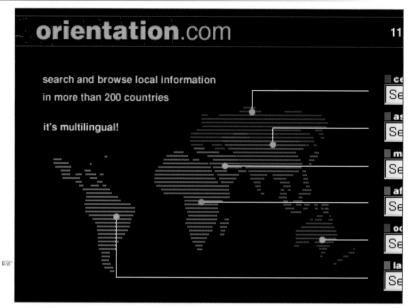

sixdegrees

This excellent chat site works on the basis that anyone is separated from everyone else by six connections.

www.sixdegrees.com

Stick Figure Death Theatre

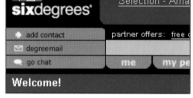

Very simple animations of stick figures meeting gruesome (and sometimes funny) ends.

www.sfdt.com

Strolling.com

Incredible site that takes you on a virtual stroll around London, Paris, and New York, (specifically the World Trade Center).

www.strolling.com

UFO Mind

An outstanding portal site that has links to thousands of sites covering aliens, UFOs, and all things paranormal. If you're a fan of *The X-Files* then this site, and its links, will keep you busy for hours.

www.ufomind.com

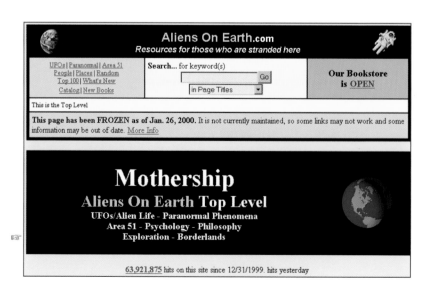

The Ad Graveyard

Ads that were never seen or were pulled soon after release - and for good reason!

www.zeldman.com/ad.html

Alien Abduction

Not a serious conspiracy theory in sight, just a tongue firmly planted in a cheek.

www.alienabductions.com

Alien Abductions Incorporated

For those who truly believe in the phenomena of alien abduction.

www.abduct.com

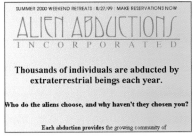

AllCam.com

Find almost any web cam from this diverse source listings site.

www.allcam.com

Annoy.com

If you want to get something off your chest, try this site first.

www.annoy.com

The Anomalist

Online journal of the weird and unexplained.

www.anomalist.com

Atlantis Rising

Ancient mysteries, future science, and unexplained anomalies, all linked to the lost civilisation.

http://atlantisrising.com

Bad Fads Museum

Excellent site with small features about all those fads in fashion, collectibles, activities, and events.

www.badfads.com

Bert is Evil

Poor Bert from *Sesame Street* is blamed for everything from Kennedy's assassination to Roswell.

www.bertisevil.com

The Black Hole

Almost nothing happens here. Almost.

www.ravenna.com/blackhole

Cool Site of the Day

There are many imitations, but this is the original.

www.coolsiteoftheday.com

Death Clock

Just enter your date of birth, and how pessimistic you're feeling, and the death clock will calculate your time of death.

www.deathclock.com

Disinformation

Amazing array of strange and peculiar activities, sites, and observations about political fixes.

www.disinfo.com

Earth Cam

Great search facility for web cams.

www.earthcam.com

Fortean Times

The UK's famous weekly magazine of the kooky and creepy.

www.forteantimes.com

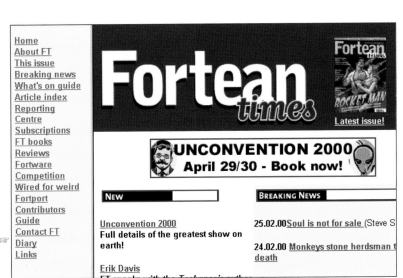

The Hampster Dance

Despite the misspelled title, this site has become world famous.

www.hamsterdance.com

The Hunger Site

Very simple site. Just visit it and a donation is made to alleviate world hunger.

www.thehungersite.com

CIAC Internet Hoaxes

All those hoaxes perpetrated online - including all the fake computer virus warnings.

http://ciac.llnl.gov/ciac/CIACHoaxes .html

Internet Traffic Report

If you're finding the net a bit slow, why not see if it's because it's overcrowded?

www.internettrafficreport.com

The Nerdman Show

Based on *The Truman Show*, this guy lives his life on the web, 24 hours a day, using 15 web cams.

www.reallifetruman.com

Outofservice.com

A great collection of mad things such as finding your *Star Wars* twin.

www.outofservice.com

What's on This Site

- NEW! Find Your Star Wars Twin
  Have you ever felt that some part of you was trapped in another galaxy, far, far away? Wo
  Our trained team of xenopsychologists will match you up with your long-lost extra-galatic s

- All About You, A Guide to Your Personality
  This test measures what many psychologists consider to be the fundamental dimensions of p

- Are you a freak?
  Another psychology test which measures your need-for-uniqueness level.

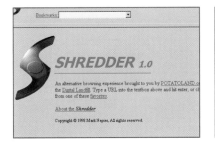

Shredder

Just enter any web address and The Shredder will display that page as a shredded work of art.

www.potatoland.org/shredder

Prayer Wheel

If you haven't got the time to pray yourself, then let the Internet keep faith for you . . .

www.prayerwheel.com

Pulp Phantom

An animated mixture of *Pulp Fiction* and *Star Wars*: The Phantom Menace. Bizarre, baby.

www.pulpphantom.com

Sausage Net

In case you need to find a cult children's TV program, try here.

www.sausagenet.co.uk

SpiritWeb

Comprehensive site that covers benign alien intervention on earth, with a view to letting it enter the Confederation of Planets.

www.spiritweb.org

Studio Creations

Complete instructions on how to build a stormtrooper outfit and other *Star Wars* props.

www.studiocreations.com

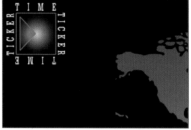

Time ticker

Find out what time it is any-where in the world . . .

www.timeticker.com

Totally Absurd

A great range of bizarre inventions that have actually been patented.

www.totallyabsurd.com

Trailervision

Trailers are always better than the movies, right? So why bother with the films at all?

www.trailervision.com

Urban Legends

The best myths and apocryphal stories collated and distilled for your pleasure.

www.urbanlegends.com

Useless Knowledge.com

A wonderful resource of 'useless' facts, quotations, dates, and more.

www.uselessknowledge.com

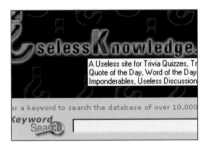

The Weird Web

Collection of odd facts, words, sayings, happenings, and the like.

www.weirdweb.com

What the Heck.com

US site that rounds up the odd, from the real world and the Internet.

www.whattheheck.com

WorldVillage.Org

What would it be like if the world's population was reduced to 1,000, but maintained the same statistics? This site shows you.

www.worldvillage.org

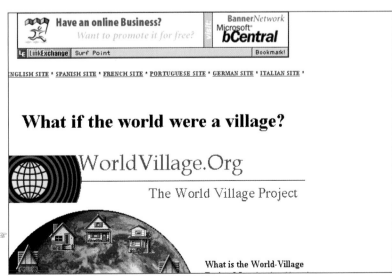

Index

@brint.com, 390
@griculture Online ,488
@nifty, 51
007.com, 258
101CD.com, 230
10-Tenths Motorsport, 207
19th Hole, The, 213
19thHole.com, 213
1Ski.com, 213, 356
1st Headlines, 151
1st Resume Store International, 418
20th Century Fox, 258
24 Hour Fitness.com, 462
4Car, 338
6 Figure Jobs.com, 418
7am.com , 151
7am.com, 151
800 Hampers, 230
800-Trekker.com, 230
A Girl's World Clubhouse, 197
A to Z Encyclopedia of Ice Hockey, 208
A2btravel.com, 350
ABC, 148, 272
About.com, 108, 324
AbsoluteChat, 112
ABTA, 356
Access Camera, 227
Access-Able, 356
ACM, 14
Acrobat, 62
Action Computer Supplies, 138
Action Online, 138
Actors Craft, 476
Actrix, 34
Ad Graveyard, The, 501
Adam's Monopoly Page, 316
Adobe, 134
Aer Lingus, 356
Aeroflot, 356
Africa News Online, 152
African ISPs, 44
Agence France Presse, 152
Ain't it Cool News, 250, 252
Air Canada, 357
Air France, 357
AJAX, 166
A-levels, 179
Alien Abduction, 501
Alien Abductions Incorporated, 501
Allbiz.com, 390
AllCam.com, 501
Allexperts.com, 174
All-Hotels, 357
All-in-One Search Page, 108
All-Internet Shopping Directory, The, 227
Allrecipes.com, 448
Allwhois.com, 108
AltaVista, 98
Alternative Medicine, 462
AlterNet, 152
Amaya, 70
Amazon Auctions/Sotheby's Amazon
   Auctions, 244
Amazon.com, 224, 246, 251
America's Job Bank, 418
American Automobile Association, 342
American Bar Association, 386
American National Bank, 376
American National Bank, The, 376
American School Directory, 179
AmericanAirlines, 357
AMG All Music Guide, 286
Amivin, 230
AMP3.com, 290
Amtrak, 357
Amusement Park Physics, 486
ANAC, 462
Ancestry.com, 326
Ancient Coins, 330
AndineT, 42
Andreessen, Marc, 21
Andy Warhol Museum, The, 476
Angelfire, 78, 120
AngliaCampus, 176
Animail, 231
Annoy.com, 501
Anomalist, The, 502
Another.com, 77
ANS/TLIC, 24
Anti-Social.com, 78
AOL, 21; AOL Australia, 35; AOL Brazil, 42;

AOL Canada, 32; AOL Germany, 38; AOL
   Hometown, 122; AOL Japan/AOL Hong
   Hong, 48; AOL UK, 28; AOL
   US/CompuServe, 24, 25
APC, 436
ApexMail, 79
Apple, 134
Appointment Plus, 418
ArabNet, 166
ArgoSphere, 180
ARPA, 11, 14, 13
ARPANET, 14, 16, 17, 19
Art Museum Image Consortium/AMICO, 472
Artcyclopedia, 472
Artificial Linguistic Computer Entity, 114
Arts & Letters Daily, 479
Asia Times Online, 153
Asian City Web, 79
Asian ISPs, 48–53
Ask a Chef.com, 448
Ask An Expert, 176
Ask Jeeves for Kids!, 194
Ask Jeeves, 104
Ask Jobs, 418
Association of Theater Artists, The, 302
Aston Martin, 342
AT&T WorldNet, 25
At-A-Glance Film Reviews, 258
Atlantis Rising, 502
Atlapedia Online, 180
Auction Beagle, 241, 246
Auction Channel, The, 246
Auction Hunter, 241, 244
Auction Insider, 244
Auctions.com, 247
Auction-Sales.com, 246
Audible.com, 290
AudioCatalyst 290
AudioFind, 108
AudioGalaxy, 290
AusBone, 35
Austalian Government, The, 168
Australia & New Zealand ISPs, 34–37
Australia's Great Train Journeys, 358
Australian Football League, 213
Autobytel.com, 338
Autoexpress, 343
Autographs for sale, 304
Autohit, 343
Automatic Weather Stations, 153
Automobile Association, The, 342
Automotive Industry Online, 343
AutoSuggestion, 340
AutoTrader, 343
Avon, 463
Babel Fish, 180
Babyworld, 195
Backgammon Galore!, 316
Bad Astronomy, 488
Bad Fads Museum, 502
BAFTA, 258
Bank of America, 376
Bank of Canada, 376
Bank of England, 376
Banksite.com, 372
BARB, 273
Barclay Square, 231
Barclays Bank, 376
Barclays Stockbrokers, 377
Bargainholidays.com, 352
BarMeister, 448
Barnes and Noble, 225
Baseball.com, 214
BBC, 270; BBC Education 181; BBC News
   146; BBC Sports 214; BBC Weather Centre
   148
Bboy.com, 79
Beastie Boys, The, 282, 290
Beauty.com, 458
BeautyCare.com, 463
Beeb, 273
Beer Travelers, 444
Beers Direct/Lastorders.com, 449
Bell, Alexander Graham, 10
Berners-Lee, Tim, 19
Bert is Evil, 502
Beseen, 123
Betty Crocker, 448
Beverage Network, The, 444
Bid Hit.com, 247
Big Little Railroad Shop, 330

Bigfoot, 104
Biglobe, 49
Bigsave.com, 231
Bikini World, The, 304
Bill, The, 273
Billboard Online, 286
Biography.com, 304
Birds in a Cheshire Garden, 326
Birdwatching.com, 330
Bizarre Stuff, 488
Bizreference.com, 388
Bla-Bla, 79
Black Hole, The, 502
BlackStar, 226
BlackVoices.com, 123
Blood-Horse, The, 214
Bloomberg.com, 370, 388
Bluecycle.com, 245
BMG Classics, 291
BMW, 344
Bn.com, 225
Boardgames.com, 314
Board-it.com, 215
Boats.co.uk, 326
Bob's Shop Window, 231
Body Shop, The, 463
BOL.com, 227
Bollywood World, 258
Bolt, 195
Bonus, 195
Boo.com, 224, 428
BookBlvd.com, 232
Books-For-Cooks, 448
Borders.com, 232
Bottled Water Web, 449
Bottomdollar.com, 232
Boxing.com, 215
BoxingPress.com, 215
Bravissimo, 436
Brint—The Biz Tech Network, 390
British Airways, 358
British Gardening On-line, 327
British Medical Journal, 464
British Midland, 358
British Shopping Links (BSL), 233
Broadway.com, 479
Broline.com, 49
Brookside, 274
BSM, 343
BT Click, 28
BT Internet, 28
Budget Rent-a-Car, 358
Buffy the Vampire Slayer, 274
BUPA, 464
Business Link, 386
Business Owners Toolkit, 388
Business Resource Center, 390
Business Week online, 391
Buy.com, 233
Buyers Index, 108
Cable & Wireless Internet, 28
Cable & Wireless Lite, 28
Calligraphy Centre, 331
Campaign for Real Ale, 449
Canadian Government, The, 168
Canadian Pacific Railways, 358
Cannes, 259
Car Museums, 345
Car Safety, 345
Care2, 77
Career Mosaic UK, 414
Career Path.com, 419
Career Shop.com, 419
Career Web, 419
Car-Imports, 344
Cars & Culture, 344
Cartoon Network, 196
Castrol, 340
Cathay Pacific, 359
Catholic Online, 79
Cats! Wild to Mild, 489
CBC, 153, 274
CBI, 391
CBS 153, 275; CBS SportsLine/Sports.com,
   206
Celebhoo, 300
Celebrities @ MTV, 302
Celebrity 1000, 305
Celebrity Addresses of the Famous & the
   Infamous, 305
Celebrity Email.com, 305

Index

Index

Credits

All illustrative material in this book is from screen grabs taken from the relevant websites. The Publisher would like to thank all those who contributed to *The Internet Atlas*.